*Properties of liquids
and solutions*

Properties of liquids and solutions

J. N. Murrell and E. A. Boucher

School of Chemistry and Molecular Sciences
The University of Sussex

JOHN WILEY & SONS LIMITED
Chichester · New York · Brisbane · Toronto · Singapore

Copyright © 1982 by John Wiley & Sons Ltd.

All rights reserved.

Library of Congress Cataloging in Publication Data:

Murrell, J. N. (John Norman)
  Properties of liquids and solutions.

  Bibliography: p.
  Includes index.
  1. Liquids.   2. Solution (Chemistry)
I. Boucher, E. A.   II. Title.
OD541.M9   541'.0422   81-21921

ISBN 0 471 10201 6 (cloth)   AACR2
ISBN 0 471 10202 4 (paper)

British Library Cataloguing in Publication Data:

Murrell, J. N.
  Properties of liquids and solutions.
  1. Liquids
  I. Title   II. Boucher, E. A.
  541'042'2   QD541

ISBN 0 471 10201 6 (Cloth)
ISBN 0 471 10202 4 (Paper)

Typeset by Preface, Ltd, Salisbury, Wilts.
Printed by Page Bros. (Norwich) Ltd

Contents

v

Preface

This book has been based upon a course of lectures given to second year students in the School of Chemistry and Molecular Sciences at the University of Sussex. To understand our choice of material and the level at which it is presented we should explain that certain courses at Sussex have been identified as core material which is given to all students in the School: chemists, biochemists, chemical physicists, materials scientists and environmental scientists.

The reasons for choosing *Properties of Liquids and Solutions* as a core course, are, we hope, obvious. Most chemical synthesis is carried out in the liquid state because reactions are on the one hand faster than in the solid state and on the other hand energetically cheaper and mechanistically simpler than in the gaseous state. Most methods of purification involve either a distribution of solutes between immiscible solvents or the partition of mixtures in solid–liquid or liquid–gas equilibria. Most biochemical and many environmental systems are in the liquid state or involve colloids or membrane boundaries between liquids. Solid–liquid equilibria are particularly important for the industrial preparation and purification of materials.

We have written the book because we found no single text that met the needs of our students. Most of the material we present can be found either in general physical chemistry texts or in monographs. However, the former generally lack the detail that is required for a course at honours degree level and the latter lack the cohesion that comes from teaching the subject as a whole and are often too advanced in their speciality. There is no shortage of suitable texts to support undergraduate teaching in, for example, spectroscopy, reaction kinetics, thermodynamics or valence theory. The absence of a comprehensive text on the liquid state probably means that it is not generally taught as a unified subject. We hope that this book will encourage others to look at it in this light.

Much of our knowledge of the liquid state derives from the physical chemistry of the nineteenth century. This is firmly based on thermodynamics and is no less important now than it was fifty years ago. However, with the development of fast, large-store digital computers our understanding of liquid properties in terms of intermolecular potentials has leapt forward making this currently one of the most active areas of research. We have tried to achieve a balance in this book between the traditional or macroscopic approach and the more modern, and complementary, microscopic approach to liquid properties.

In order to produce a text of moderate length we have assumed a prior knowledge in several important fields. First thermodynamics: we assume that all the basic thermodynamic equations have been covered elsewhere and we expect students to have had some practice in applying them, say to ideal gases or solids.

From statistical mechanics we assume prior knowledge only of the Boltzmann distribution and the partition function. There is a difficult choice here; statistical mechanics has led to substantial advances in our understanding of liquids but these are either associated with simple models of liquids that are now thought inadequate or they are connected with integral equations which we would judge to be largely outside the undergraduate curriculum. We do describe in detail the statistical approach through computer simulation because it is modern, not mathematically demanding and conceptually revealing; all very positive attributes of undergraduate material.

Finally, from quantum mechanics we require a few elementary concepts of bonding theory such as orbital, spin and covalent, which will enable us to give a review of intermolecular forces and provide the foundation of the microscopic approach.

The order in which we have chosen to cover the subject is broadly based on a pattern of increasing complexity; non-electrolytes before electrolytes before colloids, for example. We have also chosen to cover the theoretical material on intermolecular forces and liquid state models before the more experimental aspects of pure fluids and non-electrolyte mixtures. However, the reader would lose nothing by taking Chapters 4 and 6 before Chapters 2 and 3 and we would expect many courses to follow that pattern.

We are indebted to many of our colleagues for stimulating discussions during the preparation of the book, particularly Drs M. H. Ford-Smith, J. B. Pedley, G. L. Pratt and J. G. Stamper. We are particularly grateful to Drs E. R. A. Peeling and M. J. B. Evans for having read and criticized parts of the manuscript.

Chapter 1

The liquid state of matter

1.1 What is a liquid?

A simple operational definition of a liquid is that it is a medium which takes the shape of a container without necessarily filling it. In contrast, a gas both takes the shape and fills the container whilst a solid neither takes the shape nor fills it. There are, however, materials which are difficult to place on this definition. A few polymeric materials appear to be solid but with time they will flow to the shape of a container. Glasses behave similarly although their flow rate may be immeasurably slow at normal temperatures.

The operational distinction between a solid and a liquid must therefore be made more precise by referring to the time response to an applied force. We say that a material shows elastic behaviour if it returns to its original shape following the application then removal of a force. It shows inelastic or plastic behaviour if it is permanently distorted by the force.

The response of solids to a force is mainly elastic (at least for low strain), and that of liquids is mainly inelastic. However, the skipping of stones on the surface of water shows that elasticity is not completely absent in a liquid and the flowing of glass is an illustration of inelastic behaviour. The polymer known colloquially as 'silly putty' which can be moulded into an elastic ball but which will flow slowly under an applied force is a material in which both elastic and inelastic behaviour are easily illustrated.

At first sight the operational distinction between a liquid and a gas might appear to be more rigorous. However, there is a simple experiment to show that this is not so.

If one takes a sealed tube containing liquid in equilibrium with its vapour then the top of the liquid is indicated by an interface (meniscus). If the temperature of the tube is raised the density of the liquid will decrease and that of the gas increase until eventually a temperature is reached at which both densities will be equal. At point all distinction between liquid and vapour disappears and this is shown by the disappearance of the interface.[†]

[†]In 1863 Andrews described the phenomenon for carbon dioxide in these words: 'On partially liquefying carbonic acid by pressure alone and gradually raising at the same time the temperature

1

The temperature at which this occurs is called the critical temperature. As we shall see later the pressure in the tube is also a characteristic property of the liquid which is called the critical pressure. For most liquids this pressure is very high (e.g. for water it is 218 atm) so that great care is needed in carrying out the experiment.

On applying increasing pressure to a substance at a temperature above its critical temperature it simply becomes more dense: there is no point at which one can say it passes from being a gas to being a liquid. This unification of the two states of matter is expressed by using the term fluid to encompass both gas and liquid. Below the critical point gas and liquid are distinct states which can exist in equilibrium with each other. Above the critical point the two states become one.

Supercritical fluids are being increasingly used for extraction processes.† For example, supercritical CO_2 is being used commercially to decaffeinate green coffee beans. The advantages of such a process are that CO_2 is pharmacologically inert, the extractant can be recovered simply by lowering the pressure and coffee flavours are, apparently, not extracted.

A further brief comment on terminology: the words vapour and gas are often used interchangeably. Vapour is usually used when the phase is in contact with its liquid or solid. For example vapour pressure is the equilibrium pressure in the gas (vapour) above a liquid or solid. One could logically always use vapour for the phase below the critical temperature because only then can this equilibrium be established. However, we shall generally use the term gas unless it is essential to make the distinction that the substance can be placed in equilibrium with its liquid by a change in pressure alone.

Macroscopic and microscopic views

Although there is no simple and all-embracing operational distinction between a solid, liquid and gas, ice, liquid water and water vapour are obviously different and hence more scientific lines of investigation must be pursued to penetrate their differences. We shall see that progress can be made both by a thermodynamic and by a molecular description of materials, approaches which can be called the macroscopic and microscopic views respectively. Historically the thermodynamic approach has precedence as it stems from the work of Willard Gibbs and others in the late nineteenth century. The molecular approach to liquids is largely based on theories developed in the past fifty

†G. Wilke, *Angew. Chem.*, **17**, 701 (1978).

to 88 °F the surface of demarcation between the liquid and the gas became fainter, lost its curvature and at last disappeared. The space was then occupied by a homogeneous fluid, which exhibited, when the pressure was suddenly diminished or the temperature slightly lowered, a peculiar appearance of moving or flickering striae throughout its entire mass.' The latter observation which is associated with opalescence of the fluid is due to fluctuations in the density of the fluid near the critical point.

years but the major advances in our understanding of liquids that it has brought are directly linked to the advent of the electronic computer in the 1950s.

The strength of classical thermodynamics lies in the fact that its application does not rely on any knowledge of the molecular structure of matter. In fact some important generalizations about the freezing and boiling of liquids were discovered before the atomic structure of matter was universally accepted. However, the diversity of liquid-state properties can only be understood from the diversity of the shapes of molecules and the forces that act between molecules. In other words, there is probably more to be gained from the microscopic approach if we wish to understand the properties of individual systems, but the macroscopic approach leads more easily to the broad generalizations regarding the states of matter. Both approaches have as their aim the prediction and interpretation of measurable quantities.

1.2 An introduction to phase diagrams

A convenient method of representing the regions of stability of solid, liquid and gas under various conditions of temperature and pressure is by a phase diagram. The formal definition of the term phase was first given by Gibbs. It is a state of matter that is uniform in its physical state and in its chemical composition. Liquid water is a single phase, a mixture of ice and water has two phases. A gas, whether composed of a single chemical substance or a mixture of chemicals, is a single phase. A mixture of two different chemicals in the liquid state may be a single phase (the component liquids are said to be miscible) or it will form two phases; hexane and water, for example, are immiscible.

At one atmosphere external pressure water exists as a solid below 273 K, as a liquid between 273 K and 373 K and as a gas above 373 K. If the pressure is increased then the melting point of ice is lowered and the boiling point of water is raised. If the pressure is reduced below one atmosphere these trends are reversed and below 610 Pa (0.06 atm) ice passes directly to water vapour when the temperature is raised, without going through the liquid phase.† The term sublimation describes the solid–vapour conversion in either direction.

---

†The diversity of units currently in use for pressure causes difficulty for readers of the scientific literature. The SI unit is the pascal which is the pressure exerted by a force of one newton per square metre; $1 \text{ Pa} = 1 \text{ N m}^{-2}$. Unfortunately this unit is not as commonly used as many other SI units. An important and widely used unit is the atmosphere (atm) which is defined by international agreement to be exactly 101325 Pa. A useful rule of thumb is $1 \text{ Pa} \sim 10^5$ atm. Precisely 10^5 Pa also defines another unit, the bar (hence $1 \text{ bar} \sim 1$ atm) and high pressures are often quoted in kilobar (kbar). The atmosphere in turn is also standardized to the pressure of a column of mercury 760 mm high (1 atm $\equiv$ 760 mmHg). Another name for a standard mmHg is torr, after Torricelli who invented the barometer (1 torr = (1/760) standard atmosphere). In this book the pascal will be generally used for all quantitative measures of pressure but the phrase 'at one atmosphere' will be used to indicate the common laboratory conditions of a system under variable natural atmospheric pressure.

It is quite common to write the ideal gas equation $pV = nRT$ using a lower case letter for

Figure 1.1 The phase diagram for water (not to scale)

These data on water are summarized in its phase diagram, Figure 1.1. For simplification we have shown an incomplete diagram which does not record the fact that there are several different crystalline forms of ice. A further examination of the solid phases will be made in Chapter 8.

Figure 1.1 shows *areas* which are two dimensional, *lines* which are one dimensional and a *point* (at the joining of the lines) which has zero dimensions. The areas indicate the ranges of temperature and pressure within which only a single phase exists; within the boundaries indicated we can vary temperature and pressure whilst maintaining a single phase. We say that with a single phase the system has two degrees of freedom. The degree of freedom is formally defined as the number of variables that can be changed without changing the number of phases.

Two phases can coexist in equilibrium only at pressures and temperatures

pressure but upper case for temperature and volume. The reasoning is that volume is an extensive quantity (its value for the whole is the sum of values for the separate parts) and along with other extensive quantities, like energy and entropy, it is given a capital letter. Pressure, in contrast, is an intensive quantity (its value does not depend on the size of the system) and a lower case letter is used. Temperature is also an intensive quantity but the logical use of a lower case symbol could cause confusion with the use of t for time. We prefer to use capitals for pressure, volume and temperature and we will therefore write the ideal gas equation $PV = nRT$. We shall, however, conform to the common practice of using a lower case letter for vapour pressure when we wish to distinguish this from the total pressure. The vapour pressure is approximately equal to the partial pressure of a component in the vapour above the condensed phase of that component. We shall therefore use a lower case for partial pressures. Thus, Dalton's law of partial pressures will be written $P = \Sigma_i p_i$.

defined by the lines shown in Figure 1.1: the solid–liquid line, the liquid–gas line and the solid–gas line. For two phases in equilibrium if we specify one of the variables, say pressure, then the other, temperature, is determined. Along a line pressure is a function of temperature or, vice versa, temperature is a function of pressure. Along a line the system has only one degree of freedom.

The vapour pressure of a condensed phase is the pressure at which that phase is in equilibrium with its vapour. Thus the liquid–gas line gives the vapour pressure of the liquid as a function of temperature. If the external pressure is taken below the vapour pressure the liquid will boil and if it is above the vapour pressure the vapour will condense.

Three phases can coexist in equilibrium only at the intersection of the three two-phase lines, which is called a *triple point*. This is a fixed or invariant point which in the phase diagram of water has coordinates $P = 610$ Pa, $T = 273.1600$ K. Because the position of the triple point is capable of being determined with great accuracy (much greater than the ice point because that depends on maintaining the pressure at exactly 1 atm) it has been taken as the fixed point in the Kelvin scale of temperature.

The phase rule

The number of degrees of freedom for a single component such as water can be summarized mathematically by the formula

$$f = 3 - p, \tag{1.1}$$

where f is the number of degrees of freedom for a system having p phases in equilibrium. This is a simplified expression of the Gibbs phase rule which is valid for a pure substance. The complete rule, for many components, will be discussed in a later chapter.

Common experience might be thought to conflict with the pattern of Figure 1.1. On a winter's day we may see ice floating in a pond and sense that the air is saturated with water vapour. Can this mean that the conditions represent those of the triple point? The phase diagram that we have been examining applies only to a single component in an equilibrium situation and the winter's scene is neither. If we assumed equilibrium and ignored the very small dependence of vapour pressure on total pressure then the air pressure could be discounted and the partial pressure of water vapour above an icy pond would equal the triple point pressure of 610 Pa.

The fact that at a specified pressure pure ice has a definite melting point and pure water a definite boiling point is a consequence of the phase rule; there is only one degree of freedom for a single-component two-phase system. The importance of such results provides the incentive to formalize the phase rule by a proof which we give here for a single component.

Two or more phases can exist in equilibrium only if certain criteria are satisfied. For thermal equilibrium each phase must be at the same temperature; if this were not the case, heat would flow from the hotter to the colder until thermal equilibrium was reached. For mechanical equilibrium each phase must be at the same pressure; a system which does not satisfy this criterion will undergo volume changes until the pressures are equal. Finally there is a criterion arising from the second law of thermodynamics that the entropy of the system be a maximum.

If we confine our attention to changes for which the temperature, pressure and mass of the system are kept constant then the thermodynamic criterion of equilibrium is that the Gibbs free energy, G, of the system be a minimum. We will later examine this condition in some detail when the system contains more than one chemical species and when a chemical reaction may occur between these species. For the present we confine our attention to systems containing a single component.

Suppose we have two phases, labelled α and β, which are in contact at the same temperature and pressure. We let the Gibbs free energy per mole in the two phases be $G_m(\alpha)$ and $G_m(\beta)$ respectively. If we transfer dn moles from β to α whilst maintaining the same temperature and pressure the change in Gibbs free energy is

$$dG = (G_m(\alpha) - G_m(\beta))\, dn. \tag{1.2}$$

If the system is at equilibrium then $(dG/dn) = 0$ and this will only be true if

$$G_m(\alpha) = G_m(\beta). \tag{1.3}$$

Because G is a function of temperature and pressure it is useful to be explicit and write equation 1.3 as

$$G_m(\alpha; T, P) = G_m(\beta; T, P). \tag{1.4}$$

We now see that when two phases are in equilibrium the temperature and pressure cannot be varied independently because equation 1.4 must always be satisfied. In other words equation 1.4 provides a connection between the temperature and pressure at which the two phases can be in equilibrium. For two phases in equilibrium there is therefore one less degree of freedom than when only a single phase is present.

If three phases α, β and γ are in equilibrium, three equations such as 1.4 can be written. In addition to 1.4 we have

$$G_m(\alpha; T, P) = G_m(\gamma; T, P) \quad \text{and} \quad G_m(\beta; T, P) = G_m(\gamma; T, P). \tag{1.5}$$

However, any two of these equations implies the third so that there are only two independent equations. We conclude that if three phases are in equilibrium the system has two degrees of freedom less than does a single phase.

The above result can be generalized as follows: p phases in equilibrium have $p - 1$ independent free energy equalities and hence $p - 1$ less degrees of freedom than has a single phase. As there are two degrees of freedom for the single phase (T and P) we have for p phases

$$f = 2 - (p - 1) = 3 - p, \tag{1.6}$$

which is a proof of expression 1.1.

Table 1.1   Values of some critical constants for fluids

	$P_c/10^5$ Pa	T_c/K	$V_{c,m}/cm^3\ mol^{-1}$
He	2.29	5.2	57.8
H_2	13.0	33.2	65.0
N_2	33.9	126	90.1
CO_2	73.9	304	94.0
C_2H_6	48.8	305	148
C_6H_6	49.2	562	260

Data from *Handbook of Chemistry and Physics*, 59th Edn, CRC Press (1978).

The critical point

The liquid–gas line in a phase diagram terminates at the high temperature end at the critical point. For water (Figure 1.1) the parameters of the critical point are $T_c = 647.30$ K and $P_c = 2.20 \times 10^7$ Pa. Table 1.1 shows a selection of critical point data. Note that critical temperatures occur in a very wide range from a few degrees kelvin for helium to above 10^4 K for some metals. The critical temperature is roughly a constant ratio of the normal boiling point, $T_c \approx 1.5\ T_b$, and we will comment on this fact in a later chapter. Critical pressures also cover a wide range, and systems which are liquid at room temperature and atmospheric pressure normally have critical pressures above 100 atm.

Figure 1.1 brings out the points we have made about the unification of the liquid and gaseous phases above the critical point. It is also clear that by taking a suitable (P, T)-path in the phase diagram it is possible to pass from a point in which the phase is gaseous to one in which it is liquid without crossing the gas–liquid line. All that is necessary is, first, to raise the temperature keeping the pressure constant until T_c is exceeded, second, to increase the pressure keeping the temperature constant until P_c is exceeded and finally, to reduce the temperature below T_c.

Density and compressibility

A liquid under normal pressures has a density which is not too dissimilar from that of the solid; this is true over the whole liquid range from the melting point to the boiling point. Generally the liquid is less dense than the solid at the melting point, but there are a few exceptions of which water is one; ice floats on water. Silicon, germanium and tin are other examples where the liquid is more dense than the solid. This can be explained by the fact that the solids have rather open crystal structures with the low coordination number of four.

Another similarity between normal liquids and solids is that they have a low compressibility, which is an important property for the successful operation of hydraulic transmission systems. We can infer from this that there is not a great deal of free space between the molecules in a normal liquid and in this respect they resemble the solid phase.

The above statements about density and compressibility do not apply to liquids near their critical points which are much less dense and quite compressible. Water, for example, has a density of only 0.32 g cm^{-3} at its critical point so that it expands in volume by about a factor of three on going from its normal melting point to the critical point. A liquid close to its critical point has more free space between the molecules than does the normal liquid.

Crystalline solids

There is no evidence that any substance has a critical point on the solid–liquid boundary line. No matter how high the pressure there is always a sharp distinction between liquid and solid and a discontinuous change in volume on passing across the phase boundary. This result does not conflict with our earlier statement that it is difficult to categorize glasses and some plastic materials as solids or liquids. A phase diagram represents the regions of existence of thermodynamically stable species. Systems can be kinetically stable in the sense that they do not change during the time scale of an experiment, but they are not then subject to the laws of equilibrium systems. It is, for example, possible to cool a liquid below its freezing point without it freezing (called supercooling) providing there is an absence of nucleating centres. Liquids that become very viscous close to their freezing point are very slow to crystallize and will, on further lowering of the temperature, become glasses.

The thermodynamic distinction we have to make, therefore, is not between a liquid and a solid, but between a liquid and a *crystalline* solid. A crystal is defined as a material which possesses a periodic repetition of some basic microstructure, this repetition extending three-dimensionally over macroscopic distances. We say that a crystal is a macroscopically ordered system, and specifically the molecules in a crystal possess long-range order in both the positions of their centres and their orientations. Gases and liquids do not possess this long-range order but, as we shall see in the next section, liquids are not devoid of all order.

1.3 Order in liquids

Dilute gases are without order in the spatial arrangement of their molecules. If the probability per unit volume of finding a molecule in the gas whose centre is at the point $\mathbf{r}$ in space is $P(\mathbf{r})$, then the probability per unit volume of finding simultaneously one molecule at $\mathbf{r}$ and another at $\mathbf{s}$ will be

$$P(\mathbf{r}, \mathbf{s}) = P(\mathbf{r}) \times P(\mathbf{s}) = P^2(\mathbf{r}) \tag{1.7}$$

providing that the distance between the two molecules, $|\mathbf{r} - \mathbf{s}|$, is larger than

Figure 1.2   The pair probability function for a dilute gas as a function of the distance between their centres. The van der Waals diameter of the gas molecule is d, and P_∞ is a constant that depends on the density of the gas. The maximum at d is due to the attractive forces that exist between molecules (see chapter 2). The higher the temperature, the less prominent will be this maximum

the sum of their van der Waals radii. In other words, providing that the two molecules are not attempting to occupy the same region of space their probabilities for being at particular points are uncorrelated.

Figure 1.2 shows schematically the pair probability function for a dilute gas and we can take this as being typical of a phase with no order. This may be contrasted with the probability function for a close-packed crystal lattice of spherical molecules which is shown in Figure 1.3. For this the pair probability function shows peaks and for an ideal lattice these peaks persist to infinite distance.

Diffraction

It is well known that a crystal lattice will produce a diffraction pattern from scattered monochromatic radiation whose wavelength is of a similar order of

Figure 1.3   The pair probability function for a cubic close-packed solid. The first peak corresponds to 12 nearest neighbours at a distance d

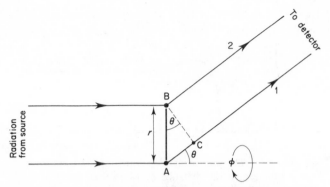

Figure 1.4   Scattering of a beam by two scattering centres A
and B where AB is perpendicular to the beam

magnitude to the lattice spacing in the crystal. By analysis of this pattern the distances between the atoms in the crystal can be determined. Both X-rays and monoenergetic neutrons (whose wavelength λ is given by the de Broglie relationship $\lambda = h/p$ where h is Planck's constant and p is the momentum) can be obtained with wavelengths of the order of 0.1 nm (1Å) and these are suitable for such diffraction studies.

A monatomic gas (e.g. Ne) gives rise to no diffraction pattern, showing that there is no regular spacing between the atoms. Molecular gases do show diffraction,† but this is due to the regular spacing between the atoms within a molecule and not between atoms in different molecules. Liquids occupy an intermediate position between the crystalline solid and the gas. They do show diffraction as a result of regular spacing between atoms in different molecules but the diffraction peaks are less sharp than those produced by a solid.

A rigorous derivation of the diffraction formula for a liquid goes beyond the mathematical level of this book but an outline of it can be given. Consider first a monochromatic beam being scattered by two centres A and B through an angle θ as shown in Figure 1.4. Beam (1) will travel further than beam (2) by $\delta = r \sin \theta$, before it reaches the detector. If this distance is an integer number of wavelengths ($\delta = n\lambda$) the two beams will arrive at the detector in phase and an amplified signal will be detected. If the path distances differ by an extra half wavelength ($\delta = (n + \frac{1}{2})\lambda$) the two beams will be out of phase and there will be no signal. The detector will then show a series of maxima and minima as one sweeps through the angle θ, analogous to the diffraction pattern produced by visible light from a double slit.

Suppose that AB is a diatomic molecule; δ will then also depend on the angle (α) between AB and the incident beam. It might be thought that averaging over all angles α would eliminate the diffraction pattern but this is

---

†This is most readily seen in electron scattering rather than in X-ray or neutron scattering as the scattering probability is much greater for electrons.

not so because there is more chance of finding molecules with large α than with small. If all orientations in space are equally probable then the number of molecules making an angle α with the incident beam is proportional to $\sin \alpha$. It can be shown that after averaging over α the intensity of the scattered beam is given by the expression

$$I(s) \propto \frac{\sin(sr)}{sr},\qquad(1.8)$$

where

$$s = \frac{4\pi}{\lambda}\sin\frac{\theta}{2}.\qquad(1.9)$$

$\mathrm{Sin}(sr)$ is an oscillating function hence $I(s)$ will oscillate and decay with increasing s or θ. All azimuthal angles ϕ relative to the incident beam are equally probable so that the diffraction pattern will consist of concentric rings around a centre which is the undeflected beam, these rings gradually dying out for large angles. This would be the typical electron diffraction pattern from a gas of diatomic molecules.

The radial distribution function

If we turn now to a monatomic liquid then we no longer have a fixed distance r between the scattering centres.† The spread of possible distances can be described by a probability function which defines mathematically the chance of finding two atoms separated by r. This function is called the radial distribution function $g(r)$. To be more precise it is defined such that from one atom there exists a second lying between r and $r + dr$ with probability $4\pi r^2 g(r)\,dr$.

The intensity of the scattered X-ray or neutron beam produced by a liquid is obtained by multiplying equation 1.8 by the above probability function and integrating over all values of r, thus

$$I(s) = A \int_0^\infty 4\pi r^2\, g(r)\left(\frac{\sin sr}{sr}\right) dr,\qquad(1.10)$$

where A is an appropriate constant which depends on the scattering strength of the atoms and beams in question. Expression 1.10 enables us to calculate the scattering pattern knowing the radial distribution function. In practice there is more interest in determining $g(r)$ from the experimentally determined scattering pattern.

Expression 1.10 can be rewritten as the following Fourier integral

$$sI(s) = A \int_0^\infty [4\pi r\, g(r)]\sin(sr)\,dr,\qquad(1.11)$$

---

†Even for a diatomic molecule r is not absolutely fixed due to vibrational motion; the short-time average of r is, however, fixed.

and using the inverse Fourier theorem this can be transformed into

$$4\pi r\, g(r) = \frac{2}{A\pi} \int_0^\infty sI(s)\sin(sr)\, ds, \qquad (1.12)$$

whence

$$g(r) = \frac{1}{2A\pi^2 r} \int_0^\infty sI(s)\sin(sr)\, ds. \qquad (1.13)$$

Thus knowing $I(s)$ and the constant A it is possible to determine $g(r)$.

One of the most striking illustrations of the difference between a solid and a liquid is a comparison of the X-ray diffraction of the two phases close to the melting point. Figure 1.5 shows this for powdered and liquid aluminium near the melting point. Analysis of the diffraction patterns leads to the radial distribution functions also shown in Figure 1.5. Notice that the sharp pattern

Figure 1.5 The X-ray diffraction intensities from powdered and liquid aluminium close to the melting point. $4\pi r^2 \rho g(r)$ is the probability of finding two atoms separated by r in a material of density ρ. (From H. Ruppersberg and H. J. Seeman, Z. Naturforsch. **20a**, 104 (1965))

of the powder gives on analysis a distribution function which also has relatively sharp oscillations and these persist to large distances. The liquid, in contrast, has a smoother diffraction pattern and only the first two oscillations in $g(r)$ are prominent. On the evidence, there is order in liquid aluminium as far as second neighbours but not significantly beyond that.

We will return to the question of order in a liquid later in the book with particular reference to models of the liquid state, and to liquid crystals which occupy a position between the liquid and the crystalline states.

1.4 Classes of liquids

We hope to show in this book that there is a unity in the modern approach to the liquid state. However, one must not understate the difference between one liquid and another. Helium, aluminium, water and benzene in their liquid states have widely different properties. The corresponding solids are also very different from one another. These differences can be attributed to differences in the intermolecular potentials in these condensed phases and we shall therefore preface our discussion of different classes of liquids and liquid mixtures by reviewing, in the next chapter, the theory of interatomic and intermolecular forces.

Table 1.2 lists the phase transition temperatures for the four liquids just mentioned, and two other properties, density and viscosity. Liquid helium has unique properties and for this reason we will not give it much attention in this book. The interested reader is advised to go to a specialist text.† It is unique because the lightness of the atoms and the weakness of the He–He interatomic potential lead to a fluid whose properties must be interpreted by quantum mechanics; for all other fluids classical mechanics is generally sufficient.‡

Table 1.2   Properties of some widely different liquids

	He	C_6H_6	H_2O	Al
T_m/K	0 (25 atm)	279	273	933
T_b/K	4.21	353	373	2740
T_c/K	5.20	562	647	7740
$\rho(T_m)/\text{g cm}^{-3}$	0.125 (4.2 K)	0.899	1.000	2.380
$\eta(T_m)/\text{cP}$	0.003 (4.2 K)	0.85	1.79	1.39

T_m, T_b and T_c are the melting, boiling and critical temperatures respectively. ρ is the density and η the viscosity at the melting point (for He the boiling point). A convenient unit of viscosity is the centipoise, $cP = 10^{-3}$ kg m^{-1} s^{-1}.

†J. Wilks. *An Introduction to Liquid Helium*, OUP, Oxford (1970).
‡For helium the de Broglie wavelength of translational motion $\lambda \sim \hbar/(mkT)^{\frac{1}{2}}$ is of the same order as, or larger than, the interatomic distance.

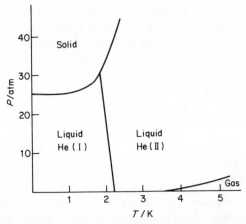

Figure 1.6 The phase diagram for ^{4}He. There is evidence for more than one type of solid but the separate solid phases have not been included in the diagram

Figure 1.6 shows the phase diagram for helium at low temperatures. There are in fact two isotopes of helium, ^{3}He and ^{4}He, which have been studied separately and we show only the phase diagram of the common isotope ^{4}He. The diagram is unique in three respects. Helium is the only pure substance for which two liquid phases can coexist in equilibrium. These liquids are labelled He(I) and He(II) as shown and the phase boundary line between them is called the λ line. He(I) behaves like a normal liquid but He(II) has special properties such as a vanishing viscosity as T approaches zero; by virtue of this property it is called a superfluid.

Helium is the only substance which cannot be solidified at atmospheric pressure however low the temperature. The minimum pressure required to produce the solid is 25 atm. The third unique feature is that there is no boundary line between the solid and the gaseous phases.

At the other extreme of liquid range temperatures aluminium typifies the class of liquid metals which is also generally dealt with in specialist texts. We draw attention to the special features of the energies of liquid metals in the next chapter.

Water is such an important liquid that it will be given a chapter to itself in this book so we defer comment at this stage. Benzene is in many respects typical of the wide class of liquids which are formed by non-polar organic molecules, and as these are in many respects simpler than water and similar liquids they will be discussed in the first half of this book.

Chapter 2

Intermolecular forces

2.1 General principles

The existence of solid and liquid phases is a manifestation of the attractive forces that act between molecules. It is customary to refer to these as intermolecular forces† or van der Waals forces with the implication that they are different in degree and in kind from the forces that hold atoms together within a molecule, the so-called intramolecular or valence forces. The extent to which there are such differences is a question that will be examined later.

We made the point in Chapter 1 that the properties of liquids can be interpreted or predicted at two levels, the microscopic and the macroscopic. It is only in the first of these descriptions that the intermolecular force occurs explicitly. If we wish to understand the properties of liquids in terms of the properties of their component molecules then that understanding must originate in their intermolecular forces.

We begin with a few remarks about force and energy. If two molecules are far apart there is an attractive force drawing them together. If the molecules are very close to one another there is a repulsive force tending to push them apart. There is a distance, the equilibrium or van der Waals distance, at which the force is zero. It is, as we shall see, often more informative to discuss this interaction between molecules using the intermolecular energy, rather than the force. The intermolecular energy (also called the potential energy) is defined as the difference between the total energy of the molecules and the sum of the separate molecular energies. The intermolecular force is minus the gradient or slope of the intermolecular energy.

At infinite separations the intermolecular energy is zero. When two molecules approach one another the intermolecular energy becomes initially negative; it reaches its lowest value at the van der Waals distance and, if the molecules are brought closer together than this the energy increases and eventually becomes positive. For a pair of atoms this energy, $U(R)$, is only a

---

†Not all liquids are composed of molecules; liquid argon and mercury are not, for example. We use 'molecular' to encompass atomic species.

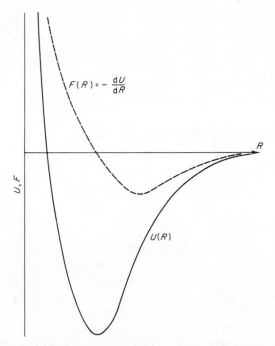

$$F(R) = -\frac{dU}{dR}$$

$U(R)$

Figure 2.1 Schematic form of the interatomic potential energy as a function of R the atomic separation. The force is given by $-dU/dR$

function of R, the intermolecular distance: a typical form for $U(R)$ is shown in Figure 2.1.

Empirical and ab initio

For a pair of molecules the intermolecular potential is a function of their relative orientation as well as of R, the distance between their centres.† We can therefore think of U as being a hypersurface and the force acting on the molecules in any orientation is given by the gradient of U at the appropriate point. There are three ways in which we can determine the function U: by *ab initio* calculation, by empirical and by semi-empirical means. The words *ab initio* mean from first principles and to follow this route we have to solve the Schrödinger equation for the electrons for different positions of the nuclei. There is a theorem, due to Born and Oppenheimer, that the energies obtained in this way give the potential energy we require.

For very simple systems (e.g. two helium atoms) it is possible to obtain almost exact solutions of the Schrödinger equation. For slightly more compli-

†In general the orientation of each molecule relative to the axis R is described by three angles, but as the potential energy is independent of a rotation of both molecules by the same amount about R the potential energy is a function of only five angles and R.

cated systems (complicated in this sense means having more electrons or more atoms) such as two neon atoms or hydrogen molecules it is possible to obtain a potential which is quite accurate but usually not as good as the best estimate that can be obtained by other means. For even more complicated systems (e.g. two water molecules) one cannot at present obtain very accurate solutions of the Schrödinger equation, but the level which can be achieved will often give a better potential than can be obtained empirically. With the rapid advance of computer technology there is a parallel advance in our ability to obtain accurate intermolecular potentials by *ab initio* calculation. For many systems such potentials will be as good or better than those determined empirically or semi-empirically.

The word empirical means from experiment. Any experimental observation which can be interpreted theoretically on the basis of the intermolecular potential is capable, in principle, of leading to a potential which is consistent with that observation. However, there are two difficulties with this approach. First, there is not usually a unique potential curve that reproduces a particular experimental observation although the more data one has available the narrower the range of acceptable potentials. Second, there is usually no simple analytical route for going from the experimental observation to the potential, and one generally has to make the connection by trial-and-error. One assumes a form of the potential and calculates the appropriate experimental result. The difference between this and the observed experimental result is used as a basis for adjusting the form of the potential.

It is almost impossible to achieve a satisfactory potential by trial-and-error if one has no preknowledge of the form of the potential. For that reason the most satisfactory potentials are usually achieved by semi-empirical means in which some *ab initio* evidence is used to deduce the general features of the potential. To take one example, it can be shown from theory that the interatomic energy for two inert gas atoms at large internuclear distances is proportional to R^{-6}, hence all accurate semi-empirical potentials for these systems are made to satisfy this limiting behaviour.

Many-body energies

It is quite common to assume that the total intermolecular energy in the solid or liquid states is a sum of the energies of the molecules interacting in pairs and, as we shall see, there is theoretical support for this assumption. In this case we can derive empirical or semi-empirical potentials from experiments that only involve pairwise interactions, and these are mainly experiments on dilute gases. Collisions in a dilute gas are sufficiently infrequent that they nearly all occur between pairs of molecules, with far fewer involving three or more molecules colliding simultaneously. We shall discuss the statistical mechanics of the imperfect gas in Section 3.3 with the particular objective of seeing how gas properties can be used to derive the pair potential.

In liquids and solids molecules have simultaneous contacts with several neighbours so that there is no fundamental reason why the bulk properties should depend only on the pair potential. If there are significant contributions to the intermolecular potential from molecules interacting three or more at a time (so-called many-body energies) then these will influence the properties of the liquid. Turning the argument the other way round: if the properties of the liquid are used to deduce an empirical pair potential with the assumption that the many-body terms are negligible, then that empirical potential may have little resemblance to the pair potential deduced from gas phase properties or from *ab initio* calculations.

There are reasons, which we shall discuss in the next section, for believing that for liquids composed of inert gas atoms or non-polar molecules the many-body terms can be neglected. For these systems empirical pair potentials deduced from liquid state properties are very similar to the true pair potentials. For liquids composed of polar molecules the many-body terms are probably not negligible, although the situation may well have to be examined for each system of interest. We will give some attention to this point when we come to examine the properties of liquid water in Chapter 8.

Potentials for metals

There is certainly one class of liquid for which the many-body energies are far from negligible, and that is the liquid metals. The high electrical conductivity of metals shows that electrons are not bound to particular atoms or molecules, but are delocalized over the whole bulk phase. The so-called free-electron model, in which the electrons move in a potential which is constant over the whole phase, is a good first approximation to the electronic states of metals, and for this the total energy depends on the size and shape of the phase, but not on the arrangement of the nuclei.

It would require too large a detour in the development of our subject to cover the theory of the metallic bond, and we must refer the interested reader to specialist texts.[†] We wish only to make the point that the empirical pair potentials which have been deduced from diffraction data on liquid metals, are quite different from those of, say, the inert gas liquids. Figure 2.2 shows a typical example and we draw attention to the oscillations in the region of large R. These oscillations are a manifestation of the fact that $U(R)$ represents the potential for two atoms in the presence of all other atoms in the system. Such potentials therefore depend on factors such as the density of the liquid, and hence show a slight dependence on temperature.

The term 'effective pair potential' should be used for pair potentials deduced empirically from the properties of any liquid for which the many-

[†]For example, N. H. March, *Liquid Metals*, Pergamon Press, Oxford (1968); T. E. Faber, *Introduction to the Theory of Liquid Metals*, Cambridge U.P., Cambridge (1972); M. Shimoji, *Liquid Metals*, Academic Press, London and New York (1977).

Figure 2.2 The effective pair potential for liquid sodium at 373 K. The potential was deduced by applying the Percus–Yevick equation (mentioned briefly in section 3.4) to the analysis of the X-ray diffraction data for liquid sodium. (W. S. Howells and J. E. Enderby, *J. Phys.*, C, **5**, 1277 (1972))

body energies are not negligible. This will distinguish such a potential from the true pair potential for two atoms or molecules interacting in the absence of any others.

Inter- and intramolecular energies

We return now to the opening statement in this chapter regarding the difference between intermolecular and intramolecular energies. A typical chemical bond has a binding energy of more than 200 kJ mol^{-1}; the typical binding energy of neighbouring molecules in a liquid is below 10 kJ mol^{-1}. However, there are intermediate cases. The so-called hydrogen bond energy which occurs in water and other hydroxylic solvents may be as large as 25 kJ mol^{-1}. Donor–acceptor molecular complexes (e.g. trimethylamine–SO_2) can have binding energies up to 50 kJ mol^{-1}.[†] Although there is not a sharp boundary between the strongest intermolecular bond and the weakest intramolecular bond, the great majority fall clearly into one category or the other and it is therefore convenient to discuss them from different points of view.

[†]The reader should turn to a book on valence theory for a fuller discussion of these. For example, J. N. Murrell, S. F. A. Kettle and J. M. Tedder, *The Chemical Bond*, Wiley, Chichester (1978); R. McWeeny, *Coulson's Valence*, Oxford U.P., Oxford (1980).

Because the intermolecular energy is a small part of the total energy of the system it is possible to utilize a technique of quantum mechanics called the perturbation method to develop the theory of intermolecular energies. Perturbation theory has two pedagogic advantages over the other commonly used technique of quantum mechanics which is the variation method. First, it provides a connection between the intermolecular energy and properties of the interacting molecules, and second, it provides a subdivision of the intermolecular energy into a sum of physically interpretable parts. Its disadvantage is that, in general, it is not as accurate as the variation method nor as easy to implement on a computer. The variation method is almost always the technique which is chosen for calculating intramolecular energies (chemical bond energies), because these are a much larger part of the total energy.

We give in the next section an outline of the perturbation theory of intermolecular energies and direct the reader elsewhere for a fuller treatment.[‡]

Short- and long-range energies

The most important classification of the various contributions to the intermolecular energy is into short-range and long-range energies. A long-range energy is one that varies at large R as some inverse power of R; say R^{-n}. The Coulombic energy between charges falls into this category having $n = 1$. A short-range energy is one that varies at large R as $\exp(-kR)$, where k is a constant. There is no definite value of R at which short-range energies end and long-range begin. Rather we should think that these contribute to the total energy at all R, but beyond a certain point only the long-range contributions are important. Short-range energies have their origins in the overlap of the wave functions or orbitals of the interacting atoms or molecules. The chemical bond is essentially a short-range energy; the repulsive forces that keep atoms or molecules apart in a solid or liquid are also of this category. Long-range energies do not depend on orbital overlap and, as we shall see in the next section, they can be qualitatively understood from arguments based upon classical electrostatics.

Figure 2.3 shows the interatomic potential for two neon atoms and its division into attractive, long-range, and repulsive short-range, terms. The van der Waals' minimum occurs at the value of R at which the slopes of the two terms are equal in magnitude but opposite in sign. It can be seen that the short-range term is a steeply rising function of R. Indeed, one can say very roughly, that the van der Waals minimum occurs at the distance at which the repulsion starts to be noticeable.

Because the repulsive energies rise steeply when the wave functions of the interacting systems overlap we can introduce as a crude approximation the concept that atoms and molecules have definite sizes and shapes. If atoms

[‡]For example, Chapters 2 and 3 in *Rare Gas Solids*, Eds. M. L. Klein and J. A. Venables, Academic Press, London and New York (1976).

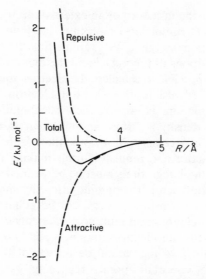

Figure 2.3 Calculated attractive and repulsive energies of Ne–Ne as a function of R

were miniature ball bearings the repulsive energy would rise vertically when R equalled the sum of the atomic radii of the two atoms. Although this is an oversimplification it is an important idea because, as we show in Chapter 3, some important features of the liquid state are predicted by models which assume a 'hard-shape' repulsive energy.

In the remainder of this chapter we wish to do two things: to describe the origins and characteristic features of the contributions to the intermolecular potential; and to describe the functional form of semi-empirical potentials that have been commonly used in the theory of the liquid state. For our requirements in the rest of this book the second of these two tasks is the more important, but, as we have already noted, the form of empirical potentials is primarily based on theoretical considerations, and it is therefore appropriate that we tackle these first.

2.2 Long-range energies†

Long-range energies can be divided into three types, electrostatic, induction and dispersion energies. To calculate the first of these we need only know the distribution of charge within the molecules: this is made up of point positive charges from the nuclei and a diffuse negative charge from the electrons. To calculate the second two we need to know how the electrons in a

---

†This and the next section will be of interest mainly to those readers who have a strong interest in the theoretical basis of intermolecular forces.

molecule move under the influence of an external electric field. This effect is referred to as the polarization of a molecule; the induction and dispersion energies are polarization energies. We examine first the electrostatic energy.

If we know the positions of the nuclei and the distribution of the electrons in the molecules, it is possible to calculate the electrostatic energy by summing the nuclear–nuclear repulsion, the electron–electron repulsions and the electron–nuclear attraction. However, such calculations are quite difficult because the electron density is diffuse and an integration over all elemental electron interactions is necessary. Moreover, there is, to a large extent, cancellation of the attractive and repulsive terms making up the total electrostatic energy so that the integrations must be performed with high accuracy.

A much simpler approach is to combine attractive and repulsive terms in such a way that the electrostatic energy can be equated to the energy of interaction of the net charges and multipole moments of the molecules. The resulting expression for the electrostatic energy is known as the multipole expansion. We do not give the formal derivation of this expansion in this book, but note two important points regarding its validity.† First, the expansion is valid only if there is negligible overlap of the electron clouds of the two molecules and second, for the expansion to be convergent in the first few terms, the distance between the centres of the two molecules must be large compared with the linear dimensions of the two molecules. Broadly speaking, it is only when the two molecules are far apart that the multipole expansion is valid and rapidly convergent. At short distances, say less than van der Waals' separations, the multipole expansion will provide only a qualitative guide to the electrostatic energy, and to obtain an accurate value it is usually necessary to sum the individual Coulombic energies as already described.

Electric moments

The first moment of a charge distribution is called the dipole moment. Two point charges $+\delta$ and $-\delta$ separated by a distance r have a dipole moment δr directed along the line from the positive to the negative charge. A more general definition of the dipole moment for a molecule is given in the appendix to this chapter. The traditional unit for molecular dipole moments is the debye.‡ A molecule has no dipole moment if it possesses a centre of symmetry or if it has three mutually perpendicular planes of symmetry. Thus HCl and CH_3F have dipole moments, H_2 and CH_4 do not.

The second moment is called the quadrupole moment and is given the symbol Θ. For molecules like N_2 and CO_2 which have no dipole moments the quadrupole is the first non-zero moment. Typical quadrupolar charge distri-

†For a derivation see A. D. Buckingham, *Quart. Revs.*, **13**, 183 (1959); and Chapter 1, *Intermolecular Interactions from Diatomics to Biopolymers*, Ed. B. Pullman, Wiley-Interscience, Chichester (1978).
‡1 debye $= 10^{-18}$ e.s.u. $= 3.3356 \times 10^{-30}$ C m.

Figure 2.4   Coordinates for the electrostatic energy
between charges and dipole moments

butions are cigar shaped or disc shaped. For highly symmetrical (nearly spherical) molecules like CH_4 the first non-zero moment is the octopole (3rd moment) and for SF_6 it is the 4th moment. For a perfectly spherical charge distribution with no net charge (e.g. a neon atom) all moments are zero.

The multipole expansion for the electrostatic energy is an expansion in powers of R, where R is the distance between the centres (usually taken as the centres of mass) of the two molecules. The first term is the Coulomb energy between the net charges q_a, q_b of the two molecules[†]

$$q_a q_b / 4\pi\varepsilon_0 R. \tag{2.1}$$

The second term is the interaction between the charge on one molecule and the dipole moment μ of the other. Because the dipole is a vector quantity the energy depends on the orientation of the dipoles; in terms of the angular variables defined in Figure 2.4 it is

$$(q_b \mu_a \cos \theta_a - q_a \mu_b \cos \theta_b)/4\pi\varepsilon_0 R^2. \tag{2.2}$$

Equation 2.2 is more compactly written in vector notation

$$(q_b \boldsymbol{\mu}_a \cdot \boldsymbol{R} - q_a \boldsymbol{\mu}_b \cdot \boldsymbol{R})/4\pi\varepsilon_0 R^3, \tag{2.3}$$

where $\boldsymbol{R}$ is the vector distance of B from A.

The first non-zero contribution to the multipole expansion for neutral but dipolar molecules is the dipole–dipole energy

$$-\mu_a \mu_b (2 \cos \theta_a \cos \theta_b - \sin \theta_a \sin \theta_b \cos \phi)/4\pi\varepsilon_0 R^3, \tag{2.4}$$

which in vector form is

$$\left(\frac{\boldsymbol{\mu}_a \cdot \boldsymbol{\mu}_b}{R^3} - 3 \frac{(\boldsymbol{\mu}_a \cdot \boldsymbol{R})(\boldsymbol{\mu}_b \cdot \boldsymbol{R})}{R^5} \right) /4\pi\varepsilon_0. \tag{2.5}$$

The most favourable (most negative energy) orientations of two dipoles are colinear head-to-tail or side-by-side (antiparallel).

The full expressions for the higher terms in the multipole expansion are rather complicated and will not be given here.[‡] For charged systems there is

[†] $4\pi\varepsilon_0 = 1.11 \times 10^{-10}$ C V m^{-1} = 1 e.s.u.
[‡] A. D. Buckingham *loc. cit.*

Table 2.1 Electrostatic energies obtained from the multipole expansion
with the multipoles terminated at different order

	LiH($R = 14a_0$)		HF($R = 6a_0$)	
	$\rightarrow\rightarrow$	$\uparrow\downarrow$	$\rightarrow\rightarrow$	$\uparrow\downarrow$
Dipoles	−40.6	−20.3	−54	−27
Dip. + quad.	−39.4	−19.8	−30	−18
Dip. + quad. + oct.	−41.7	−19.0	−56	−12
Est. series limit	−42	−19	−49	−15

Distances and energies in atomic units. $a_0 = 0.5295$ Å, unit of energy 10^{-4} $E_h = 0.2626$ kJ mol^{-1}. The diatomic bond lengths are $3.02a_0$ and $1.73a_0$ for LiH and HF respectively, J. T. Bröbjer and J. N. Murrell, *Chem. Phys. Letters*, **77**, 601 (1981).

another term like 2.7 which is proportional to R^{-3} due to the interaction of the charge on one molecule with the quadrupole of the other. The terms in R^{-4} are charge–octopole and dipole–quadrupole, and so on. A result that summarizes the whole series is that the mth moment of one molecule interacting with the nth moment of another gives an energy proportional to $R^{-(m+n+1)}$. The charge can be included in this formula by considering it to be the zeroth moment.

Table 2.1 gives two examples of the rate of convergence of the multipole expansion. Although dipole and quadrupole moments are often known from experiment this is not generally the case for higher moments. However, quite accurate values for these can be obtained for small molecules from quantum mechanical calculations, and such values have been used to give the results in Table 2.1. The values of R chosen for these calculations are roughly the van der Waals distances for the dimers. It is known that at shorter distances the overlap of the electron clouds of the two molecules leads to errors in the multipole expansion.

The results of Table 2.1 show that the multipole expansion converges rapidly for the LiH dimer but slowly for the HF dimer. This is due not only to the different values of R in the two cases but also because the higher multipole moments are larger, relative to the dipole, for HF than for LiH. These results show that care is needed in calculating electrostatic energies by the multipole expansion.

For molecules which have no dipole moments but large quadrupole moments such as CO_2 ($\Theta = -14 \times 10^{-40}$ C m^2 $= -4.2 \times 10^{-26}$ e.s.u.), the quadrupole–quadrupole contribution to the electrostatic energy can be quite large. For example, side-by-side CO_2 molecules separated by 4 Å will have a positive energy from this source equal to

$$\frac{9\,\Theta^2}{16\pi\varepsilon_0 R^5} = 3.9 \times 10^{-21} \text{ J } (= 2.3 \text{ kJ mol}^{-1}). \tag{2.6}$$

Figure 2.5 The polarization of an atom by a neighbouring positive charge

Polarization energies

We turn now to the polarization energies which are due to changes in the electron distribution within the molecules when they come within each other's influence. The electric fields arising from the permanent moments of one molecule will induce moments in a neighbour, and the interaction between permanent and induced moments will lead to an attraction between the two: this is called the induction energy. The type of electron displacement is illustrated for a simple case in Figure 2.5. The induction energy can be large for interacting ions or molecules with large dipole moments, but it will be small for nearly spherical molecules like CH_4 and SF_6, because these have no low-order moments, and the electric fields in their vicinity are small. It will be zero for inert gas atoms as these have no moments of any order.

Although an inert gas atom has no permanent moments it can possess time varying (instantaneous) moments due to fluctuations in its electron distribution. These instantaneous moments will induce moments in a neighbouring molecule, and there will be an energy of interaction between the two. Although the instantaneous moments average over time to zero, the polarization energy that is associated with them does not average to zero. It is this energy that is called the dispersion energy. A rigorous theory of dispersion energies can only be obtained by quantum mechanics. This theory was first derived by F. London, and hence dispersion energies are often referred to as London energies.

The extent to which the electron density in an atom or molecule is polarized by an external field is measured by a quantity α called the polarizability, which is defined as the dipole moment induced by a unit applied field $\mathscr{E}$,[†]

$$\mu_{ind} = \alpha \cdot \mathscr{E} . \tag{2.7}$$

Both μ_{ind} and $\mathscr{E}$ are vector quantities so that α is a tensor having components α_{xx}, α_{xy} etc. For spherical systems $\alpha_{xx} = \alpha_{yy} = \alpha_{zz} = \alpha$ and $\alpha_{xy} = \alpha_{yz} = \alpha_{zx} = 0$. For non-spherical systems the average polarizability, a scalar quantity, is

---

†Some texts include a factor $4\pi\varepsilon_0$ in this expression, but we prefer the convention in which this is subsumed within α.

defined by

$$\alpha = \tfrac{1}{3}(\alpha_{xx} + \alpha_{yy} + \alpha_{zz}) \qquad (2.8)$$

The quantity α/ε_0 has the dimension of volume, and its value is roughly proportional to the molecular volume. For example, for N_2 α is approximately $12a_0^3\varepsilon_0$ and for benzene approximately $70a_0^3\varepsilon_0$. The polarizability of a molecule like benzene is very anisotropic as the electrons are much more mobile for movement parallel to the plane of the molecule than for movement perpendicular to the plane: this is due to the delocalized π electrons of the conjugated double bonds.

Induction energies

The induction energies can be calculated by substituting the expression for the induced moment (2.7) for one of the dipole moments which occur in expressions 2.2 or 2.4. For example, if molecule A has a charge q_a this will give a field at B proportional to $q_a R^{-2}$, and the induced dipole moment will be proportional to $q_a \alpha_b R^{-2}$. The interaction energy of this charge with the induced moment is proportional to $q_a^2 \alpha_b R^{-4}$. The full expression with appropriate factors is (assuming an isotropic polarizability)

$$E_{\text{ind}} = -\tfrac{1}{2}q_a^2\alpha_b/(4\pi\varepsilon_0)^2 R^4 \qquad (2.9)$$

Note that induction energies are always negative because the charge or permanent moment always induces a moment in the sense that their interaction is attractive. This is illustrated in Figure 2.6, which shows the direction of the induced dipole arising from the field of a permanent dipole for various orientations of two molecules. The induction energy for a molecule with a polarizability α_b in the field of a dipole moment μ_a, when averaged over all

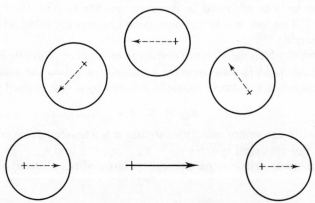

Figure 2.6   The direction of an induced dipole relative to a
permanent dipole

orientations, is given by the following expression

$$E_{ind} = -\frac{\mu_a^2 \alpha_b}{(4\pi\varepsilon_0)^2 R^6} \tag{2.10}$$

Dispersion energies

Figure 2.6 can also be used to show that the dispersion energy is always negative. If the permanent dipole is replaced by a temporary dipole then the induced dipoles will always be in such a direction that they are attracted to the temporary dipole. For example, if the temporary dipole is reversed, all the induced dipoles will reverse. Thus, even if the average of the temporary dipole is zero, as it must be for a molecule without a permanent dipole moment, the average of the interaction energies with which it is associated will not be zero.

The electrostatic field at a distance R from a dipole is proportional to R^{-3}, hence the induced moments will, from equation 2.7, also be proportional to R^{-3}. As dipole–dipole energies are proportional to R^{-3} (2.4), dipole–induced dipole energies will be proportional to R^{-6}. It is therefore customary to write the dispersion energy as

$$E_{disp} = -C_6/R^6, \tag{2.11}$$

where the coefficients C_6 can be deduced empirically or by calculation. For atoms or nearly spherical molecules C_6 is independent of the relative orientation of the systems. For other molecules C_6 will be angle dependent but in most cases only spherical averages are known. Table 2.2 gives some typical values for C_6. These are quoted in atomic units so that to obtain the energy in atomic units one must insert in equation 2.11 the appropriate value of R in atomic units.

Expression 2.11 is the first term in an expansion in $1/R^2$ for the dispersion energy, with higher terms (C_8/R^8 etc.) arising from the interaction of induced

Table 2.2   Values of the dispersion energy coefficient $C_6/E_h a_0^6$ defined by expression 2.11

A \ B	H	He	Ne	H_2	N_2	CH_4
H	6.50	2.83	5.6	8.7	21	30
He	2.83	1.47	3.0	4.1	10	14
Ne	5.6	3.0	6.3	8.2	21	29
H_2	8.7	4.1	8.2	13	30	43
N_2	21	10	21	30	73	100
CH_4	30	14	29	43	100	150

Values are from A. Dalgarno, *Adv. Chem. Phys.*, **12**, 143 (1967). $E_h a_0^6 = 9.573 \times 10^{-80}$ J m^6.

multipoles of higher order (quadrupoles etc.). The values of C_8 and C_{10} are known for simple systems like the inert gas atoms, but these higher terms are usually less than 10% of the leading term.

An approximate relationship between the dispersion energy and the polarizabilities of the interacting systems was derived by London using perturbation theory

$$E_{\text{disp}} = - \frac{3I_a I_b}{2(I_a + I_b)} \cdot \frac{\alpha_a \alpha_b}{(4\pi\varepsilon_0)^2 R^6}. \tag{2.12}$$

I_a and I_b are ionization potentials of the two systems. For two identical atoms or molecules this formula becomes

$$E_{\text{disp}} = - \frac{3\alpha^2 I}{4(4\pi\varepsilon_0)^2 R^6}. \tag{2.13}$$

It can be seen from expressions 2.10 and 2.12 that for dipolar molecules the induction and dispersion energies are both proportional to R^{-6}. Using the London formula for the dispersion energy, 2.13, the ratio of the induction energy to the dispersion energy is approximately $\mu^2/\alpha I$. The size of this factor in a typical case is shown by the data in Table 2.3. The induction energy is only 2% of the dispersion energy. As polarizabilities are roughly proportional to molecular volumes it is, in general, only for small molecules with large dipole moments that the induction energy is important. For ionic systems the induction energy (an R^{-4} term as shown by equation 2.9) may also be large, but in this case the electrostatic energy is by far the most important contribution to the long-range energy.

Pair additivity

The final point we give attention to in this section is the pair additivity of the long-range energies. For example, if we have three molecules A, B and C in mutual proximity then we wish to know whether the total intermolecular energy is equal to the sum of A–B, B–C and A–C pair energies. Any deviation can be attributed to a three-body energy.

The electrostatic energy is exactly pair additive: for example, the electrostatic energy for three point charges is the sum of the three Coulombic energies for the charges interacting in pairs. It can be shown by perturbation

Table 2.3 Data relevant to the induction and dispersion energies between HCl molecules

$\mu = 1.08\ \text{D} = 3.60 \times 10^{-30}\ \text{C m}$
$\alpha = 2.6 \times 4\pi\varepsilon_0\ \text{Å}^3 = 2.9 \times 10^{-40}\ \text{J}^{-1}\ \text{C}^2\ \text{m}^{-1}$
$I = 12.75\ \text{eV} = 2.04 \times 10^{-18}\ \text{J}$
$\dfrac{\mu^2}{\alpha I} = 0.022$

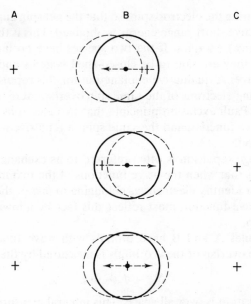

Figure 2.7 An illustration of the non-pair
additivity of induction energies

theory that the dispersion energy is also exactly pair additive in the R^{-6} term
(2.11), with non-additive contributions only appearing in higher powers of
$1/R$.†

The induction energy is not pair additive as can be seen easily by qualitative
argument. Figure 2.7 shows the displacement of the electrons of an atom
towards a neighbouring positive charge. If a second positive charge is placed
at the same distance on the other side of the atom, then the fields from the
two positive charges will cancel and there will be no displacement of the
centre of the electron cloud, only a symmetrical distortion as shown. There is
therefore a charge-induced dipole energy with one charge present but no such
term with two charges present. The net induction energy is therefore not the
sum of the induction energies arising from one charge being there without the
other. It is because of the possible importance of induction energies in determining the properties of polar liquids that one must be cautious in assuming a
pair-additive potential for such systems.

2.3 Short-range energies

Short-range energies arise from the overlap of electron densities of the
interacting molecules. If the two species have unpaired electrons (e.g., H,

†For a proof of this see Chapters 2 and 3 in *Rare Gas Solids*, Eds. M. L. Klein and J. A.
Venables, Academic Press, London and New York (1976).

CH_3) then by pairing the electron spins so that the net spin angular momentum is zero, an attractive short-range energy is obtained. This is the origin of intra-molecular (valence) energies. If the two species have no unpaired electrons (e.g., He, CH_4) they are said to be closed-shell systems and the short-range energy is repulsive. A qualitative explanation for this repulsion is that when orbitals containing electrons of the same spin overlap there is an approaching violation of the Pauli exclusion principle that two electrons cannot have the same orbital wave function and the same spin; a repulsive force is associated with this violation.

The short-range repulsion is often referred to as exchange repulsion. The reason for this is that when the wave functions of the two molecules overlap we can no longer identify electrons as belonging to one or the other molecule and the total wave function must reflect this fact by allowing for exchange between the two.

If two molecules A and B have orbitals with wave functions ϕ_a and ϕ_b respectively, the overlap of these orbitals is measured by the overlap integral

$$S = \int \phi_a \phi_b \, dv, \tag{2.14}$$

where the integration is over all space. This integral measures the amount of space which is common to both wave functions. If A and B are far apart the orbitals ϕ_a and ϕ_b will not overlap significantly and S will be effectively zero.

A common feature of the wave functions of atomic and molecular orbitals is that they decay exponentially to infinity. It follows that the overlap integral also decays exponentially as the distance between the two molecules goes to infinity. To give a specific example, the overlap integral between two hydrogen 1s atomic orbitals has the form

$$S = (1 + R + R^2/3)\exp(-R). \tag{2.15}$$

As is shown in the appendix to this chapter, the exchange energy involves the product of two orbital overlap functions, $\phi_a \phi_b$, so that the exchange energy is approximately proportional to S^2. As the exchange energy is rather difficult to calculate but the overlap integral easy, this provides a useful route to the estimation of exchange energies. The following approximate relationship was suggested by Mulliken

$$E_{ex} = kS^2/R \tag{2.16}$$

where k is a constant whose value depends on the type of orbitals involved. A more general approach is to assume that the exchange energy is of the form

$$E_{ex} = A \exp(-bR) \tag{2.17}$$

where A and b are parameters whose values are to be determined empirically. Expression 2.17 is known as the Born–Mayer potential.

The exchange energy can generally be taken as pair additive. To obtain a significant three-body exchange energy it is necessary for there to be some region of space where there is simultaneously an overlap of the wave functions of three molecules, and this would only occur if the pair overlaps were exceptionally large. In other words it would only occur in very repulsive situations which are not of any significance for the liquid state.

The hydrogen bond

Amongst those systems where the intermolecular energy is exceptionally large the hydrogen bond is by far the most important for the liquid state. In Chapter 8 we will examine in detail the intermolecular potential for water molecules, but a few more general comments are in order at this point.

The hydrogen bond is a structure in which a hydrogen atom is partly bonded to two electronegative atoms, most commonly nitrogen, oxygen or a halogen atom, the three atoms being usually colinear. In most cases the hydrogen is more strongly bound to one atom (A) than the other (B), the A–H bond being almost the same length as in the uncomplexed system, A–H and the other bond B–H being longer than a normal chemical bond. In a few strong complexes the hydrogen is symmetrically placed between A and B.

Recent *ab initio* calculations on hydrogen bonded complexes have confirmed the early view that the main contribution to the binding energy comes from the electrostatic energy between the dipolar A–H bond and a partial negative charge on the electronegative atom B. For the stronger complexes, however, there is a significant contribution to the energy from a valence-type interaction arising from the overlap of orbitals of A–H with those of B. This interaction leads to a partial transfer of electrons from B to the A–H bond.[†]

A negative (stabilizing) energy arising from the overlap of orbitals of closed-shell systems (as distinct from the exchange repulsion already discussed) is commonly explained by the Mulliken theory of charge-transfer or donor–acceptor complexes. We again refer the reader elsewhere for details.[‡] A point that should be made, however, is that the relationship of charge-transfer to exchange energies has some similarity to the relationship of induction and dispersion to electrostatic energies. Charge-transfer energies can be thought of as involving exchange and polarization, and the alternative description exchange-polarization is often used. Like induction energies, charge-transfer energies are not pair additive.

Table 2.4 summarizes some of the conclusions that have been reached in the last two sections.

2.4 Empirical and semi-empirical potentials

Although it is possible to predict from quantum mechanics the general functional form of the intermolecular potential, it is only for relatively simple atoms or molecules that we can obtain potentials in this way which are

---

[†]For a more detailed discussion see L. C. Allen, *J. Amer. Chem. Soc.*, **97**, 6921 (1975).
[‡]J. N. Murrell, S. F. A. Kettle and J. M. Tedder, *The Chemical Bond*, Ch. 15, Wiley, Chichester (1978).

Table 2.4 Characteristic properties of the perturbation contributions to intermolecular energies

Type	Range	Attractive or repulsive	Pairwise additive
Electrostatic	Long	Either	Yes
Exchange	Short	Repulsive	Yes
Dispersion	Long	Attractive	Yes
Induction	Long	Attractive	No
Exchange polarization or charge transfer	Short	Attractive	No

sufficiently accurate to provide a very good fit to the bulk properties of gases, liquids and solids. As explained in the first section of this chapter, a more successful route for obtaining accurate potentials is to combine some theoretical knowledge on the form of a potential with experimental information on the values of parameters which occur in the potential. This is called the semi-empirical method.†

Even if a potential is known not to be an accurate representation of the true potential, an analysis of the type of bulk properties that it can give may be revealing. For example, the simplest pair potential for atoms is the hard-sphere function. If an atom is modelled by a hard-sphere of diameter σ the potential will be zero for $R > \sigma$ and infinity for $R < \sigma$ with a discontinuity at $R = \sigma$. This function is illustrated in Figure 2.8(a). It can be shown that the hard-sphere potential, when introduced into statistical theories, reproduces qualitatively many of the properties of a fluid: the thermal conductivity and viscosity are two examples, and the value of σ can be chosen to give the best fit to such properties. It also leads to a bulk phase which has a solid–liquid phase change. The important inference from such an analysis is not that the hard-sphere potential is an accurate representation of the potential, but that the particular properties mentioned are primarily dependent on the repulsive part of the potential, and for such properties the van der Waals attractive well is much less important.

To obtain a liquid–gas phase change it is necessary to use a potential which has a minimum. The simplest potential which possesses this can be obtained by combining a square-well attraction with the hard-sphere repulsion as shown in Figure 2.8(b). Unfortunately this potential has not proved to be mathematically very easy to use in theories of fluids and, as it is a long way from being a realistic potential, not a great deal of attention has been given to it in the scientific literature.

---

†A very detailed account of the method of determining intermolecular energies from experimental data is contained in *Advances in Chemical Physics, Volume 12, Intermolecular Forces*, Ed. J. O. Hirschfelder, Interscience, London and New York (1967).

Figure 2.8   A comparison of simple empirical potentials. (a) hard-sphere, (b) square-well, (c) Lennard-Jones (equation 2.18), (d) (exp–6), $[U = 9 \times 10^4 \, \varepsilon \exp(-10R/\sigma) - 4\varepsilon \, (\sigma/R)^6]$

The potential which has been the basis of most analytical studies of atomic fluids and is at the same time a reasonably close representation of real potentials has the form

$$U = 4\varepsilon \left[\left(\frac{\sigma}{R} \right)^{12} - \left(\frac{\sigma}{R} \right)^{6} \right]. \tag{2.18}$$

It is called the Lennard-Jones or L-J potential after its originator. It is also often called the 6–12 potential being one member of the family

$$U = A \left[\left(\frac{\sigma}{R} \right)^{m} - \left(\frac{\sigma}{R} \right)^{n} \right], \qquad m > n, \tag{2.19}$$

where m and n are integers. These potentials are zero at $R = \infty$ and $R = \sigma$, and have a minimum at

$$R_{\min} = \sigma \left(\frac{m}{n} \right)^{\frac{1}{m-n}}, \tag{2.20}$$

of depth

$$U_{\min} = A \left[\left(\frac{n}{m} \right)^{\frac{m}{m-n}} - \left(\frac{n}{m} \right)^{\frac{n}{m-n}} \right]. \tag{2.21}$$

For the L-J potential $R_{\min} = 2^{1/6}\sigma$, $U_{\min} = -\varepsilon$ as indicated in Figure 2.8(c).

At large R the L-J potential is asymptotic to an R^{-6} curve and hence it has the correct form to reproduce the long-range dispersion energy between closed-shell atoms and molecules. For $R < \sigma$ the first term in the potential dominates and making this proportional to R^{-12} ensures a rapid rise in the repulsive branch of the curve. There is no physical significance in taking $m = 12$, but a mathematical advantage in having $m = 2n$ for the evaluation of certain integrals that enter the calculation of fluid properties.

There is now general agreement that one gets closer to exact interatomic potentials by taking the repulsive part of the potential to be an exponential; the theoretical arguments for this were given in the last section. The most commonly employed simple function is

$$U = A \exp(-kR) - C_6/R^6, \tag{2.22}$$

which is usually called the (exp − 6) potential. This function has the merit that both the long-range attraction and short-range repulsion are functions that are supported by theoretical analysis. A typical function is shown in Figure 2.8(d).

All the functions illustrated in Figure 2.8 have so few constant parameters (from one to three) that the values of these parameters can be optimized by fitting theoretical predictions to experimental data and, as explained in the first part of this chapter, these data are usually obtained from the properties of gases. However, no simple analytical function, either those we have described or others, gives an exact representation of the data. To obtain agreement between theory and experiment at the highest possible level most workers have employed different functions for different ranges of R. It is then necessary to impose the condition that U shall be a smooth function over the complete range of R, and this places further restrictions on the parameters. Very accurate pair potentials for the inert gases have been obtained in this way.†

The current situation for the potentials between molecules is one of active research, but there is no widely held view on what are the best semi-empirical functions to employ. One popular approach is to assume that the potential is a sum of atom–atom pair potentials using functions of the type illustrated in Figure 2.8: a sum of L–J potentials has been most commonly used. For example, the intermolecular potential between two N_2 molecules would be the sum of four N–N pair potentials. For polar molecules it is common to add to such terms an electrostatic energy in the form of the multipole expansion. The potential between two HCl molecules would therefore be the sum of H–H, Cl–Cl and H–Cl pair potentials, plus electrostatic terms such as expression 2.5 obtained from dipole and quadrupole moments.

The most complicated fluid which has been extensively subjected to theoretical analysis is water and the potentials employed for such studies will be described in Chapter 8.

†For example, an accurate Ar–Ar potential has been published by J. M. Parson, P. E. Siska and Y. T. Lee, *J. Chem. Phys.*, **56**, 1511 (1972).

2.5 Long-range macroscopic attraction

The existence of long-range attractive forces between molecules and macroscopic particles or between two macroscopic particles, is very significant for an understanding of several topics that are dealt with in the last three chapters of this book: colloid stability, wetting phenomena, membrane properties, etc.[†] To account for these forces it is necessary to extend the theory of molecule–molecule interactions in two ways. First, it is necessary to sum up the forces from all the molecules that make up the macroscopic particles, and second, a correction has to be made to the long-range forces when they operate over macroscopic distances (typically greater than 500 Å).

We have seen (2.11) that the long-range dispersion energy between two molecules has the form $-C_6/R^6$, where C_6 is of the order of 10^{-78} J m^6 atom^{-1}. The sum of such contributions for all molecules in a macroscopic particle will depend on the shape of the particle. The most important cases are when the particle has a planar face, which can be considered as infinite in area, and is of infinite thickness (this is called the semi-infinite solid), and when the particles are spheres of equal radii. In these cases the total dispersion energy can be obtained by integrating expression 2.11 between certain limits. The following are the most important results.

(1) For a molecule at a distance R from the surface of a semi-infinite solid the energy is

$$E = -\frac{\pi n C_6}{6R^3},\tag{2.23}$$

where n is the number density of molecules (number per m^3) in the solid.

(2) For two semi-infinite solids whose faces are parallel and separated by a distance R, the energy per unit area of face is given by

$$E = -\frac{H}{12\pi R^2},\tag{2.24}$$

where H is known as the Hamaker constant, which for this system is given by

$$H = \pi^2 n^2 C_6.\tag{2.25}$$

(3) For two spheres of radius a whose centres are d apart, the energy is

$$E = -\frac{H}{6}\left\{\frac{2}{D^2-4} + \frac{2}{D^2} + \ln\left(\frac{D^2-4}{D^2}\right)\right\},\tag{2.26}$$

where $D = d/a$. If the spheres are large compared with the shortest distance between the surfaces ($d \approx 2a$) then the Hamaker constant is also given by expression 2.25, and this is the usual assumption.

The most important point to make about expressions 2.23, 2.24 and 2.26, is

---

[†]P. Richmond, *Colloid Science*, Specialist Periodical Report, Chem. Soc., vol. 2, (1975); A. W. Adamson, *Physical Chemistry of Surfaces*, 3rd edn, Wiley, Chichester (1977).

that the energy depends on a smaller inverse power of the separation than does the molecule–molecule energy. As a result these energies are significant over much larger distances than the molecule–molecule energy.

In section 2.2 we gave the following qualitative explanation of dispersion forces: a temporary dipole on one molecule induces a dipole on a neighbouring molecule and there will be an attraction between these two dipoles. In standard quantum mechanics this interaction is considered to be instantaneous, but in a more advanced theory, quantum electrodynamics, it is recognized that it takes time for the interaction to be passed between the molecules by an electromagnetic radiation field. For large separations this results in some dephasing of the temporary and induced dipoles, and hence some reduction in the dispersion force. Such a reduction was first postulated by Verwey to explain the apparently small value of dispersion energies between colloidal particles at large distances. The first detailed theory by quantum electrodynamics was by Casimir and Polder in 1948.

If the temporary dipoles in a molecule fluctuate with a frequency v this will be associated with radiation of wavelength $\lambda = c/v$. If the distance between the molecules is comparable with or greater than λ then the dephasing of the temporary and induced dipoles will be significant. Typical wavelengths are those associated with electronic transitions in the molecules, 10^3–10^4 Å (10^2–10^3 nm), and it is at such distances or longer that one refers to the forces as being very-long-range or retarded. Casimir and Polder showed that in this region the dipole–dipole dispersion energy varied as R^{-7} rather than R^{-6}. The retarded forms of the macroscopic interactions given in 2.23, 2.24 and 2.26 also increase by one power of R in the denominator.

The London theory of dispersion energies relates the C_6 coefficient to polarizabilities of the molecules (2.12). In 1956 Lifshitz showed that it was possible to relate macroscopic dispersion energies directly to macroscopic properties of the interacting particles and the intervening medium. The relevant property is the dielectric constant (relative permittivity), which, as we show in Chapter 8, is the macroscopic analogue of polarizability. The Hamaker constant that appears in 2.24 and 2.26 can be determined from a knowledge of the dielectric constant as a function of frequency although the method is quite complicated and we give no details here.†

Hamaker constants for single materials are typically of the order of 10^{-19} J and some values calculated by the macroscopic approach are given in Table 2.5. The presence of a liquid medium between the particles, rather than a vacuum or air, lowers appreciably the dispersion energy, and it also shortens the distance at which retardation sets in. For a system of particles 1 and 2 separated by an intervening medium 3 the effective Hamaker constant for the particles is given by

$$H_{12,3} = H_{12} + H_{33} - H_{13} - H_{23}. \tag{2.27}$$

†P. Richmond, *loc. cit.* D. B. Hough and L. R. White, *Adv. Colloid Interf. Sci.*, **14**, 3 (1980).

Table 2.5   Values of the Hamaker constant for different
media, calculated from macroscopic theory

	$H/10^{-20}$ J
Water	3.0–6.1
Ionic crystals	5.8–11.8
Metals	22
Silica	8.6
Quartz	8.0–8.8
Hydrocarbons	6.3
Polystyrene	5.6–6.4

Where a range of values is given this reflects different methods of
calculation. J. Visser, *Surface and Colloid Science*, Ed. E. Matijević,
vol. 8, Wiley–Interscience, Chichester (1976).

Note that if the medium (3) has the same dielectric properties as 1 and 2,
then there is effectively no interaction between the particles.

Finally, it should be mentioned that there has been much interest in the
direct experimental measurement of the attractive forces between macroscopic systems at sub-micron distances, notably the work of Tabor and
co-workers on mica.[†] There has been a broad measure of agreement with
modern theory down to separations of about 1 nm.

Appendix 2

The net charge of a molecular species is obtained by summing over the
nuclear charges eZ_α and integrating over the electron distribution. If $\rho(r)$ is
the electron probability density then

$$q = e\left(\sum_\alpha Z_\alpha - \int \rho(r)\, dv\right). \tag{A2.1}$$

The first moment is the dipole moment which is a vector quantity whose x
component is, for example, given by

$$\mu_x = e\left(\sum_\alpha Z_\alpha x_\alpha - \int \rho(r).x\,.dv\right). \tag{A2.2}$$

The second moment, or quadrupole, is a tensor with components Θ_{xx}, Θ_{yy},
Θ_{zz}, $\Theta_{xy} = \Theta_{yx}$, etc., given by the expressions

$$\Theta_{xx} = \frac{e}{2}\left(\sum_\alpha Z_\alpha(3x_\alpha^2 - r_\alpha^2) - \int \rho(r)(3x^2 - r^2)\, dr\right), \tag{A2.3}$$

$$\Theta_{xy} = \frac{3}{2}e\left(\sum_\alpha Z_\alpha x_\alpha y_\alpha - \int \rho(r).xy\, dv\right) \quad \text{etc.} \tag{A2.4}$$

[‡]J. M. Israelachvili and D. Tabor, *Proc. Roy. Soc.*, **A331**, 19 (1971).

For a molecule with a three-fold or higher symmetry axis (e.g. CH_3F or a linear molecule) there is only one independent component of the quadrupole tensor. If z is taken as the symmetry axis, then $\Theta_{zz} = -2\Theta_{xx} = -2\Theta_{yy}$, $\Theta_{xy} = \Theta_{yz} = \Theta_{zx} = 0$.

Only the first non-zero moment of a molecule is independent of the origin of the coordinate system. For example, suppose the origin is displaced in the x direction by a so that $x' = x - a$, then expression A2.2 becomes

$$\mu'_x = e\left(\sum_\alpha Z_\alpha x'_\alpha - \int \rho(r).x' \, dv\right)$$

$$= e\left(\sum_\alpha Z_\alpha(x - a) - \int \rho(r)(x - a) \, dv\right)$$

$$= \mu_x - ae\left(\sum_\alpha Z_\alpha - \int \rho(r) \, dv\right)$$

$$= \mu_x - aq. \tag{A2.5}$$

Hence for a neutral molecule ($q = 0$), $\mu'_x = \mu_x$, but for a charged species this is not the case. Likewise for a dipolar molecule the quadrupole is dependent on origin.

In the multipole expansion of the electrostatic energy R is the distance between the origins of the multipole moments of the two molecules, and hence the individual terms in the multipole expansion are origin dependent both in their numerators (the multipoles) and their denominators (powers of R). However, the total electrostatic energy is independent of origin. It is usual to choose the centre of mass of a molecule for the multipole origin and this generally leads to the most rapid convergence of the multipole expansion.

We turn now to a brief discussion of the exchange energy. If molecule A has an electron (labelled 1) with a wave function Φ_a and species B an electron (2) with wave function Φ_b then the wave function of the pair of electrons is $\Phi_a(1)\Phi_b(2)$. However, as electrons are indistinguishable an equally acceptable wave function is $\Phi_a(2)\Phi_b(1)$. There is a fundamental postulate of quantum mechanics that the total wave functions for electrons must change sign if we exchange the labels of two electrons: this is called the antisymmetry principle. Thus the only combination of the two product wave functions that is an allowed wave function for the AB pair is[†]

$$\psi = N(\Phi_a(1)\Phi_b(2) - \Phi_a(2)\Phi_b(1)), \tag{A2.6}$$

where N is a normalizing factor.

We can calculate the energy of the system with the wave function A2.6 from the quantum mechanical formula

$$E = \int \psi H \psi \, dv, \tag{A2.7}$$

[†]The antisymmetry rule applies to space and spin of the electrons so Φ must be a space–spin function or 'spinorbital'. The lower case ϕ used in 2.14 represents an orbital without indication of spin.

where H is the Hamiltonian and the integration is over all space. Substituting A2.6 into A2.7 gives

$$E = N^2 \int (\Phi_a(1)\Phi_b(2) - \Phi_a(2)\Phi_b(1)) H (\Phi_a(1)\Phi_b(2) - \Phi_a(2)\Phi_b(1)) \, dv,$$

$$(A2.8)$$

and, on multiplying out the terms we obtain four integrals, two of which are of the type

$$N^2 \int \Phi_a(i)\Phi_b(j) H \Phi_a(i)\Phi_b(j) \, dv, \qquad (A2.9)$$

where i and j are 1 or 2. These give the electrostatic contribution to the intermolecular energy discussed in the last section. The other two integrals are of the type

$$-N^2 \int \Phi_a(i)\Phi_b(j) H \Phi_a(j)\Phi_b(i) \, dv, \qquad (A2.10)$$

and these give the exchange energy, the word exchange referring to the relationship between the functions on the two sides of H.

It would need more detailed discussion on the nature of the Hamiltonian and the functions Φ to explain why the exchange energy is positive for the overlap of closed-shell systems, because this only becomes evident when the explicit form of the integrals is examined. However, we note that the integral A2.10 involves the overlap density $\Phi_a\Phi_b$ for both electrons 1 and 2 and hence A2.10 will be approximately proportional to the square of the overlap integral S (expression 2.14).

Chapter 3

Theories and models of the liquid state

3.1 Introduction

A successful theory of the liquid state will be one that explains the bulk properties of the liquid from a knowledge of the intermolecular potential. In the bulk we are dealing with a very large number of molecules ($\sim 10^{23}$) and we know by the principles of statistics that at equilibrium the time fluctuations of bulk properties will be very small and can generally be ignored. Statistical thermodynamics provides the analytical connection between the intermolecular potential and thermodynamic observables such as pressure and free energy. Non-equilibrium statistical mechanics provides a similar connection for time-dependent properties such as viscosity and thermal conductivity.

The statistical equations can be solved exactly or with high accuracy for gases and solids but, for reasons which will be explained later, they are very difficult to solve for liquids. Indeed, a rather advanced knowledge of statistical mechanics is needed to understand the most successful statistical theories of liquids and we shall make only passing comments on these in this chapter. Even the statistical theory of the imperfect gas, which we shall cover in detail, requires a good grounding in statistical thermodynamics and readers without this are advised to omit section 3.3.

An alternative approach to a theory of liquids has been through the use of physical models and in the next section we will describe work along this line that was undertaken by Bernal and others. These models have improved our conceptual understanding of the nature of liquids but they have not proved very helpful for the quantitative prediction of liquid-state properties.

In recent years a method has been developed for modelling liquids which has been conceptually valuable and has proved capable of giving a quantitative interpretation of bulk properties. This method uses a modern computer with fast operation and large core store to simulate the behaviour of a large number of atoms or molecules interacting under some assumed potential function. No computer is large enough (nor likely to be) to handle directly the interaction of 10^{23} particles but, as we shall see, techniques exist for dealing with much smaller numbers (10^2–10^3) which will give results not significantly different from the true bulk. These techniques will be described in section 3.5.

Before the era of computer simulation there was considerable interest in relatively simple statistical models of the liquid state which were extensions of the statistical theories of solids. The *cell theory* of Lennard-Jones and Eyring's *significant liquid structure theory* are two of these. It cannot be said that they have an important place in modern liquid state theory because it is now accepted that the imperfect solid is a poor approximation to a liquid. The interested reader is directed to other books for an account of these theories.[†]

The treatment of liquids as imperfect gases is also not without serious criticism, but it at least has the merit of being relevant to fluids above the critical state. For this reason we give more attention to the statistical theory of the imperfect gas in section 3.3 than might be thought justified in a book on liquids. We must emphasize, however, that normal liquids are neither imperfect gases nor imperfect solids. There is at present no theory of the liquid state which is satisfactory for all types of liquid and all conditions of temperature and pressure.

3.2 Physical models

The physical models developed by Bernal and others have been based on the proposition that the structure of liquids can be represented by the random close packing of hard or almost hard shapes. If one is thinking of a monatomic fluid, for example, then the model might be a cluster of ball bearings which has not been shaken down to a regular close-packed structure.

One of the first physical models examined by Bernal was a cluster of plasticine balls.[‡] The relationship between the balls was determined by compressing the cluster so that the balls developed planar contact faces, that is, they became irregular polyhedra. When this model was dismantled it was found that the average number of faces of these polyhedra was 13.6 and the most commonly occurring face was pentagonal. A regular close-packed arrangement of spheres would give 12-faced polyhedra with rhombic faces. Only tetrahedra, cubes and octahedra of the regular solids can be packed in an ordered array to fill space completely; polyhedra with pentagonal faces such as the dodecahedron cannot. Bernal therefore inferred that random close packing and pentagonal arrangements were necessarily connected.

Further examination of a randomly close-packed steel ball model, by

[†]H. Eyring and M. K. Jhon, *Significant Liquid Structures*, Wiley, London and New York (1969); J. A. Barker, *Lattice Theories of the Liquid State*, Pergamon Press, Oxford (1963).

[‡]The three dimensional random packing of gelatine spheres was earlier examined by W. E. Morrell and J. H. Hildebrand, *J. Chem. Phys.*, **4**, 224 (1936), and before that others had studied packing in two dimensions. Bernal, however, was the first to emphasize the geometrical features of random close packing.

Figure 3.1 The radial distribution function for an assembly of hard spheres of diameter σ at high density. The continuous curve is the result of a computer simulation such as will be described in section 3.5 and the histogram is the result of a ball-bearing experiment by Bernal and King. The figure was taken from J. S. Rowlinson, *Disc. Faraday Soc.*, **49**, 30 (1970)

Bernal and by Scott, led to a radial distribution function for hard spheres which is in good agreement with that found by computer simulation as shown in Figure 3.1. The coordination numbers in the model, defined by the number of neighbours whose centres were less than 1.05 diameters from a chosen atom, were found to vary between four and eleven with an average of nine. This agrees well with the result of computer simulation and the experimental value for neon determined by diffraction studies which is 8.8.

Scott's steel ball experiments led to a density for random close packing of 0.86 times the density of regular close packing and this also agrees well with, for example, the value of 0.87 for the ratio of the densities of solid and liquid argon at its melting point.

3.3 Statistical thermodynamics

Statistical thermodynamics is a scheme by which thermodynamic observables can be calculated as averages over molecular properties. In this chapter we first show how it may be applied to calculate the properties of the imperfect gas as this establishes the route for determining empirical potentials as described in the previous chapter. The analysis of the imperfect gas also shows one way that progress can be made for liquids.

All thermodynamic functions can be obtained from a quantity which plays a central role in statistical mechanics called the partition function. If a system has a set of discrete energy levels E_i, the partition function is defined by

$$Q = \sum_i \exp(-E_i/kT). \tag{3.1}$$

For an ensemble of systems with the same volume which are in thermal equilibrium the probability that a specified member has an energy E_i is[†]

$$P(E_i) = \exp(-E_i/kT)/Q. \tag{3.2}$$

Discrete energy levels arise in quantum mechanics for the electronic, vibrational and rotational states of molecules and for the translational states of atoms and molecules confined to finite volumes. By taking the system to be an individual molecule and substituting the appropriate expressions for these energies into equation 3.1 one can deduce the molecular partition function and the thermodynamic stability of the species through the expression

$$A - A(T = 0) = -kT \ln Q, \tag{3.3}$$

where A is the Helmholtz free energy.

This procedure, which is probably familiar to most chemists, takes no account of the intermolecular potential. As the total energy for N molecules is not the sum of N separate molecular energies it is not strictly justified to take the system (in the statistical mechanical sense) to be an individual molecule, rather, it must be a set of N interacting molecules. In this case to make progress in the evaluation of equation 3.1 it is necessary to write the total energy as a sum of the internal energies, $E_{k,A}$, of the molecules (electronic, vibrational and rotational), the translational energies of the molecules and U the intermolecular potential

$$E_i = \sum_A (E_{k,A} + E_{trans,A}) + U. \tag{3.4}$$

Expression 3.4 contains an important assumption which is that the intermolecular potential U is independent of the internal state (labelled k) of the molecules. The intermolecular potential is independent of the vibrational and rotational states of the interacting molecules[‡] but it is not independent of their electronic states. However, for most molecules at normal temperatures only the lowest (ground) electronic state contributes significantly to the partition function and hence, without serious error, it can be taken as the

---

[†]Terms such as 'system' and 'ensemble' have precise meanings in statistical mechanics. We direct the reader to specialist books on the subject for these and also for the derivation of 3.2 and the expressions relating Q to thermodynamic observables. The following two books are recommended: F. C. Andrew, *Equilibrium Statistical Mechanics*, Wiley, London and New York (1963). G. S. Rushbrooke, *Introduction to Statistical Mechanics*, Oxford (1949).
[‡]This is contained within the Born–Oppenheimer separation of electronic and nuclear motion.

intermolecular potential appropriate to all molecules being in their ground states.

The configurational integral

Because we have, by expression 3.4, written the total energy as a sum of component energies the partition function 3.1 for a system of N molecules can be expressed as a product of component partition functions.[†] It can be shown that Q has the form

$$Q = \left(\frac{q_{\text{int}}q_{\text{t}}}{V}\right)^N \frac{Q'}{N!} \tag{3.5}$$

where q_{int} and q_{t} are the internal and translational partition functions for a single molecule and Q' is called the configurational integral. The internal partition function depends on the vibrational and rotational energies of the molecule, and it can be evaluated readily using the harmonic-oscillator and rigid-rotor models. However, as it has no role in our later analysis we have no need to quote its explicit form.

The translational partition function can easily be evaluated and for molecules of mass m contained in a volume V the result is

$$q_{\text{t}} = (2\pi mkT/h^2)^{3/2}V. \tag{3.6}$$

We note therefore that q_{t}/V is independent of volume and hence the volume dependence of Q is the same as the volume dependence of Q'.

A final point to note about expression 3.5 is the appearance of $N!$ in the denominator. This is associated with the indistinguishability of identical molecules in the system. However, the factor is only appropriate for identical molecules under conditions in which they can rapidly interchange their positions (i.e. in gases and liquids) and it must be omitted if this is not the case (i.e. for solids). In principle, identical molecules which have fixed places in a lattice are distinguishable.

The configurational integral is defined by

$$Q' = \int \ldots \int_{3N} \exp(-U/kT) \, dq, \tag{3.7}$$

where U is the total intermolecular potential energy appearing in equation 3.4. The integration is over the $3N$ coordinates that define the positions of the centres of mass of the molecule and any rotational coordinates of the molecules which are parameters in the intermolecular potential.[‡]

[†]This is because of the mathematical identity

$$\exp(-\sum_i a_i) = \prod_i \exp(-a_i).$$

[‡]A qualification must be made that 3.7 is only valid when the motion of the centres of mass of the molecules can be treated by classical mechanics. The existence of negative regions (van der Waals' minima) of the intermolecular potential as illustrated in Figure 2.8 will be associated with discrete bound states. Except for very light atoms or molecules these discrete state are sufficiently close together that they can be treated as a continuum and classical mechanics applied. For helium the corrections for quantum behaviour are very important; for light atoms such as neon they are small and standard procedures exist for making a quantum correction.

If N is the number of molecules in a macroscopic sample (10^{23}) there will be no hope of evaluating this integral unless it can be factored into products of integrals of smaller dimension. At first sight it might appear that this is relatively straightforward because, as argued in section 2.1, the inter-molecular potential is predominantly composed of pair potentials with smaller contributions from three-body and higher terms. Unfortunately this does not, of itself, lead to factorization of the configurational integral as can be seen from the following example.

Consider a system of three atoms interacting by pair potentials $U(R_{ij})$ so that the total interatomic potential is

$$U = U(R_{12}) + U(R_{23}) + U(R_{13}). \tag{3.8}$$

The variables of integration q are the coordinates of the centres of mass of the atoms whereas the R_{ij} are the distances between the centres, the two being related by expressions such as

$$R_{12} = ((qx_2 - qx_1)^2 + (qy_2 - qy_1)^2 + (qz_2 - qz_1)^2)^{1/2}. \tag{3.9}$$

Thus if we integrate over the position coordinates of atom 1, the part of the integral which depends on the position of atom 1 is

$$\exp((-U(R_{12}) - U(R_{13}))/kT), \tag{3.10}$$

and the resulting integral will be a function of the positions of atoms 2 and 3. For a system of N atoms, integration over the position coordinates of any one atom does not lead to a constant but to a function which depends on the positions of the other $N - 1$ atoms, hence the total integral cannot be expressed as a product of independent integrals.

In contrast, we note that for solids the situation is much simpler because it is usually assumed that U is a function (usually a harmonic function) of the displacement of an atom from its lattice site and it does not depend explicitly on the distances between the atoms. Thus one can write

$$U = \sum_i U(q_i), \tag{3.11}$$

whence 3.7 reduces to a product of N single-atom integrals

$$Q' = \prod_{i=1,N} \int \exp(-U(q_i)/kT) \, dq_i, \tag{3.12}$$

which can be evaluated knowing the functional form of $U(q_i)$. An extension of this result was developed into the cell theory of liquids by Lennard-Jones and co-workers.

The cluster expansion

The way forward for liquids and gases is to make an expansion of the integrand of the configurational integral. To illustrate this approach we again assume that the total potential is pair additive and write

$$U = \sum_{ij(j<i)} U_{ij}, \tag{3.13}$$

where $U_{ij} \equiv U(R_{ij})$ is a pair potential. A function f_{ij} called the Mayer function is defined by

$$f_{ij} = \exp(-U_{ij}/kT) - 1, \qquad (3.14)$$

whence, from 3.7 and 3.13,

$$Q' = \int \ldots \int_{3N} \prod_{ij} (1 + f_{ij}) \, d\boldsymbol{q} \qquad (3.15)$$

The product in 3.15 can now be expanded to give

$$Q' = \int \ldots \int_{3N} \left(1 + \sum_{ij} f_{ij} + \sum_{ij} \sum_{kl \neq ij} f_{ij} f_{kl} + \ldots \right) d\boldsymbol{q}, \qquad (3.16)$$

which is called the cluster expansion. The first term is independent of the intermolecular potential or, giving it another perspective, is the only term which appears in the ideal gas limit of the intermolecular potential being zero. The terms linear in f represent the interaction of molecules in pairs, and the higher terms represent the interaction of molecules three or more at a time.

The first term in the cluster expansion is easily evaluated. For interacting atoms the $3N$ dimensional integral over the complete volume V which they occupy is equal to V^N. The second term is evaluated by first noting that all the U_{ij} (hence all the f_{ij}) are equivalent; therefore each of the $N(N-1)/2$ terms of this kind must give the same contribution to the integral. Taking f_{12} as a typical term and integrating over the coordinates of all other atoms leads to the following expression for Q'

$$Q' = V^N + \tfrac{1}{2} N^2 V^{N-2} \iint f_{12} \, d\boldsymbol{q}_1 \, d\boldsymbol{q}_2 + \text{higher terms}, \qquad (3.17)$$

where we have replaced $N(N-1)$ by N^2, a justified approximation for large N. The higher terms are evaluated in a similar way and reduce to integrals over the positions of three or more atoms.

The b integral

For atomic systems U_{ij} is a function only of R, the distance between the atoms, and no orientational variables are involved. The integral over f_{12} in 3.17 can in this case be reduced further (see Appendix 3.1) to give the following result

$$Q' = V^N \left[1 - \frac{2\pi N^2 b}{V} + \ldots \right], \qquad (3.18)$$

where

$$b = -\int_0^\infty f_{12}(R) R^2 \, dR = \int_0^\infty (1 - e^{-U_{12}(R)/kT}) R^2 \, dR. \qquad (3.19)$$

The integral b can be readily evaluated by numerical techniques if the interatomic potential $U(R)$ is known, and it has been extensively studied for the L-J potential (2.18). One of the few potentials for which an analytical integration is possible is the hard-sphere potential (Figure 2.8(a)). For this potential, $U(R)$ is infinite in the region $0 < R < \sigma$ and integration in this range gives $\sigma^3/3$. For the region $R > \sigma$, $U(R)$ is zero and so in this range there is no contribution to the integral. Thus for the hard-sphere model we have $b = \sigma^3/3$ and

$$Q' = V^N \left[1 - \frac{2\pi N^2 \sigma^3}{3V} + \ldots \right]. \tag{3.20}$$

Because σ^3 is of the order of a molecular volume, $N^2 \sigma^3/V$ must be of the order of N, which, for a macroscopic sample is of the order 10^{23}. Moreover, higher terms in the cluster expansion 3.16 are of the order of higher powers of N, so that the cluster expansion as it appears in Q' is extremely divergent and there would be no justification for terminating it at the second term. However, thermodynamic observables depend on $\ln Q$, as can be seen from 3.3. The contribution from Q' to the Helmholtz free energy is, from 3.18

$$A - A(T = 0) = -kT \ln Q' = -kTN \left[\ln V + N^{-1} \ln \left(1 - \frac{2\pi N^2 b}{V} + \ldots \right) \right], \tag{3.21}$$

and because a logarithmic function is a very slowly divergent function of its argument, the cluster expansion for A can be shown to be convergent, at least for dilute gases.[†] In fact the correct result can be obtained by treating the second term in the cluster expansion as small and using the approximation $\ln(1 + x) = x$ for small x. In this limit 3.21 becomes, for one mole (with $N = \mathcal{N}, k\mathcal{N} = R$)

$$A - A(T = 0) = -RT \left(\ln V - \frac{2\pi \mathcal{N} b}{V_m} \right). \tag{3.22}$$

Of particular interest is the pressure of the system which can be obtained from the relationship

$$P = -\left(\frac{\partial A}{\partial V} \right)_T. \tag{3.23}$$

Differentiating 3.22 we obtain the result

$$P = \frac{RT}{V_m} \left(1 + \frac{2\pi \mathcal{N} b}{V_m} \right). \tag{3.24}$$

If b is zero, 3.24 is the perfect gas equation. The term in b is a correction which approaches zero as the molar volume increases. Analysis of further

---

[†]The full analysis is quite complicated and was first given by Ursell, *Proc. Camb. Phil. Soc.*, **23**, 685 (1927).

terms in the cluster expansion and their contribution to P shows that 3.24 comprises the first two terms in an expansion for P in powers of $1/V_m$. These terms will be related to an empirical equation for the pressure in section 3.6.

We can now return to an examination of the size of the b-term and its contribution to the pressure using the hard-sphere model for simplicity ($b = \sigma^3/3$). Taking argon as our example, σ is approximately 3.4 Å. The molar volume of gaseous argon at 273 K and 1 atm is 22.4 dm³ and the molar volume of liquid argon at 87 K is 28.6 cm³. From these data one obtains values for the dimensionless quantity $2\pi \mathcal{N} b/V_m$ of 2.2×10^{-3} for the gas, and 1.7 for the liquid. The b-term is therefore a small correction to the pressure for the gas, but a large correction for the liquid and the cluster expansion terminated at the first correction term is unlikely to give the correct pressure for the liquid state. We will return to an examination of expression 3.24 for gases in section 3.6 in order to show how experimental measurement of (P, V, T)-properties can be used to deduce b, and hence allow parameterization of the intermolecular potential.

Although it is clear from the above analysis that the cluster expansion 3.16 terminated at the linear terms is inadequate for liquids, the ideas which are behind it have proved valuable. J. E. Mayer and others have made an extensive analysis of the cluster integrals using graph theory techniques to reduce and sum the terms.[†] Although these techniques have not been sufficient to allow a direct solution to the configurational partition function (3.16) for liquids they have proved useful in alternative statistical approaches to liquids based on distribution functions, and it is this aspect that we explore in the next section.

3.4 Distribution functions

In discussing the concept of order in a liquid in section 1.3 we introduced an important function in the theory of liquids called the radial distribution function, $g(r)$. This and similar functions play a central role in the more advanced statistical theories of liquids, and although we will not be describing such theories in great detail it is important to see the general direction in which the subject is progressing.

The instantaneous state of a system of N particles in classical mechanics is described by specifying the $3N$ momenta and $3N$ position variables of the particles. We start by defining a function $f^{(N)}$ which gives the probability of finding the particles in a specified classical state. The probability that particle 1 will have momentum between p_1 and $p_1 + \mathrm{d}p_1$ and position between q_1 and $q_1 + \mathrm{d}p_1$, and simultaneously particle 2 has momentum between p_2 and $p_2 + \mathrm{d}p_2$, etc., is

$$f^{(N)}(p_1 \ldots p_N, q_1 \ldots q_N) \, \mathrm{d}p_1 \ldots \mathrm{d}p_N \, \mathrm{d}q_1 \ldots \mathrm{d}q_N. \tag{3.25}$$

[†]J. E. Mayer and M. Goeppert-Mayer, *Statistical Mechanics*, Wiley, New York (1940).

To obtain a general N-particle configurational probability function which describes the positions irrespective of momenta, we can integrate over the momentum variables and obtain

$$n^{(N)}(q_1 \ldots q_N) = \int \ldots_{3N} \int f^{(N)}(p_i, q_i) \, dp_1 \ldots dp_N. \qquad (3.26)$$

However, even this function has no direct relevance to experiment when N is large, because no experiment can give information about the simultaneous positions of all particles in the system. What can be deduced is some inform-ation about the relative positions of small numbers of particles and particu-larly, as we have seen in section 1.3, about the distribution of pairs of particles.

The distribution functions for small numbers of particles can be obtained from 3.26 by successive integrations over the position variables. Thus if we know $n^{(N)}$ we can find by integration $n^{(N-1)}$, $n^{(N-2)}$, etc., down to $n^{(1)}$. The general recurrence formula is

$$\int n^{(K+1)} \, dq_{k+1} = (N - K)n^{(K)}, \qquad (3.27)$$

which means that the integral is equal to the distribution function for K particles multiplied by the number of particles encountered in performing the integration over the whole volume. In an isotropic fluid the probability of finding a particle in a volume dq_1 is independent of q_1, hence we have

$$n^{(1)} = N/V \quad \text{and} \quad \int n^{(1)} \, dq_1 = N. \qquad (3.28)$$

From 3.27 the integral of the pair distribution function is given by

$$\int n^{(2)}(q_1, q_2) \, dq_2 = (N - 1)n^{(1)} = N(N - 1)/V. \qquad (3.29)$$

The radial distribution function $g(r)$ is related to $n^{(2)}$ by the expression

$$n^{(2)}(q_1, q_2) = n^{(1)}(q_1)n^{(1)}(q_2)g(r) = (N^2/V^2)g(r). \qquad (3.30)$$

As r approaches infinity, $g(r)$ approaches one, and in this limit the probability of finding one particle at q_1 and a second at q_2 is the product of the two one-particle probabilities.

For a system in equilibrium $n^{(N)}$ will be proportional to $\exp(-U/kT)$, where U is the total potential energy, as defined by 3.4, for the N particles. The proportionality constant is equal to $N!/Q'$, where Q' is the configurational integral (equation 3.7). This can be confirmed by integrating both sides of the expression

$$n^{(N)} = \frac{N!}{Q'} \exp(-U/kT), \qquad (3.31)$$

over the coordinates of all N particles and using the integration formula 3.27.

By successive integrations over the coordinates of each particle, expressions for the lower order distribution functions can be obtained and, in particular,

$$n^{(2)} = \frac{N!}{(N-2)\,!Q'} \int \ldots \int \exp(-U/kT)\,\mathrm{d}\boldsymbol{q}_3 \ldots \mathrm{d}\boldsymbol{q}_N \qquad (3.32)$$

Thus to calculate these distribution functions from the intermolecular potential requires a similar, and as difficult, an integration as does the calculation of Q'.

Integral equations

The advanced statistical theories to which we have referred earlier, provide approximations to the distribution function $n^{(2)}$ and to $g(r)$. One of the most important ideas that has been used is contained in the Kirkwood superposition approximation

$$n^{(3)}(\boldsymbol{q}_1, \boldsymbol{q}_2, \boldsymbol{q}_3) = \frac{V^3}{N^3}\, n^{(2)}(\boldsymbol{q}_1, \boldsymbol{q}_2)n^{(2)}(\boldsymbol{q}_2, \boldsymbol{q}_3)n^{(2)}(\boldsymbol{q}_3, \boldsymbol{q}_1). \qquad (3.33)$$

This states that the probability of finding particles at $\boldsymbol{q}_1, \boldsymbol{q}_2, \boldsymbol{q}_3$, is proportional to the product of the three pair probabilities. The equation is exact if the three particles are far apart, and from this limit one deduces that the factor $(V/N)^3$ must be included for correct dimensionality. The equation will not be exact if the particles are close together (if 1 and 2 are close together this will influence the probability that 3 is close to 1), but the errors arising from the approximation do not appear to be large. Integration of both sides of 3.33 over the position variables of one particle leads on the left to $n^{(2)}$ (by 3.27), and on the right to an integral involving $n^{(2)}$. This is therefore an integral equation for $n^{(2)}$ and such equations have been developed and analysed by Born, Green and Yvon.

The other important direction that has been followed in the statistical mechanics of fluids starts from an expansion of $\ln g(r)$ in powers of $1/V$, using similar techniques for analysing clusters of particles to those of Mayer which were described in the last section. Two theories, known as the hypernetted chain (HNC) and Percus-Yevick (PY) theories have been developed in this way and are currently in active use at the research level. For the derivation and analysis of these equations we refer the reader to more advanced texts.[†]

Finally we note that for molecules there is interest not only in the distribution functions for the centres of mass, but also in distribution functions for orientation. For example, for an assembly of linear molecules one would be interested in the probability that a second molecule has its centre of mass at a distance R from the first, and that it subtends angles of θ_a, θ_b, ϕ, as

[†]C. A. Croxton, *Introduction to Liquid State Physics*, Wiley, Chichester (1975). J. P. Hanson and I. R. McDonald, *Theory of Simple Liquids*, Academic Press, London and New York (1976).

defined in Figure 2.4. Distribution functions containing this information are particularly important for analysing the liquid–crystal phase which will be described in Chapter 5.

Velocity correlation

We saw in section 1.3 that gases, liquids and solids are distinguished by having very different radial distribution functions. Spatial distribution functions describe the time-averaged relative positions of molecules in the phase. The way that the position or velocity of a molecule evolves with time is also characteristic of the phase. In gases molecules move rapidly through large distances and are deflected only on collision with other molecules. In solids the molecules oscillate about their lattice sites and only rarely jump between sites. In liquids the molecules move around like dancers in a crowded ballroom; they progress slowly with frequent collisions.

The function which brings out most clearly differences in the time evolution of gases, liquids and solids is called the velocity autocorrelation function. It is defined by

$$\psi(t) = \langle v(0) \cdot v(t)\rangle / \langle v(0)^2\rangle, \tag{3.34}$$

where $v(0)$ is the velocity of a molecule at a particular time and $v(t)$ the velocity of the same molecule at a time t later. The brackets indicate averages over all molecules in the system; $\langle v(0)^2\rangle$ is the average squared velocity of the molecules.

Figure 3.2   The velocity autocorrelation function for typical solid, liquid and gas. The liquid curve is a calculation by B. J. Berne and G. D. Harp, *Adv. Chem. Phys.*, **17**, 63 (1970)

At $t = 0$, $\psi(t)$ is equal to unity. When t becomes very large the molecule may still be moving with a speed similar to that at $t = 0$, but the direction in which the molecule is travelling will be completely unrelated to its direction at $t = 0$ because of all the collisions that have occurred in this time. Because the numerator of 3.34 is a scalar product (i.e., proportional to the cosine of the angle between the vectors $v(0)$ and $v(t)$) the average value of this scalar product will approach zero as t approaches infinity. However, the rate and manner in which it approaches zero is very different for gases, liquids and solids.

In a dilute gas the mean free path of a molecule (the average distance between collisions) is large and on collision a molecule is more likely to suffer a small deflection than a large deflection. For this reason $\psi(t)$ approaches zero slowly and smoothly. In a solid a molecule will oscillate about its lattice site and for a simple harmonic motion $\psi(t)$ will also have harmonic form with the same frequency as the vibration.

In a liquid the velocity autocorrelation function starts initially like that of a solid, showing an oscillatory form due to the collision of a molecule with its neighbours. However, the motion is not harmonic and the molecule has a short memory of its initial velocity. Thus $\psi(t)$ is oscillatory but the amplitude of the oscillations decays quite rapidly to zero.

Figure 3.2 shows the typical behaviour of $\psi(t)$ that we have described above. The liquid state function is one that has been calculated for liquid CO using the method of computer simulation to be described in the next section.

3.5   Computer simulation

With the present generation of large electronic computers it is possible to solve the classical equations of motion for up to about 10^3 particles interacting through some analytical pair potential of the type described in section 2.4. One can then calculate the time-average or time-dependent properties of this system and compare these with the properties of a real fluid. If it can be established that the number of particles considered is large enough to represent a macroscopic sample, then the comparison between computer experiment and physical experiment provides a measure of the accuracy of the pair potential and of the assumption that the total potential is pair additive.

Of course 10^3 particles will not behave in the same way as 10^{23} particles. Such a small sample would have a large surface area relative to its volume and, as we shall see in a later chapter, molecules at the surface have different energies from molecules in the bulk. We can, however, get around this difficulty by supposing that our particles are confined in a small cubic volume and that this volume, together with its pattern of positions and momenta of the particles, is translated with infinite repetition along the three edges of the cube. In other words the elementary cube has the same relationship to the whole fluid as does a unit cell of a crystal to the whole crystal lattice. An

Figure 3.3 Construction of a macroscopic
fluid from an elementary cell (two dimensions).
Note that particle labelled A, for example, has
the same relative position and momentum in
each cell

instantaneous picture of a two-dimensional fluid in this model is shown in
Figure 3.3. The arrows associated with each point indicate the momenta of
the particles.

It is clear from Figure 3.3 that we have not modelled a true fluid by our
translational operation because, as has been stressed in section 1.3, a fluid has
no long-range order. However, providing the range over which the interparticle potential acts is less than half the side length of the cell (d) then the
total potential in which a particle finds itself is not influenced by the artificial
translational symmetry. Thus particle A_5 might interact with B_5 but not with
B_4 or B_6 which are more than $d/2$ away. Similarly A_5 can interact with C_2 but
not with C_5 etc. In other words particle A is influenced by the potential of
only one B, C, D . . . particle.

For short-range potentials, we can therefore simulate a fluid by a relatively
small number of particles at normal densities and indeed the first successful
computer calculations by Alder and Wainwright in 1959 on hard spheres used
only 32 particles in the cell. For long-range potentials it is necessary to have
large cells and hence at normal densities large numbers of particles. In
particular, for ions there is the difficulty that the Coulomb potential between
equivalent particles diverges, and there are problems with convergence even
for dipolar molecules. Techniques have been devised to account for these
long-range interactions, but they still have controversial features so we will
not elaborate the point.

A further point that can be seen from Figure 3.3 is that during the
trajectory a particle will encounter the cell wall; particle B is an example of

this. However, if the cell walls have no physical reality then as one particle passes out of a cell (e.g., B_5 from the central cell in Figure 3.3) then another (e.g., B_6) will enter from the other side. Thus the model conserves particle density when this is averaged over the elementary cell.

Molecular dynamics

The amount of computer time that is required to simulate the dynamics of 10^3 molecules can be large even on the fastest computers. Small molecules in liquids randomize their positions and orientations in about 10^{-12} s, so that one needs to simulate about 10^{-10} s of physical time to obtain an average representation of the liquid, and this may require an hour or more of computing time. For molecules which have complicated potentials this time would have to be increased considerably, or the number of molecules reduced, for calculations to be feasible. Non-rigid molecules (i.e. those which are allowed to vibrate) present another order of magnitude of difficulty, and little has been done in this area to date.

Molecular dynamics calculations are carried out using standard numerical integration procedures for coupled differential equations. An initial starting configuration is chosen, usually a regular array, and momenta assigned in a random manner subject to a restraint provided by the total energy of the system. After a relatively short computing time the transient effects of the starting configuration will have died out and this part of the trajectory is discarded as having no physical significance. From then on the positions and momenta of the particles are recorded as a function of time and used to calculate time-dependent or time-averaged properties, in particular the radial distribution function.

Phase transitions are not easy to reproduce by computer simulation because long-range correlation is artificially built into the model as we have noted, yet one should record for historical interest the important result obtained by Alder and Wainwright that both solid and fluid phases can be reproduced for hard spheres and that the phase change occurs when the volume V is approximately 1.4 times the close packed volume V_0.[†]

Figure 3.4 shows the typical trajectories obtained in the solid and liquid phases and Figure 3.5 shows the pressure–volume relationships deduced in the high and low density regions. If V/V_0 is close to 1.4 then starting with a regular configuration the trajectories are solid-like, but if one starts with an irregular configuration they are liquid-like.

Monte Carlo method

To calculate equilibrium configurational properties of a fluid it is not, of course, necessary to know the time dependence of the particle motion; it is

[†]B. J. Alder and T. E. Wainwright, *J. Chem. Phys.*, **31**, 459 (1959).

Figure 3.4　Trajectories of hard spheres in the solid (S) and liquid (L) phases from the results of Alder and Wainwright. Calculations were on 32 particles which underwent approximately 3000 collisions. Only the trajectories of half the particles are shown. We are indebted to Professor B. J. Alder for providing original photographs for this figure

Figure 3.5 Pressure–volume relationship for hard spheres as deduced by molecular dynamics calculations. The solid–liquid phase change occurs at approximately $V/V_o = 1.4$

sufficient to have just a selection of configurations from which an appropriate average can be extracted. The fact that a trajectory passes through a set of configurations allows this method to be used for configurational averages, although inherent in this is the so-called ergodic assumption that time averages of dynamical systems are equivalent to statistical mechanical averages. A less costly method of calculating these averages on a computer is to construct a random set of configurations and average over them without bothering about the momentum variables or the time evolution of a configuration.

It is possible to construct a random configuration for N particles by selecting $3N$ random numbers and to use these to define the positional coordinates of the particles. For example if the first random number is ζ, lying between the limits 0 and 1, then an x coordinate for particle 1 given by

$$x = (2\zeta - 1)k, \tag{3.35}$$

will lie somewhere in the limits $-k \leqslant x \leqslant k$. Such an approach to the construction of a random set of configurations is referred to as the Monte Carlo method, the connotation with games of chance being evident.

The average value of a property $X(q_i)$, which is a function of the coordinates of the particles, in a system that obeys Boltzmann statistics, is

$$\bar{X} = \frac{\int e^{-U(q_i)/kT} X(q_i) \, dq_i}{\int e^{-U(q_i)/kT} \, dq_i}, \tag{3.36}$$

where $U(q_i)$ is the potential energy. If we therefore generate a large number, M, of configurations and calculate the value of X for each, $\bar{X}$ can be approximated by

$$\bar{X} = \sum_{i=1}^{M} P_i X_i, \qquad (3.37)$$

where

$$P_i = \frac{e^{-U_i/kT}}{\sum_{i=1}^{M} e^{-U_i/kT}}, \qquad (3.38)$$

is the probability of configuration i arising. Calculating $\bar{X}$ in this way is called the crude Monte Carlo method.

The crude Monte Carlo method described above for choosing and weighting the configurations is extremely inefficient because most configurations produced are highly improbable for a real fluid. Most configurations produced by a set of random numbers will have some atoms lying on top of one another, that is, some particles will be so close together that the potential energy U_i will be extremely high. What is needed therefore is a method of selecting configurations directly so that they occur in the set with probability P_i, and if this is the case then we can replace 3.37 by

$$\bar{X} = \frac{1}{M} \sum_{i=1}^{M} X_i. \qquad (3.39)$$

A procedure for achieving this was proposed by Metropolis and co-workers in 1953, and it is this which, for liquid state computer simulation, is generally called the Monte Carlo method. A detailed description of the procedure is given in Appendix 3.2.

Apart from the confirmation of important concepts of the fluid state by computer simulation it should be emphasized that many measurable quantities can be accurately reproduced given a suitable pair potential. Thus even early calculations by Wood and Parker in 1957 using small numbers of particles showed that with a Lennard-Jones potential for argon, with parameters fitted to the second virial coefficient, the thermodynamic properties of liquid argon could be quite accurately reproduced. Some later results by McDonald and Singer are given in Table 3.1. The results can be improved by further refinement of the potential.

The computer simulation of molecular, as distinct from atomic, fluids is in its early days but there is good evidence to suggest that experimental data, particularly diffraction data, will be reproduced by relatively simple intermolecular potentials.[†] For example, a hard core model for CS_2 with parameters shown in Figure 3.6 has given good agreement with X-ray scattering

†Several papers on this topic were presented in 'Structure and motion in molecular liquids', *J.C.S. Faraday Disc.*, **66**, (1978).

Table 3.1 P, V, T, data for argon[†]

| T/K | V_m/cm^3 | P/atm | | $-\bar{U}/kJ\ mol^{-1}$ | |
		exp.	calc.	exp.	calc.
97.0	28.48	214	200 ± 14	5.799	5.912
97.0	28.95	141	141 ± 10	5.736	5.807
108.0	28.48	451	433 ± 12	5.690	5.803
108.0	31.72	16	-16 ± 10	5.204	5.247
117.0	28.48	619	605 ± 16	5.581	5.740
117.0	29.68	386	399 ± 14	5.393	5.519
117.0	30.92	219	174 ± 13	5.209	5.347

[†]Calculated by I. R. McDonald and K. Singer, *J. Chem. Phys.*, **50**, 2308, (1969) from a Lennard-Jones pair potential. The statistical error in calculating the average configuration internal energy is estimated at $\pm 8 \times 10^{-3}$ kJ mol^{-1}.

data. We restate a point made earlier that for strongly polar molecules the electrostatic contribution to the potential must certainly be allowed for and will probably have an important influence on the liquid structure.

3.6 Equations of state

For a perfect gas the equation relating pressure, volume and temperature, is

$$P = RT/V_m. \tag{3.40}$$

For a real gas there are small deviations from this equation and for liquids it is not valid at all. However, in principle more complicated equations can be found which represent the (P, V_m, T) behaviour through the whole fluid range and these can be written in the alternative forms

$$P = \psi(V_m, T) \quad \text{or} \quad \phi(P, V_m, T) = 0 \tag{3.41}$$

Figure 3.6 A hard-core model for CS$_2$. The diameters of the sulphur and carbon atoms are 3.5 Å and 3.0 Å respectively. (S. I. Sandler and A. H. Narten, *Mol. Phys.*, **32**, 1543 (1976))

Figure 3.7   Three isotherms for carbon dioxide. The area between the broken curve is the region where liquid (L) and vapour (V) coexist

where ψ and ϕ are functions of the variables in brackets. These are called equations of state for the fluid.

Figure 3.7 shows the pressure–volume curves for CO_2 for three temperatures; one above the critical temperature, one below and one at T_c, the critical temperature. These curves are typical of all fluids and, as we show later, by a suitable scaling of pressure, volume and temperature all fluids are found to fit quite closely to a common set of curves.

At temperatures above T_c there is only one fluid phase. At low pressures the P–V isotherm is hyperbolic, conforming to the perfect gas law (3.40), but at high pressures the fluid becomes much less compressible than a perfect gas and the isotherm rises much more steeply than does a hyperbola. At temperatures below T_c the isotherms are approximately hyperbolic (the deviation from the perfect gas law will later be examined in more detail) until a pressure is reached at which the first drop of liquid appears.

We have seen in section 1.2 that when a single component has two phases in equilibrium there is only one degree of freedom, so that if this is used to specify the temperature, then the pressure is fully determined. In other words, no matter what amount of liquid we have in equilibrium with gas the pressure is a constant (at a given T) although the volume can vary. If, however, the volume is decreased until the system is totally liquid then the compressibility drops immediately to a very low value, that is, V changes very little with a further increase of pressure.

If a family of (P, V_m) isotherms is plotted at temperatures below the critical temperature the points of discontinuity which mark the boundaries of the liquid–gas equilibrium fall on a curve which is shown by the broken line in Figure 3.7. The curve in its left-hand branch gives the molar volume of the liquid, and in its right-hand branch the molar volume of the gas when these are in equilibrium. The top of the curve is the critical point at which these two volumes are equal, that is, the densities of the gas and liquid phases are equal at the critical point.

The (P, V_m) isotherm at the critical temperature is gas-like at low pressures and liquid-like at high pressures, and the critical point is a point of inflexion which satisfies the criteria

$$\left(\frac{\partial P}{\partial V}\right)_T = 0, \qquad \left(\frac{\partial^2 P}{\partial V^2}\right)_T = 0, \qquad \left(\frac{\partial^3 P}{\partial V^3}\right) < 0. \tag{3.42}$$

The first of these conditions means that $V^{-1}(dV/dP)_T$, the isothermal compressibility, is infinite at the critical point. In practice, the fluid is infinitely compressible only over an infinitesimal range of pressures.

The behaviour of other thermodynamic quantities as the critical point is reached is a matter of some complexity. The experimental result is that the Helmholtz free energy, A, is not an analytical function of V and T at the critical point, and the specific heat at constant volume, which is given by

$$C_v = (\partial U/\partial T)_V = -T(\partial^2 A/\partial T^2)_V \tag{3.43}$$

is infinite. We refer the reader to more advanced texts for a more detailed discussion of the critical state.[†]

Van der Waals' equation

The first quantitatively successful equation of state of a fluid that describes the (P, V_m) curves of the liquid and gaseous branches was that of van der Waals. This is usually written in the form

$$(P + a/V_m^2)(V_m - b) = RT, \tag{3.44}$$

which can be rearranged to

$$P = \frac{RT}{V_m - b} - \frac{a}{V_m^2}. \tag{3.45}$$

In this equation a and b are empirical parameters which can be given a physical interpretation. The parameter b, for example, can be taken to represent the nearly incompressible volume of randomly, close-packed, molecules. We see from 3.45 that this parameter occurs in the first term and has the effect of raising the pressure above its perfect-gas value. The parameter a is associated with the attractive forces between molecules and these will decrease the pressure below its perfect-gas value. The term a/V_m^2 is called the internal pressure of the fluid.

[†]For example, J. S. Rowlinson, *Liquids and Liquid Mixtures*, 2nd edn, Ch. 3, Butterworth, London (1969).

From these physical arguments one could expect some temperature dependence of both the van der Waals parameters. Experiment shows that this is more important for the attractive term and an equation of state was proposed by Berthelot which contains a temperature-dependent internal pressure.

$$(P + a/TV_m^2)(V_m - b) = RT. \tag{3.46}$$

This equation is considered to be a slight improvement over the van der Waals equation.

If the van der Waals equation is differentiated with respect to V and the critical point conditions 3.42 applied, one obtains the following relationships between the critical constants and the van der Waals parameters a and b:

$$P_c = a/27b^2, \qquad T_c = 8a/27Rb, \qquad V_{c,m} = 3b. \tag{3.47}$$

Moreover, the ratio

$$Z_c = P_c V_{c,m}/RT_c, \tag{3.48}$$

which is called the compression factor at the critical point, has the value $3/8 = 0.375$, and hence is independent of a and b. Table 3.2 shows experimentally determined values of Z_c and the van der Waals parameters for a number of fluids. It is seen that Z_c is always a little less than the van der Waals value, the smallest values being for polar molecules.

Other equations of state can be analysed in a similar manner to the van der Waals equation. The Berthelot equation, for example, also gives $Z_c = 0.375$, but an equation due to Dieterici

$$P = \frac{RT}{(V_m - b)} \exp(-a/RTV_m), \tag{3.49}$$

Table 3.2 Values of the compression factor at the critical point and the van der Waals constants (*Handbook of Chemistry and Physics*, 59th Edn, CRC Press, 1978)

	Z_c	a/dm^6 atm mol^{-1}	$100b/dm^3$ mol^{-1}
He	0.306	0.034	2.370
Ne	0.308	0.211	1.709
H_2	0.305	0.244	2.661
N_2	0.291	1.390	3.913
CO_2	0.275	3.592	4.267
H_2O	0.227	5.464	3.049
NH_3	0.242	4.170	3.707
C_2H_6	0.285	5.489	6.380
C_6H_6	0.274	18.00	1.154

The van der Waals constants are not determined solely from critical point data according to 3.47, but are optimized for the whole (P, V_m, T) behaviour.

leads to $Z_c = 0.271$, which is rather closer to most experimental values. However, Dieterici's equation is very poor at high pressures.

The equation of state for the hard-sphere model of a gas has been known quite accurately for many years. The Percus-Yevick equation, for example (see page 50), gives the equation of state

$$P = \frac{RT}{V_m}\left(\frac{1 + \eta + \eta^2}{(1 - \eta)^3}\right),$$ (3.50)

where $\eta = \pi\rho\sigma^3/6$; ρ is the density of the gas and σ is the hard-sphere diameter (Figure 2.8(a)). This equation agrees very well with pressures determined by computer simulation. Without attractive forces between the molecules there can be no liquid–gas phase change. Thus the hard-sphere model can only represent a fluid above its critical point. However, the hard-sphere model is a much more accurate representation of the effect on pressure of the short-range repulsive forces between molecules than is the first term in the van der Waals' equation (3.45). For this reason equations of state which are extensions of the hard-sphere result (3.50), can be very accurate. For example, Carnahan and Starling have proposed an equation

$$P = P_0 - \frac{a}{T^{1/2}V_m(V_m + b)},$$ (3.51)

where P_0 is given by 3.50, which is very much better than any of the other two-parameter equations of state mentioned above.[†]

Law of corresponding states

Although the critical constants of fluids cover very wide ranges (see Table 1.1), it is found empirically that the critical temperature is generally about 1.5 times the normal boiling point, and the critical volume is about three times the molar volume of the normal liquid. This suggests that if the pressure, volume and temperature are scaled to the values of the critical constants, then all fluids should obey, approximately, the same equation of state. This idea was first explored by van der Waals. He defined reduced variables by

$$P_r = P/P_c, \qquad V_r = V_m/V_{c,m}, \qquad T_r = T/T_c,$$ (3.52)

and noted that different gases at the same reduced volume and temperature exerted approximately the same reduced pressure. This is called the law of corresponding states.

We have already seen that the critical constants of fluids that obey the van der Waals equation are related to the parameters a and b by 3.47. It follows that one can replace a and b in the van der Waals equation by P_c, $V_{c,m}$ and T_c, and, after rearrangement, the equation can be written in reduced variables in

---

[†]An excellent review of this and other equations of state is given by D. Henderson, ch. 1, Equations of state in engineering and research, *Adv. in Chem.*, **182** (1979).

Figure 3.8   Isotherms of the reduced van der
Waals equation

the form

$$P_r = \frac{8T_r}{3V_r - 1} - \frac{3}{V_r^2}.$$ (3.53)

Figure 3.8 shows isotherms of the reduced van der Waals equation at three values of T_r. For $T_r > 1$ the isotherms have no turning points and have the general features of fluid isotherms above the critical point. For $T_r = 1$, the isotherm shows the required point of inflexion at $P_r = V_r = 1$. For $T_r < 1$, however, the isotherms have two turning points and they do not exhibit the constant pressure region which is associated with the gas–liquid equilibrium.

The van der Waals equation predicts that below the critical temperature an increase in pressure can lead to an increase in volume which is physically impossible. One can, however, obtain physically acceptable isotherms from the van der Waals equation by replacing the region having the two turning points by a straight line such that the two cut-off areas (shown in Figure 3.8) are equal.† This rule, known as Maxwell's equal area rule, is proved in Appendix 3.3.

Figure 3.9 shows the compression factor $Z = PV_m/RT$ at 273 K for some small molecules. At low pressures gases are more compressible than the

†The van der Waals equation is analytical (i.e. differentiable to all orders) for all values of P, V and T, whereas the isotherms for real fluids are not analytical at the points of onset of the two-phase region. Thus the failure of the van der Waals equation to represent the isotherms in the two-phase region is a failure possessed by any analytical equation of state.

64

Figure 3.9 The compression factor as a function of pressure at $T = 273$ K. (Data from E. P. Bartlett *et al.*, *J. Amer. Chem. Soc.*, **52**, 1363 (1930) and H. M. Kvalnes and V. L. Gaddy, *J. Amer. Chem. Soc.*, **53**, 394 (1931))

perfect gas due to the long-range attractive forces between the molecules; at high pressures they are less compressible due to the short-range repulsive forces. If such data are plotted in reduced variables, they all fall close to the same curve. This is shown in Figure 3.10 for a large number of molecules and several different values of the reduced temperature.

One can attribute the law of corresponding states to the fact that similar molecules have similar functional forms for their intermolecular potentials. For example, suppose two molecules A and B have L-J potentials (2.18) but with different values for the parameters ε and σ.

$$V_{AA} = 4\varepsilon_A[(\sigma_A/R)^{12} - (\sigma_A/R)^6], \tag{3.54}$$

$$V_{BB} = 4\varepsilon_B[(\sigma_B/R)^{12} - (\sigma_B/R)^6]. \tag{3.55}$$

Because ε is an energy scaling parameter in the Lennard-Jones potential and kT has dimensions of energy, we expect systems A and B to behave similarly

Figure 3.10   Reduced compressibility factor Z_r as a function of reduced temperature and pressure for a variety of gases. (From Gouq—Jen Su, *Ind. Eng. Chem.*, **38**, 803 (1946))

with respect to their population of energy states if

$$\frac{\varepsilon_A}{kT_A} = \frac{\varepsilon_B}{kT_B} \quad \text{or} \quad \frac{T_A}{T_B} = \frac{\varepsilon_A}{\varepsilon_B}. \tag{3.56}$$

Likewise as σ is a scaling parameter for the distance between molecules and volume is of dimensions distance cubed, then gas A in volume V_A should have similar pair interactions to gas B in volume V_B if

$$\frac{V_{A,m}}{V_{B,m}} = \left(\frac{\sigma_A}{\sigma_B}\right)^3. \tag{3.57}$$

As pressure has the dimensions RT/V we then expect the ratio of the pressures to be

$$\frac{P_A}{P_B} = \left(\frac{\varepsilon_A}{\varepsilon_B}\right)\left(\frac{\sigma_B}{\sigma_A}\right)^3. \tag{3.58}$$

Let us put this another way; if temperature is measured in units of ε/k, volume in units of σ^3 and pressure in units of ε/σ^3 then the two fluids should obey the same equation of state

$$\phi(P^*, V^*, T^*) = 0, \tag{3.59}$$

where

$$P^* = \sigma^3 P/\varepsilon, \qquad V^* = V_m/\sigma^3, \qquad T^* = kT/\varepsilon, \tag{3.60}$$

are dimensionless variables. In particular, they should have the same critical constants (P_c^*, V_c^*, T_c^*). Because

$$P^*/P_c^* = P/P_c = P_r, \quad \text{etc.} \tag{3.61}$$

then the two fluids should obey the same reduced equation of state with variables (P_r, V_r, T_r).

The above argument can be generalized for any intermolecular potential in which there is a single energy scaling factor and a single distance scaling factor. We can also invert the argument: if an empirical equation of state can be found which in the reduced variables (P_r, V_r, T_r) holds for a number of different fluids then we deduce that the pair potentials of the molecules in all these fluids have the same functional form

$$V = \varepsilon f(R/\sigma), \tag{3.62}$$

where ε and σ are energy and distance scale factors respectively. Such fluids are said to belong to the same conformal family.

One consequence of the law of corresponding states is that the boiling point of a fluid at a fixed reduced pressure is a universal fraction of the critical temperature. Because the critical pressures of most fluids are similar ($\sim$50 atm) and boiling points on an absolute scale are relatively insensitive to pressure, we conclude that the normal boiling point ($P = 1$ atm) is a fixed fraction of the critical temperature; found experimentally to be approximately 2/3.

A further generalization is that other thermodynamic properties of conformal families such as enthalpy, entropy and heat capacity can be given common functional forms when expressed in terms of the reduced variables. Figure 3.11 shows such a graph for heat capacity. This was prepared by Hougen and Watson by averaging the data for H_2, N_2, CO, NH_3, CH_4, C_3H_8 and C_5H_{12}.

The virial expansion

We showed in section 3.3 that with some approximations one can derive a relationship (3.24) between the pressure of a gas and an integral over a function of the intermolecular potential. Knowing the pair potential U_{12} it is a straightforward matter to calculate the relevant integral (3.19) and hence to deduce the pressure. It is, however, of more common interest to make the connection in the reverse direction; that is, to take experimentally determined

Figure 3.11 The difference between the heat capacity of a gas and its perfect gas value (C_p^0) as a function of reduced pressure and reduced temperature (logarithmic scale). (O. A. Hougen and K. M. Watson, *Chemical Process Principles* part II, Wiley, London and New York (1947))

pressures and from them to deduce the pair potential. The analysis is not as simple as it might appear because the available data are relatively insensitive to certain features of the potential.

This is illustrated in Figure 3.12, which shows the pair potential for argon and the function f_{12} at 87 K. The b-integral (3.19) is an integral over f_{12} weighted by R^2, and it is clear from the figure that the main contribution to the integral comes from the region of the potential around the minimum. The integral will be relatively insensitive to the short and very long-range parts of the potential. Indeed, the only feature of the repulsive branch of the potential that is likely to be deduced with reasonable accuracy from the experimental data is the point at which U_{12} crosses the R-axis (the parameter σ in Figure 2.8).

The most convenient way of making the connection between (P, V, T)-data and the intermolecular potential is through an equation of state for gases known as the virial equation (first used by Kammerlingh-Onnes and Keesom in 1912). It is in the form of an expansion of the pressure in powers of V^{-1}.

$$P = \frac{RT}{V_m}\left[1 + \frac{B(T)}{V_m} + \frac{C(T)}{V_m^2} + \ldots\right]. \tag{3.63}$$

$B(T)$ is known as the second virial coefficient, $C(T)$ is the third virial coefficient, etc. It is important to note that they are functions of temperature.

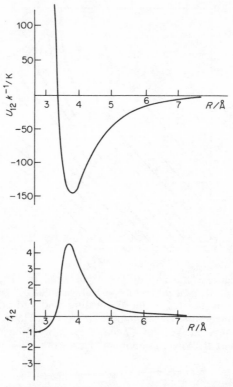

Figure 3.12 The pair potential for argon and
the resulting function $f_{12} = \exp(-U_{12}/kT) - 1$,
at 87 K

The relationship between the b integral and $B(T)$ can be obtained by equating the terms of order $(V_m)^2$ in 3.24 and 3.63.

$$B(T) = 2\pi \mathcal{N} b = 2\pi \mathcal{N} \int (1 - e^{-U_{12}/kT}) R^2 \, dR \qquad (3.64)$$

From the cluster expansion of the configurational integral which was described in section 3.3, it can be shown that the third virial coefficient depends on both the pair potential and the three-body potential.

Figure 3.13 shows the second virial coefficient of argon as a function of temperature. $B(T)$ is negative until rather high temperatures are reached. The change in sign occurs at the Boyle temperature (412 K for argon) and at this temperature the gas is, to order $1/V_m$, behaving as a perfect gas. At the Boyle temperature the effects of the attractive and the repulsive parts of the potential just cancel in the b integral.

Table 3.3 lists some Ar_2 pair potentials that have been optimized by a least-squares procedure to $B(T)$. The L-J, square-well and (exp − 6) potentials were described in Chapter 2 (see Figure 2.8). The Kihara potential is a

Figure 3.13   Second virial coefficient of argon as a function of temperature. A smooth curve has been drawn through data from the following references: R. D. Weir *et al., Trans. Faraday Soc.*, **63**, 1320 (1967); E. Whalley *et al., Can. J. Chem.*, **31**, 722 (1953). The first of these papers has a very good description of the experimental technique

modified L-J potential with an extra parameter to improve the repulsive branch. The L-J potential is the only two-parameter potential in the list and it is significantly poorer than the others in fitting $B(T)$. The square-well potential gives a surprisingly good fit to the data although in both the depth of the well and the value of σ it is very poor when compared with the very accurate potential of Parson and co-workers; this is a complex potential deduced from atomic beam scattering that also fits $B(T)$ with high accuracy.

The above example shows that one must be cautious in accepting a potential which is based solely on second virial data. Different types of experi-

Table 3.3   Parameters of argon pair potentials which have been optimized to second virial coefficients

Potential	$\sigma/\text{Å}$	ε/kK	r.m.s./$\text{cm}^3 \text{ mol}^{-1}$
L-J	3.504	118	2.02
Kihara	3.314	147	0.51
Square-well	3.067	93	0.49
(exp − 6)	3.302	152	0.54
Parson *et al.*	3.354	141	—

A. E. Sherwood and J. M. Prausnitz, *J. Chem. Phys.*, **41**, 429 (1964); J. M. Parson, P. E. Siska and Y. T. Lee, *J. Chem. Phys.*, **56**, 1511 (1972) r.m.s. is the root mean square error.

ment probe different regions of the potential, and hence a combination of data from different experiments is a much sterner test of a potential than is extensive data from a single type of experiment. Some of the most useful data for providing information about pair potentials comes for gas-transport properties, and this is our next topic for examination.

3.7 Transport properties

Up to this point we have been concerned mainly with the properties of fluids in equilibrium, a state of equilibrium being characterized by a uniformity of properties throughout the volume of the system and a constancy of these properties with time. We shall now discuss briefly some important properties of non-equilibrium fluids, properties which are technologically important and have a bearing on the molecular interpretation of fluid behaviour.

Although the fundamentals of non-equilibrium statistical mechanisms and thermodynamics are not so well established as their equilibrium counterparts this is not through lack of attention by scientists. The kinetic theory of gases was developed in the second half of the nineteenth century and culminated in the Boltzmann transport equation, which describes the time evolution of the phase space probability density $f^{(N)}(p, q)$ (3.25), for an N particle system in which collisions are occurring. Boltzmann's great achievement was to show that this kinetic equation incorporates the fundamental irreversibility of many-particle systems which is contained in the principle that spontaneous change occurs in the direction of increasing entropy.

The Boltzmann equation can be solved for gases by assuming that only binary collisions occur between molecules. Transport properties such as viscosity can then be related to parameters of these collisions (e.g. angles of deflection) which can be calculated from the intermolecular potential. As for the treatment of virial coefficients, we can proceed in the opposite direction and deduce potentials from transport properties.[†] For dense fluids, however, there are still substantial problems in obtaining analytical solutions of the transport equations and their mathematical complexity makes them inappropriate for detailed discussion in this book.

An alternative approach to non-equilibrium processes which is based upon an extension of thermodynamic principles is known as the phenomenological approach. This term implies that the equations which are used are based upon experimental observation rather than on any underlying assumptions about the molecular interactions in the system. The approach was formalized by Onsager in 1931 although many of the equations used and general principles were known much earlier.

The essential pattern of the phenomenological equations is based on the

---

[†] S. Chapman and T. A. Cowling, *The Mathematical Theory of Non-uniform Gases*, C.U.P. (1939).

observation that the rate of flow of some property, which we shall represent by the vector flux J is proportional to a generalized force, F, which is in turn derived from the gradient of some property, ϕ. Thus we can write

$$J \propto F, \tag{3.65}$$

or

$$J \propto \text{grad } \phi. \tag{3.66}$$

The proportionality factors are called the phenomenological coefficients. These equations can be extended to situations in which there is more than one flux (e.g. matter and heat) and it was this generalization that was the key idea in Onsager's theory.

Let us take an example: the flux of thermal energy is proportional to the temperature gradient in the system. Thus the z-component of the flux can be written

$$J_z(\text{thermal energy}) = -\kappa(\mathrm{d}T/\mathrm{d}z), \tag{3.67}$$

which is known as Fourier's law. The negative sign is inserted because a flux towards increasing z (J_z positive) will occur when there is a negative temperature gradient. The constant κ is called the coefficient of thermal conductivity.

A second example is the flow of matter down a concentration gradient. The relevant equation is

$$J_z(\text{matter}) = -D(\mathrm{d}C/\mathrm{d}z), \tag{3.68}$$

where C is the concentration and D is called the diffusion coefficient. Equation 3.68 is known as Fick's first law of diffusion (his second law relates to a differential equation for C but it has no relevance to our present discussion).

Viscosity

Finally we turn to the transport property which has probably most importance for pure liquids and that is the viscosity. Viscous forces appear only when adjacent parts of a fluid are moving with different velocities. Thus in the flow of liquid down a pipe the liquid layer which is actually in contact with the pipe is stationary and the central region is moving with maximum velocity. Common experience is that a high-viscosity liquid like treacle will flow more slowly than a low viscosity liquid like water for a given applied pressure difference.

The above experimental arrangement provides a simple method for measuring liquid viscosities. Poiseuille's formula for the flow of liquid in a capillary of radius R and length l is

$$\frac{\mathrm{d}V}{\mathrm{d}t} = (P_1^2 - P_2^2)\pi R^4/16l\eta P. \tag{3.69}$$

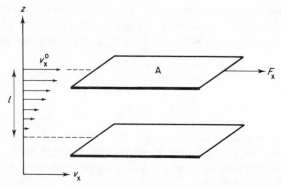

Figure 3.14 The laminar flow of a fluid between a moving upper plate and a fixed lower plate

V is the volume flowing, P_1 and P_2 are the pressures at each end of the tube, P is the pressure at which the volume is measured and η is the coefficient of viscosity. The rate of flow of liquid is measured as a function of the applied pressure and interpreted by the above formula.

For the basic transport equation for viscosity we require the flux of some quantity which is maintained by a velocity gradient. To see what this quantity is we take a theoretically simpler arrangement than the flow down a capillary. Figure 3.14 shows two parallel plates with liquid between, the bottom plate being stationary and the top plate moving with constant velocity v_x^0. For gases and most liquids the force per unit area of the top plate required to maintain this constant velocity is found to be proportional to v_x^0 and such fluids are called Newtonian fluids. Non-Newtonian behaviour is often exhibited by very viscous fluids, typically polymer solutions and we will leave a discussion of these to a later chapter.

As the bottom layer of liquid is stationary and the top layer is moving at v_x^0 we must ask how the intermediate layers are moving. The simplest assumption, and one that can be confirmed by experiment, is that the velocity is changing linearly with distance between the plates as indicated in Figure 3.14. The fluid is then said to be in a state of laminar flow characterized by a velocity gradient

$$\frac{\mathrm{d}v_x}{\mathrm{d}z} = \frac{v_x^0}{l}. \tag{3.70}$$

The experimental situation can then be summarized in the equation

$$\frac{F_x}{A} = \frac{\eta v_x^0}{l} = \eta\left(\frac{\mathrm{d}v_x}{\mathrm{d}z}\right), \tag{3.71}$$

where η is the coefficient of shear viscosity; its SI unit is $\mathrm{kg\ m^{-1}\ s^{-1}}$.

Let us now imagine the fluid to be divided into layers of molecular thickness. There will be a constant exchange of molecules between layers and these molecules will be carrying momentum in the x direction which will tend to bring the two layers to the same speed; the molecules from the faster layer will speed up the slower and these from the slower layer will slow down the faster. It is the applied force F_x which conteracts this drag. We therefore see that the flux which is associated with the velocity gradient is a flux of momentum in the x direction. We can therefore write an expression analogous to 3.67 and 3.68 as follows

$$J_z(x \text{ momentum}) \propto \left(\frac{dv_x}{dz}\right), \tag{3.72}$$

where the proportionality constant will be the coefficient of viscosity with appropriate units.

As we have already indicated, the transport coefficients can be calculated on a molecular basis from the kinetic theory of gases, the key parameter being the average distance travelled by molecules between collisions (the mean free path). For liquids such a theory is inapplicable as the concept of distinct binary collisions is inappropriate to a liquid.

From gas kinetic theory it is predicted that viscosity is independent of pressure and proportional to the square root of the absolute temperature. These predictions are confirmed by experiment. For liquids, however, the experimental behaviour is quite different. Liquid viscosities have an exponential dependence on temperature as described by the formula

$$\eta = A \exp(\Delta E_{vis}/RT). \tag{3.73}$$

Figure 3.15 shows a graph of log η against $10^3 \text{ K}/T$ for CCl_4.

Figure 3.15 A graph of log $(\eta/\text{kg m}^{-1} \text{ s}^{-1})$
against T^{-1} for CCl_4

Figure 3.16 The relationship between fluidity $(1/\eta)$ and the ratio of free to filled volume for CCl_4. (Data from J. Hildebrand, *J.C.S. Faraday Disc.* **66**, 151 (1978))

It has been customary to interpret ΔE_{vis} as an activation barrier that the molecules must overcome before the liquid can flow. Hildebrand has argued against this interpretation and has pointed out that η is an extremely sensitive function of molar volume, liquids flowing very freely when expanded only a few per cent above their intrinsic volume. He suggested that fluidity (measured by η^{-1}) should be proportional to the ratio of free volume to occupied volume (the volume of the molecules) in the liquid. If V_0 is the occupied volume and V the actual volume, then Hildebrand's relationship is

$$\frac{1}{\eta} = B\left(\frac{V - V_0}{V_0}\right), \tag{3.74}$$

where B and V_0 are parameters deduced from the straight line graph $1/\eta$ against V. Figure 3.16 shows for CCl_4 that this interpretation is suggested by experimental data. Hildebrand attributes the empirical relationship 3.73 to the temperature dependence of the ratio $(V - V_0)/V_0$.

Appendix 3.1

The integral in 3.17 can be reduced further by choosing as independent coordinates, (X, Y, Z), the centre of mass of the two particles, and (R, θ, φ) the polar coordinates of particle 2 relative to particle 1. The volume element in these coordinates is

$$dX \, dY \, dZ \, R^2 \, dR \, \sin\theta \, d\theta \, d\varphi. \tag{A3.1}$$

Integration over X, Y and Z gives a factor V and integration over θ and φ gives a factor 4π. We therefore have

$$\iint f_{12}\, dq_1\, dq_2 = 4\pi V \int f_{12}(R)R^2\, dR. \tag{A3.2}$$

For molecules the situation is more complicated and a detailed treatment can be found elsewhere.[†]

Appendix 3.2

The Metropolis method for applying the Monte Carlo procedure to the computer simulation of a liquid is as follows:

(1) Suppose a random configuration, i, has been constructed whose energy is U_i.

(2) One particle in this configuration is selected either serially (1 to N) or randomly, and by choosing three random numbers ($\zeta_1, \zeta_2, \zeta_3$) in the interval 0 to 1 this particle is displaced along the three cartesian axes by amounts

$$x = (2\zeta_1 - 1)k, \qquad y = (2\zeta_2 - 1)k, \qquad z = (2\zeta_3 - 1)k. \tag{A3.3}$$

A new energy U_{i+1} is calculated.

(3) If U_{i+1} is less than U_i the new configuration is added to the set and this configuration becomes the starting point for a further repetition of step 2.

(4) If U_{i+1} is greater than U_i the new configuration is not immediately selected but is judged by choosing a further random number η in the range 0 to 1. If

$$\eta \leqslant \exp(-(U_{i+1} - U_i)/kT), \tag{A3.4}$$

then configuration i + 1 is added to the set and it becomes the starting point for step 2. If, however,

$$\eta > \exp(-(U_{i+1} - U_i)/kT), \tag{A3.5}$$

the configuration is rejected and the previous configuration i is counted again.

It can be seen that this procedure generates a set of configurations which are generally low in energy, and it can be shown that they occur with a Boltzmann probability. The parameter k, in A3.3 is quite important. If it is too large then many of the new configurations which are generated will be rejected. If it is too small then it will take a long time to generate a representative set. At typical liquid densities a value of k which is approximately one-fifth of the distance between nearest neighbours has been found to be a reasonable compromise, and typically about half of the generated configurations are rejected by the criterion A3.5. Averages are normally evaluated from a total of 10^4–10^5 configurations.

[†]J. O. Hirschfelder, C. F. Curtis and R. B. Bird, *Molecular Theory of Gases and Liquids*, Wiley, London and New York (1964).

Appendix 3.3

To prove Maxwell's equal area rule (page 63), we start with the formula for integration by parts

$$\int_{V_1}^{V_2} P \, dV = \left| PV \right|_{V_1}^{V_2} - \int_{V_1}^{V_2} V \, dP. \tag{A3.6}$$

Let V_1 and V_2 be the molar volumes of the liquid and gas respectively, when they are in equilibrium at the same temperature and pressure. For an isothermal change $V \, dP$ is equal to dG the change in Gibbs free energy. As liquid and gas in equilibrium have the same molar free energy, dG must be zero, hence A3.6 becomes

$$\int_{V_1}^{V_2} P \, dV = P(V_2 - V_1). \tag{A3.7}$$

The left-hand side of this equation is equal to the area under the van der Waals isotherm and the right-hand side is the area under the straight line joining the points (P, V_1) and (P, V_2). These two areas will be equal only if the areas in Figure 3.8 are equal.

Chapter 4

Thermodynamic properties of pure liquids

4.1 Thermodynamics of phase equilibria

In this chapter we examine the thermodynamics of liquids having one chemical component, placing particular emphasis on the solid–liquid and liquid–gas phase equilibria. Other aspects of pure liquids such as liquid surfaces will be dealt with in Chapters 12 and 13.

We write this chapter on the assumption that the reader is familiar with the definitions of the main thermodynamic variables, with the equations linking these variables and with the criteria for equilibrium. The following introductory remarks are meant to refresh the memory but not to be comprehensive. The necessary criterion for spontaneous change in a closed system maintained at constant temperature and pressure is that there shall be a decrease in the Gibbs free energy, which is related to the enthalpy and entropy by

$$G = H - TS. \tag{4.1}$$

The rate at which spontaneous change occurs depends on mechanistic (kinetic) factors which we do not cover in this chapter. For example, diamond is thermodynamically unstable relative to graphite at room temperatures, but is kinetically completely stable. Likewise if the temperature of a liquid is taken rapidly below its freezing point, the liquid may form a glass rather than the thermodynamically more stable crystalline solid.

The chemical potential

G, H and S are extensive quantities, that is, their values are proportional to the amount of material in the system. For single-component systems their values per mole are given the symbols G_m, H_m and S_m. The molar Gibbs free energy is an extremely important quantity and it is given another symbol, μ, and name, the chemical potential. For multicomponent systems the concept

78

of molar quantities must be extended, and this topic is dealt with in Chapter 7. We only emphasize at this point that μ has greater generality than G_m, but that it is equal to G_m for a pure substance.

For thermal equilibrium between phases, each phase must be at the same temperature. For mechanical equilibrium between phases (in the absence of external fields), each phase must be at the same pressure. If these two conditions are met, then the criterion for total equilibrium between phases is that their chemical potentials shall be equal, i.e., there is also physicochemical equilibrium. We note that μ is like T and P in being an intensive property of the system, and is also like T and P in providing a criterion of equilibrium.

In mechanical systems the direction of spontaneous change is that which leads to a decrease in the mechanical potential. Thus a ball rolls downhill because its potential (gh, where g is the acceleration due to gravity and h is its height) decreases. In chemical systems the direction of spontaneous change is that which leads to a decrease in μ, the chemical potential.

The most stable phase of a pure substance at a particular temperature and pressure is the one with the lowest chemical potential. At low temperatures μ will be dominated by H_m and ordered structures with strong interactions between the molecules (i.e. a solid) will be favoured. At high temperatures μ will be dominated by the factor TS_m and a system with the greatest entropy or disorder will be favoured, which is the gas. The liquid state is therefore an intermediate situation in which there is a balance between H_m and TS_m.

Figure 4.1 shows schematically the variation of μ with temperature for solid, liquid and gas. The dashed lines show the continuation of the functions into temperature ranges where the phase is not the most stable. The melting

Figure 4.1 Schematic representation of the chemical potential for solid, liquid and gas as a function of temperature (fixed pressure)

point is the temperature at which the intersection of $\mu(s)$ and $\mu(l)$ occurs; the boiling point is at the intersection of $\mu(l)$ and $\mu(g)$.

The simplicity of Figure 4.1 disguises its importance. Let us take one example. Suppose we make some change to the system which lowers the chemical potential of the liquid state but leaves $\mu(s)$ and $\mu(g)$ unchanged. Such a change will have the effect of *lowering* the melting point and *raising* the boiling point of the system. We will see in a later chapter that this can be achieved by dissolving an involatile solute in the liquid.

As the stability of a phase depends on temperature and pressure we are interested in knowing how the Gibbs free energy varies with temperature and pressure. The key to this information is the equation

$$dG = V\,dP - S\,dT, \tag{4.2}$$

which tells us how small changes in pressure and temperature lead to a small change in G. dG is called an exact differential because a finite change in G depends only on the difference between its values in the initial and final states. ΔG does not depend on the path (in P, T space) by which this change was carried out and, in particular, on whether the change is carried out reversibly or not. From 4.2 the partial derivatives of G are given by

$$\left(\frac{\partial G}{\partial P}\right)_T = V, \tag{4.3}$$

and

$$\left(\frac{\partial G}{\partial T}\right)_P = -S. \tag{4.4}$$

Similar expressions hold also for the molar quantities, hence we can write

$$\left(\frac{\partial \mu}{\partial P}\right)_T = V_m \quad \text{and} \quad \left(\frac{\partial \mu}{\partial T}\right)_P = -S_m. \tag{4.5}$$

The function S has a special place amongst the extensive quantities of thermodynamics in that its absolute value can be determined and not, as for H and G, just relative values. The reason for this is contained in the third law of thermodynamics which can be stated as, 'all perfect crystals at absolute zero have zero entropy'. From this reference point absolute entropies can be deduced at other temperatures and these entropies are always positive. We, therefore, make the important deduction from 4.5 that at constant pressure the chemical potential of a system always decreases with increasing temperature, and that the rate of decrease is greatest for those states with the greatest entropy. Figure 4.1 is consistent with these conclusions.

The difference in the chemical potentials of two states of a single component at the same temperature and pressure is, from 4.1

$$\Delta\mu = \Delta H_m - T\Delta S_m = \Delta U_m + P\Delta V_m - T\Delta S_m. \tag{4.6}$$

80

For two phases in equilibrium $\Delta\mu$ is zero so that

$$\Delta H_m = T\Delta S_m. \qquad (4.7)$$

Both melting and vaporization are endothermic processes, hence they are accompanied by an increase in both enthalpy and entropy. The molar volume will also generally change and so will ΔU_m.

If V_m and S_m are discontinuous at a phase change then it follows from 4.5 that $(\partial\mu/\partial P)_T$ and $(\partial\mu/\partial T)_P$ are also discontinuous. This is illustrated in Figure 4.1 where the slope of μ is discontinuous at the melting and boiling points. A phase change having these thermodynamic characteristics is called a first-order phase transition.

There are other phase changes in which there is no change in volume or entropy although there will be a discontinuity in the derivatives of these quantities with temperature or pressure at the phase change. In these cases $(\partial\mu/\partial P)_T$ and $(\partial\mu/\partial T)_P$ are continuous at the phase transition but the second derivatives of μ are discontinuous. Such transitions are called second-order phase changes; paramagnetic–ferromagnetic changes in a solid are of this type. Figure 4.2 summarizes the temperature behaviour of the thermodynamic quantities we have referred to as first-order and second-order phase transitions.

Effect of pressure and temperature

From expression 4.3 we can deduce the effect of pressure on the melting

Figure 4.2 Changes in thermodynamic quantities at first- and second-order phase transitions

Figure 4.3 The effect of an increase in pressure on the chemical potentials of solid, liquid and gas, and the resulting increase in the melting and boiling temperatures

and boiling points. On passing from liquid to gas there is always a large increase in volume so that an increase in pressure will raise $\mu(g)$ much more than $\mu(l)$. From Figure 4.3 it is clear that this will increase the temperature at which the liquid boils. The change is consistent with le Chatelier's principle that a system in equilibrium tends to move in a direction which minimizes any outside perturbation. That is, an increase in pressure will move the system towards the phase with the smaller volume.

In general the solid to liquid phase change is also accompanied by an increase in volume so that an increase in pressure raises the melting point as in Figure 4.3. However, in a few cases, the most important being water, there is a decrease in volume on melting so that for these systems an increase in pressure will lower the melting point. It is common knowledge that applying sufficient pressure to ice will cause it to melt.

We can derive from 4.2 an expression which gives us the effect of pressure on the temperature of a phase change. Suppose we make changes in P and T in such a way that two phases α and β remain in equilibrium. We then have for one mole of each phase

$$d\mu(\alpha) = V_m(\alpha)\, dP - S_m(\alpha)\, dT, \tag{4.8}$$

and

$$d\mu(\beta) = V_m(\beta)\, dP - S_m(\beta)\, dT, \tag{4.9}$$

and, if equilibrium is maintained then

$$\mu(\alpha) = \mu(\beta) \quad \text{and} \quad d\mu(\alpha) = d\mu(\beta). \tag{4.10}$$

We can therefore write

$$V_m(\alpha) \, dP - S_m(\alpha) \, dT = V_m(\beta) \, dP - S_m(\beta) \, dT, \tag{4.11}$$

or

$$\Delta V_m \, dP = \Delta S_m \, dT, \tag{4.12}$$

where Δ is the difference between quantities for the two phases. Equation 4.12 can be rearranged to give

$$\frac{dP}{dT} = \frac{\Delta S_m}{\Delta V_m} = \frac{\Delta H_m}{T \Delta V_m}, \tag{4.13}$$

which is called the Clapeyron equation. This equation is exact and applies to any phase change.

Both ΔH_m and ΔV_m are always positive for the solid $\rightarrow$ gas and liquid $\rightarrow$ gas phase changes hence we conclude that the corresponding boundary lines in the P, T phase diagram (which are the lines along which equilibrium of the two phases is maintained) always have positive slope. This is also true in most cases for the solid $\rightarrow$ liquid line with water again being an exception (see Figure 1.2).

For the solid $\rightarrow$ liquid phase change we can make use of the fact that ΔH_m and ΔV_m do not vary appreciably with pressure or temperature, and integrate 4.13 to give

$$P = P_0 + \left(\frac{\Delta H_{melt}}{\Delta V_{melt}}\right) \ln(T/T_0), \tag{4.14}$$

where (P_0, T_0) is some known point on the phase boundary line. This expression will, however, be accurate only over a short temperature range.

For the solid $\rightarrow$ gas and liquid $\rightarrow$ gas transitions we cannot make this approximation, because the volume of a gas is pressure and temperature dependent. An alternative is to use the fact that the gas has a much larger molar volume than the liquid or solid hence we can write, for a perfect gas

$$\Delta V_m = V_m(g) = RT/P. \tag{4.15}$$

On substitution in 4.13 this gives us an equation known as the Clausius–Clapeyron equation

$$\frac{dP}{dT} = \frac{P \Delta H_m}{RT^2}, \tag{4.16}$$

which can be written in the alternative form

$$\frac{d(\ln P)}{d(1/T)} = -\Delta H_m, \tag{4.17}$$

where ΔH_m is the enthalpy change for the solid $\rightarrow$ gas or liquid $\rightarrow$ gas transitions.

If one measures the vapour pressure of a liquid as a function of tempera-

Figure 4.4   A graph of $\ln P$ against T^{-1} for water
from the critical point to the ice point

ture (the vapour pressure is the pressure at which the liquid and vapour are in equilibrium at a specified temperature) then it is generally found that a graph of $\ln P$ against $1/T$ is nearly linear over a wide range of temperature. This is illustrated for water in Figure 4.4 which shows the temperature range from the ice point to the critical point.

Under these circumstances one can deduce an empirical expression for the vapour pressure

$$\ln(P/P_0) = -A\left(\frac{1}{T} - \frac{1}{T_0}\right), \tag{4.18}$$

which is clearly valuable for interpolation purposes. However, the temptation to compare 4.18 with an integrated form of 4.17 which assumes that ΔH_m is independent of temperature

$$\ln(P/P_0) = -\frac{\Delta H_m}{R}\left(\frac{1}{T} - \frac{1}{T_0}\right), \tag{4.19}$$

must be resisted because ΔH_m is far from being constant over such a wide temperature range. In fact ΔH_m must be zero at the critical point for there the properties of liquid and vapour coincide.[†] We know also that the assumptions made in deriving 4.16 are invalid close to the critical point because the gas

---

†Note that the ratio $\Delta S_m/\Delta V_m$, which appears in 4.13, is indeterminate at the critical point, although (dP/dT) is certainly finite. Application of l'Hôspital's rule does not resolve the matter as differentiating still leaves an indeterminate ratio. We have commented earlier (page 60) on the strange behaviour of some thermodynamic parameters at the critical point.

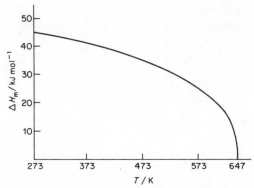

Figure 4.5   The enthalpy of vaporization of
water as a function of temperature

does not then have a much larger molar volume than the liquid; they become
equal at this point. In short, expression 4.18 can be used to deduce the
enthalpy of vaporization only in the low pressure regions where the Clausius–
Clapeyron assumptions are valid. The enthalpy of vaporization of water as a
function of temperature is shown in Figure 4.5.

Entropy changes on melting and vaporization

The entropy change on melting a solid is generally rather small but varied
in its magnitude. Values usually occur in the range $10–40$ J K^{-1} mol^{-1}. There
are several contributions to this. In the first place there is the so-called
communal entropy which is associated with the fact that exchange of molecules between lattice sites in a solid does not occur whereas exchange
between positions in a liquid does. We mentioned this point in section 3.3
when discussing the factor $N!$ that occurs in expression 3.5. The contribution
from this is about 8 J K^{-1} mol^{-1} and the inert gases have entropies of melting
which are roughly this value. For polyatomic molecules the main contribution
arises from the change of lattice vibrations of the solid to restricted trans-
lations and rotations in the liquid.

For the liquid to gas transition the entropy change is larger and for most
molecules it is approximately 85 J K^{-1} mol^{-1}. This constancy is known as
Trouton's rule and it can be understood from the fact that gases have a much
greater degree of disorder than liquids, hence differences in the amount of
order possessed by one liquid and another are small compared with the
change on going to the gas. However, as Hildebrand has emphasized, the
gases produced at the normal boiling points of liquids do not all have the same
molar volumes because the boiling points differ. As the entropy of a gas
depends on volume and temperature we should expect to find greater constancy for the entropies of vaporization to constant molar volume and this is
generally true.

Table 4.1 The boiling point T_b and entropy of vaporization (column (1)) for some liquids. Column (2) shows
the entropy of vaporization to a constant molar volume of
49.56 dm^3

		ΔS_m/J K^{-1} mol^{-1}	
	T_b/K	(1)	(2)
Hg	630	94.1	84.1
CH_4	112	82.8	94.1
$n\,C_4H_{10}$	272	82.0	93.3
cyclo-C_6H_{12}	354	84.9	92.9
C_6H_6	353	87.1	95.0
H_2O	373	109.0	145.6
C_2H_5OH	452	139.7	149.8
CH_3COOH	392	62.3	—

See J. H. Hildebrand, *J.C.S. Faraday Disc.*, **66** (1978; R. W.
Hermsen and J. M. Prausnitz, *J. Chem. Phys.*, **34**, 1081 (1961).

From the Maxwell relation

$$\left(\frac{\partial S}{\partial V}\right)_T = \left(\frac{\partial P}{\partial T}\right)_V \qquad (4.20)$$

we can see that for a perfect gas

$$\left(\frac{\partial S}{\partial V}\right)_T = \frac{R}{V} \qquad (4.21)$$

hence the dependence of entropy on volume for a perfect gas at constant
temperature is

$$S_m(V_2) - S_m(V_1) = R \ln(V_2/V_1) \qquad (4.22)$$

Thus if we have two liquids whose boiling points differ by a factor of two
(in degrees Kelvin) then their molar volumes of gas at the boiling points will
differ by a factor of two and the contribution to the entropy difference is
$R \ln 2 = 5.8$ JK^{-1} mol^{-1}.

The fact that such a difference is small compared with the total entropy
change explains why Trouton's rule is quite good in spite of Hildebrand's
improvement.

If the entropy of vaporization differs appreciably from the Trouton constant then that indicates that there is some unusual behaviour in the liquid
or gaseous states. For example, water and ethanol can be seen from Table 4.1
to have larger than normal entropies of vaporization and that must indicate
that their liquids have a greater than normal degree of order, hence a lower
than normal entropy. This can be attributed to a hydrogen bonded structure
within the liquid. In contrast ethanoic acid has a lower than normal entropy
of vaporization, as do other aliphatic acids, and this indicates that some order
is retained in the gas phase by virtue of this dimerization.

4.2 The chemical potential of a gas

Although this book is concerned with the liquid state we cannot omit a discussion of the chemical potential of the perfect and imperfect gas for two reasons. First, above the critical point gas and liquid become a single state of matter. Second, and more important for our purposes, the simplest way of determining the chemical potential of a liquid is to determine the chemical potential of the gas with which it is in equilibrium. A final point is that our approach to non-ideality in a gas will be closely paralleled later in the book when we discuss non-ideal solutions.

If we integrate expressions 4.5 we can calculate the chemical potential at one value of temperature and pressure knowing its value at another. For example, we can write for constant T

$$\mu(P_2) - \mu(P_1) = \int_{P_1}^{P_2} V_m(P) \, dP. \tag{4.23}$$

For an ideal gas we know the dependence of the volume on pressure and hence can arrive at the result

$$\mu(P_2) - \mu(P_1) = RT \int_{P_1}^{P_2} P^{-1} \, dP = RT \ln\left(\frac{P_2}{P_1}\right). \tag{4.24}$$

In establishing tables of reference for thermodynamic quantities it is convenient to adopt standard conditions of temperature and pressure and any other variables that might influence the system. By using expressions such as 4.24 one can then calculate the changes in the relevant quantity from this so-called standard state. For an ideal gas the standard state is defined to be at a pressure of 1 atm so that if we denote the standard chemical potential by $\mu^\ominus$, we have from 4.24

$$\mu(P) = \mu^\ominus + RT \ln(P/\text{atm}). \tag{4.25}$$

A standard temperature of 298 K is also normally adopted. Changes from this temperature can be deduced from expression 4.5 if one knows the dependence of entropy on the temperature.

There is one mathematical feature of 4.25 that is worth noting. As $\ln(0) = -\infty$ it follows that the chemical potential of an ideal gas approaches $-\infty$ as the pressure tends to zero. As real gases all become ideal gases at low pressures it follows that the chemical potentials of real gases also approach $-\infty$ as the pressure approaches zero.

Fugacity

For real gases the integral in 4.23 must be evaluated from careful measurement of the pressure dependence of the molar volume. However, as gas imperfections are not usually very large it is convenient to use an expression for the chemical potential of a real gas which shows its relationship to the ideal gas. To do this we define a function f called the fugacity, which has the dimensions of pressure, by

$$\mu(P) = \mu^{\ominus} + RT \ln(f/\text{atm}), \qquad (4.26)$$

subject to the condition

$$\underset{P \to 0}{\text{Limit}} \left(\frac{f}{P} \right) = 1. \qquad (4.27)$$

It must be emphasized that the fugacity is defined by both of these expressions; 4.26 alone is not enough as that just amounts to an arbitrary division of $\mu(P)$ into two terms.

The relationship between f and P can be expressed more clearly by defining a dimensionless fugacity coefficient γ by

$$f = \gamma P, \qquad (4.28)$$

so that

$$\mu(P) = \mu^{\ominus} + RT \ln(P/\text{atm}) + RT \ln \gamma, \qquad (4.29)$$

where

$$\underset{P \to 0}{\text{Limit}}\ \gamma = 1. \qquad (4.30)$$

Although $\mu^{\ominus}$ is, from 4.26, the value of the chemical potential when $f = 1$ atm this is of no help for its determination because we do not know the pressure at this fugacity. As gases differ in their deviation from ideality $\mu^{\ominus}$ would have to be determined at different pressures for different gases. However, $\mu^{\ominus}$ can be obtained from measurements of μ at low pressures where the gas can be taken as ideal.

$$\mu^{\ominus} = \mu(P_{\text{low}}) - RT \ln f_{\text{low}} = \mu(P_{\text{low}}) - RT \ln P_{\text{low}} \qquad (4.31)$$

and values of f at high pressures are obtained from 4.23 by integrating from a low pressure ($P_1 = P_{\text{low}}$) to the pressure of interest ($P_2 = P$). From 4.23 and 4.26, we have

$$\mu(P) - \mu(P_{\text{low}}) = \int_{P_{\text{low}}}^{P} V_{\text{m}}(P)\, dP$$

$$\ln f = \ln P_{\text{low}} + \frac{1}{RT} \int_{P_{\text{low}}}^{P} V_{\text{m}}(P)\, dP. \qquad (4.32)$$

Figure 4.6 shows the dependence of γ on pressure for N_2 at 273 K. At pressures below about 300 atm γ is less than one and the gas is almost ideal. Above this pressure γ, and hence the non-ideality, increases rapidly. These two regions parallel the behaviour of the compression factor Z (see Figure 3.9) and reflect the importance of the a and b parameters of the van der Waals equation (3.44). Different gases have almost the same fugacity coefficient when they are at the same reduced temperature and pressure.

88

Figure 4.6 The dependence of the fugacity
coefficient on pressure for N_2 at 273 K

Let us now ask whether there is a physical definition of the standard state
of a real gas. If we take 4.29 as our starting point then we note that if γ
measures the whole deviation from ideality $\mu^{\ominus}$ must be taken as the chemical
potential of an ideal gas. In other words the standard state of a real gas is a
hypothetical state in which the gas is behaving ideally and in which the
fugacity is one atmosphere—that is, the pressure is one atmosphere. Thus all
real gases have the same standard state which is a hypothetical ideal gas at
$P = 1$ atm. Figure 4.7 illustrates this definition. It will be seen later in the
book that a similar approach is made to the standard states of solutions.

4.3 Single-component phase diagrams

Our first look at phase diagrams in section 1.2 had the objective of introducing terms like the triple point and critical point and emphasizing the
continuity of the fluid phase above the critical point. As we have now established the concept of the equation of state (section 3.6) and discussed the
thermodynamics of phase transitions (section 4.1) we return to the single-
component phase diagram and examine it in more detail.

The general equation of state for a single component (3.41), can be represented by a surface in three-dimensional space with pressure, temperature
and molar volume as cartesian axes. A typical surface is shown in Figure 4.8.
The single phase regions of the surface are curved in the three dimensions, the
two phase regions, e.g. liquid + gas, have zero slope along the volume axis

Figure 4.7 The chemical potentials of two real gases and their common standard state

because for a specified temperature the pressure is constant whatever the proportions of the two phases. The triple point line shows the conditions of fixed pressure and fixed temperature if all three phases are in equilibrium: the volume depends on what proportions of gas, liquid and solid are in the equilibrium mixture.

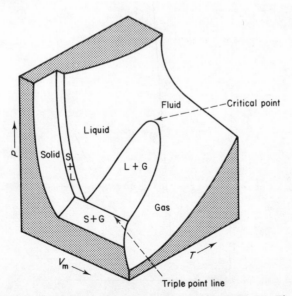

Figure 4.8 The equation of state surface $\phi(P, V_m, T)$ for a typical one-component system

The (P, T)-phase diagram shown in Figure 1.1 is a projection of the equation of state surface on the (P, T)-plane. As the two-phase regions of the surface have zero slope along the volume axis they appear as boundary lines in the (P, T)-phase diagram. The critical point is at the top of the liquid–gas boundary line so that in Figure 4.8 it is the point of maximum pressure and temperature on the liquid + gas region of the surface.

Figure 3.7 shows typical isotherms of the equation of state surface, that is it shows the line of intersection of the (P, V_m, T)-surface with (P, V_m)-planes for different temperatures. Only isotherms above the melting point of the solid were shown in Figure 3.7 but lower temperature curves could have been added which would include the solid region.

We complete this chapter by examining the (P, T)-phase diagrams of two systems, carbon dioxide and sulphur, which are shown in Figures 4.9 and 4.10. The only unusual feature of the CO_2 phase diagram is that the triple point occurs at a pressure greater than 1 atm ($T_t = 217$ K, $P_t = 5.11$ atm). Thus at normal pressures solid CO_2 sublimes and it is this property that gives it its name 'dry ice' and its value as a dry refrigerant. Cylinders of CO_2 at room temperature contain the liquid with a vapour pressure of 67 atm, but when they are discharged a CO_2 snow is produced as a result of the cooling produced by the rapid vaporization of the liquid.

Figure 4.9   The phase diagram for CO_2

Figure 4.10   The phase diagram for sulphur. The
pressure axis is not to scale. A, B and C are true
triple points. D is a pseudo-triple point between
metastable rhombic, liquid and gas

The new feature introduced for sulphur (Figure 4.10) is the existence of
two solid phases, rhombic and monoclinic. There are three true triple points
shown in the figures as A, B and C and one pseudo-triple point which is the
intersection of metastable rhombic sulphur, liquid and gas. The transition
rhombic to monoclinic is sufficiently slow that rhombic sulphur melts before
passing to the monoclinic form. Rhombic sulphur can be produced by freezing
the liquid above 1.4×10^8 Pa (1400 atm) or by rapidly condensing the
vapour onto a cold surface. In practice it is most commonly produced by
crystallization from carbon disulphide.

Liquid and gaseous sulphur are known to be mixtures of a number of
molecular species. Molecules are known with both rings and chains of sulphur
atoms and the species S_2, S_4, S_6 and S_8 are the most common forms. However,
the phase diagram is not influenced by this complexity. Whether the liquid
consists of a single type of molecule or many types it is still a single phase
because it is uniform in chemical composition.

Chapter 5

Liquid crystals—the mesophase

5.1 Order in liquid crystals

The first four chapters of this book have been concerned with the properties of pure liquids. Before turning to the more complex systems of liquid mixtures we discuss a state of matter which is intermediate between that of the crystalline solid and the liquid. This gives us the opportunity of amplifying some of the points made in the early chapters and at the same time we cover a field which in recent years has become of considerable technological importance.

In 1888 Reinitzer prepared some esters of cholesterol and noted that they had unusual melting properties. Although the crystals had a sharp melting point the melt was opaque but this opacity disappeared suddenly at a higher temperature to give a normal clear liquid.

Both he and a contemporary, Lehmann, established that the opaque state possessed anisotropic properties. This is most clearly shown by viewing thin sections between crossed polarizing plates when patterns are seen due to varying degrees of rotation of the plane of polarization by different parts of the section.

Lehmann used the term liquid crystal for this state of matter to show that it combines the properties of fluidity with that of anisotropy which is a characteristic of some crystalline solids. Despite much criticism over the years this name has remained. Friedel, in particular, stressed that the state was neither crystalline nor strictly liquid, and in 1922 he advocated the term mesophase (*meso* meaning between or intermediate) which is also widely used today.

It should not be thought that substances which exhibit a mesophase are rare. Many hundreds were prepared in the early part of this century and they were widely studied by physical chemists. Indeed, when one understands the origins of the phase one is tempted to conclude that most molecules should show a mesophase in some range of temperature and pressure, although there will be far fewer which show a mesophase at atmospheric pressure.

In this chapter we discuss the establishment of the mesophase by an appropriate choice of temperature—so-called thermotropic mesomorphism. It is also possible to establish it by an appropriate choice of solvent. This lyotropic mesomorphism will be considered in a later chapter as it connects with other topics such as surfaces, colloids and membranes.

A crystal is characterized by long-range order. This is associated with a translational symmetry that not only maintains a regularity in the lattice spacing in three dimensions, but also a regularity in the orientations of the molecules in space. In other words, the crystal possesses long-range translational order of the molecular centres and orientational order of the individual molecules.

In a mesophase some but not all of the long-range order is maintained. For a completely general molecule having three non-equivalent moments of inertia the orientational order could be maintained only along one axis, with random rotation about that axis, or along all three axes. In addition the translational order can be maintained in one, two or three dimensions. There are therefore several levels of order between the crystalline state in which all long-range order is maintained and the isotropic liquid in which no long-range translational or orientational order is maintained.

From optical studies Friedel was able to distinguish three different types of mesophase, and although further subdivisions have been suggested these are still the main categories used today.

(1) The smectic mesophase. This is a viscous state with certain properties similar to those of soaps from which the name is derived (Greek *smectos*, soap-like).

(2) The nematic mesophase. This is a mobile state which on glass surfaces frequently adopts a characteristic threaded pattern clearly visible between crossed polarizing plates. The name is likewise from the Greek: *nematos*, thread-like.

(3) The cholesteric mesophase. This is, like the nematic mesophase, a mobile state, but it is characterized by bright colours exhibited in reflected light and by a very high optical rotatory power. This phase is predominantly associated with derivatives of cholesterol, but it can be obtained from other substances. To form a cholesteric mesophase it is apparently necessary for the molecule to have a plate-like structure as, for example, cholesterol (Figure 5.1), and to be optically active.

There have been arguments over whether the cholesteric mesophase should be considered as a subclass of the smectic or of the nematic types. Many cholesteric compounds exhibit both cholesteric and smectic phases but none has been found to give both cholesteric and nematic. It appears therefore, that the molecular shapes required for cholesteric and nematic are incompatible. However, in fluidity the cholesteric is much closer to the nematic, and the addition of certain optically active compounds to some nematic mesophase will give cholesteric properties. On balance the present view is that the cholesteric mesophase should be considered as a distinct class.

Figure 5.1   The formula of cholesterol

Order in smectic and nematic mesophases

It has already been mentioned that a molecule may exhibit more than one mesophase, and this is particularly true for long molecules which can give smectic and nematic mesophases. On melting crystals of such molecules one obtains first the smectic mesophase, which on further heating turns into the nematic mesophase, and finally at a higher temperature the isotropic liquid. One can therefore conclude that the smectic mesophase has a higher degree of order than the nematic.

Friedel on the basis of his optical studies and some similarities between the shapes of thin drops of smectic fluid and soap films suggested that the smectic mesophase possessed a layered structure. This was later confirmed by X-ray studies and the layer thickness was found to be approximately equal to the length of the molecule. In contrast, X-ray studies on the nematic mesophase have shown little evidence of crystallinity, the patterns being similar to those obtained from the isotropic liquid (section 1.3). One important difference, however, is that X-ray studies carried out in the presence of applied electric or magnetic fields show that molecules in the nematic mesophase are aligned by the field. It can be concluded from this that the nematic mesophase consists of swarms of about 10^5 molecules and within each swarm there is approximate alignment but no layered structure. In other words in each swarm the molecules form an interlocking structure.

The relationship between the molecular arrangements in the crystals, the mesophase and the isotropic liquid is shown schematically in Figure 5.2. However, it must be emphasized that the orientational order in the nematic mesophase occurs only over microscopic dimensions (~100 nm) in the absence of applied fields.

There are many examples of molecules which exhibit more than one smectic mesophase. For example, the long molecule 4'-n-hexadecyl-3'-nitro-

Figure 5.2 Schematic relationship between the molecular order in the smectic and nematic mesophases and in the crystal and isotropic liquid. Perfect alignment in the mesophases should not be inferred

biphenyl-4-carboxylic acid shows three smectic phases with transition temperatures as follows:

$$\text{crystal} \xrightarrow{389.5 \text{ K}} \text{smectic I} \xrightarrow{434 \text{ K}} \text{smectic II} \xrightarrow{466.5 \text{ K}}$$

$$\text{smectic III} \xrightarrow{471.5 \text{ K}} \text{liquid}$$

Although these smectic mesophases all possess a layered structure the orientation of the molecules within a layer may be different, for example, the molecules may be tilted in some but not in others, and there may be a layer periodicity which is twice that of the simple structure by having head-to-head and tail-to-tail contacts. These are illustrated in Figure 5.3.

Liquid crystal displays

The nematic mesophase has in recent years been widely adopted for liquid crystal display devices (LCDs). They operate through their interaction with natural light either in transmission or reflection, and because they are not themselves primary light providers they consume very little power.

One type of display makes use of the fact that the nematic mesophase can

Figure 5.3   Possible alternative smectic structures to that
shown in Figure 5.2

be aligned by contact with surfaces, particularly glass surfaces. A small electric field can then be used to disturb this alignment and the change can be seen in reflected light. Another device makes use of the fact that larger fields can induce turbulence in the mesophase which produces enhanced light scattering.

The order in the cholesteric mesophase is shown most clearly by the extremely large optical rotatory power of such systems. For a normal optically active organic liquid rotations of 300° per mm would be considered large but

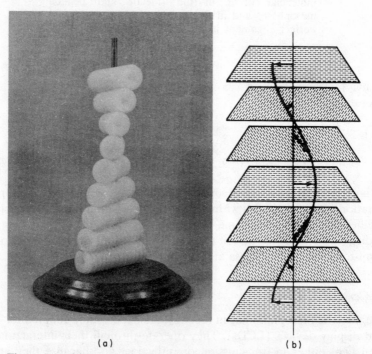

(a)   (b)

Figure 5.4   (a) Packing of chiral screws to give a helical structure. (b)
Schematic representation of the helix produced by gradually twisting
the axis of alignment of nematic-type layers

values up to 30,000° per mm have been obtained for some cholesteric meso-phases. Such large values show that there must be an ordered packing of the optically active molecules so that there is a cooperative rotation of the electric vector of the light from one molecule to another as it passes through the medium.

A simple model which illustrates the cooperative effect is shown in Figure 5.4. It consists of a set of screwed rods which are packed together so that their screws interlock along an axis perpendicular to the screw axis. This packing generates a helical array of the rods. Molecules similarly packed would produce an exceptionally large optical rotation. Figure 5.4 also shows a schematic representation of the helical structure that is obtained by gradually twisting the axis of alignment of nematic-type layers.

If the pitch of the cholesteric helix, which is the distance along the twist axis for a complete revolution of the molecular axis, is approximately equal to some wavelength in the visible spectrum then light of this wavelength will be strongly reflected by the cholesteric phase. The wavelength for maximum reflection depends on both the pitch of the helix and the angle between the helical axis and the incident ray, the connection being given by an equation similar to that of the Bragg diffraction law.

With suitable compounds the reflected colours can be obtained in any part of the visible spectrum, and in fact the pitch in the cholesteric mesophase can range from 200 nm to 8000 nm according to the molecule. Moreover the pitch changes with temperature, generally decreasing as the temperature increases, so that the reflected colours act as a sensitive temperature indicator. This has found technical and medical use in thermography, a technique whereby hot spots on surfaces are shown up by a surface coating of a cholesteric mesophase.

In concluding this section we note that there are crystalline phases in which the translational order of the molecular centres is maintained in three dimensions but in which orientational order is lost. These are frequently found for molecules which are nearly spherical so that little energy is required to allow free rotation or rotational randomization of the molecules in the crystal lattice: tertiary-butanol is one example. These phases are referred to as plastic crystals because their resistance to flow is considerably less than that of their low temperature normal crystalline form. The entropy of fusion of a plastic crystal is generally low because it possesses a greater entropy than normal crystals by virtue of the rotational randomization of molecules in the lattice.

5.2 Molecular structure and the mesophase

If one wishes to establish a phase in which long-range translational order of the molecular centres is lost, but long-range orientational order is maintained then one requires a strong rotational anisotropy in the intermolecular potential. Thus liquid crystals are formed predominantly by molecules that are plate-like or rod-like.

Anisotropy can occur both in the long-range (section 2.2) and in the short-range (section 2.3) parts of the potential. One important component to the long-range potential is the electrostatic interaction between molecules, but because liquid crystals can be formed by either polar or non-polar molecules, electrostatic forces cannot be the only factor although they are undoubtedly important.

The *para*-polyphenyls of formula

are one important class of non-polar molecules which give a mesomorphic phase for $n > 3$. It has been noted that replacing an unsaturated phenyl ring by the saturated group

changes the mesophase transition temperatures considerably. This replacement changes the long-axis polarizability considerably by removing the π-electron delocalization, and hence changing the dispersion energy. However, it makes little difference to the size of the molecule, and we can, therefore, conclude that the anisotropy of the dispersion energy plays an important role in establishing the mesophase. This is supported by the generalization that saturated long-chain organic molecules rarely form a mesophase whereas their unsaturated analogues frequently do.

The relationship between the intermolecular potential and the occurrence of a mesophase is something that can clearly be investigated by computer simulation using the methods described in section 3.5. At the time of writing relatively little has been done in this direction as the computing time required is quite high. One system that has been investigated is the orientational order of rigid rods whose centres are fixed at simple cubic lattice sites. This model was introduced by Maier and Saupe† to study the isotropic liquid → nematic phase change, but it is in fact a plastic crystal → crystal phase change. The results nevertheless are of interest.

An intermolecular potential between nearest neighbour sites was chosen of the form

$$V_{ij} = -\frac{\varepsilon}{2} (3 \cos^3 \theta_{ij} - 1), \qquad (5.1)$$

where θ_{ij} is the angle between rods i and j. This potential is the leading anisotropic term for the interaction of non-polar axial molecules providing that the dependence of ε on the intermolecular distance is allowed for. However, if the molecules have their centres fixed at lattice sites then ε can be taken as a constant.

†W. Maier and A. Saupe, *Zeit. Naturf.*, **a15**, 287 (1960).

Monte Carlo calculations† were made for various values of the parameter ε/kT. For low values (high temperatures) the system was orientationally disordered; the value of M, defined by

$$M = \tfrac{1}{2}\overline{(3\cos^2\theta_{ij} - 1)}, \tag{5.2}$$

which measures the average alignment of the molecules, being zero. As ε/kT was increased M was found to increase slowly but a discontinuous change was found at $\varepsilon/kT = 0.9$ to a new phase having a value of M approximately equal to $1/3$. A further increase in ε/kT gave a smooth increase in the order until the limiting value of $M = 1$ was reached for perfect alignment of the rods. This computer simulation therefore confirmed that the potential 5.1 was sufficient to give a plastic crystal $\rightarrow$ crystal phase change and it was argued by Maier and Saupe, probably correctly, that the same potential if used with a relaxation of the molecular centres would simulate the isotropic $\rightarrow$ nematic phase change.‡

Figure 5.5 The phase transition temperature for the *p*-*n*-alkoxybenzoic acids (G. W. Gray and B. Jones, *J. Chem. Soc.*, 4179 (1953)). Crosses show the melting points and dots the smectic–nematic and nematic–liquid transition points

†P. A. Lebwohl and G. Lasher, *Phys. Rev.*, **46**, 426 (1972).
‡This has now been confirmed: G. R. Luckhurst and S. Romano, *Proc. Roy. Soc.*, **A373**, 111 (1980).

The variation of melting point with chain length in a homologous series is frequently an erratic function of chain length. This is illustrated in Figure 5.5 by the melting points of the p-n-alkoxybenzoic acids. In contrast, the transition temperatures between mesophases, or between a mesophase and the isotropic liquid, is invariably a smooth function of chain length. In the example shown in Figure 5.5 the nematic to liquid transition temperature shows an oscillation from odd to even chain lengths, but the odd and even series lie on smooth curves.

The melting point of a compound is the temperature at which a three-dimensional ordered structure collapses to a disordered liquid, and the change is substantial. Small differences between molecules can make large changes in the way they pack in the crystal, and hence in the melting point. The change in structure between two mesophases or between mesophase and liquid is, however, relatively small, and as a result the transition temperatures are regular.

This raises the question of whether the phase changes are first or second order. In the case of p-azoxyphenetole the nematic–liquid transition has been shown to be accompanied by a small discontinuous change in volume of 0.6% compared with the solid–nematic volume change of 8.4%. Likewise small discontinuities in the enthalpy have been measured—typically only a quarter of the change found on melting. The evidence is, therefore, that transitions between mesophases or between mesophase and liquid are first order but with small discontinuities in V, H and S.

Chapter 6

Mixtures of non-electrolytes

6.1 Thermodynamic properties of liquid mixtures

In this chapter we shall be considering some important properties of liquid mixtures such as their vapour pressure and miscibility. For the moment we confine our attention to liquids which are non-electrolytes, that is, they do not significantly conduct electricity. The behaviour of such liquids follows closely certain ideal laws of mixing, and hence their thermodynamic properties can often be predicted accurately. In contrast, electrolytes, typically solutions of salts in water, show large deviations from these ideal laws, and in consequence they will be discussed in later chapters.

In addition to liquid mixtures we shall also consider in this chapter solutions of solid non-electrolytes in liquid non-electrolytes because thermodynamically the two are very similar. The word solution is used to describe a phase containing more than one substance, when for convenience one substance which is in excess (the solvent) is treated differently from the others (the solutes).

We start by defining some terms which are measures of the composition of a mixture. The most important quantity as far as the laws of mixing are concerned is the mole fraction. The mole fraction of a species A is defined as the ratio of the number of moles of A to the total number of moles of all species present in the mixture. This is written

$$x_A = n_A \Big/ \sum_i n_i, \qquad (6.1)$$

where n_i is the number of moles of species i. It follows from definition 6.1 that the sum of the mole fractions of each species in a mixture is equal to unity

$$\sum_i x_i = 1. \qquad (6.2)$$

To make up a solution with specified mole fractions requires each component to be weighed to precalculated amounts and this is a tedious operation. There are other measures of composition that are simpler for practical use. One that is commonly met in making standard solutions for volumetric

101

analysis is the molarity, which is the number of moles of a solute in 1 dm³ of solution. However, for reasons which will become clear later when we discuss changes in volume on mixing, it is not easy to determine mole fractions for a solution of specified molarity.†

A better practical measure of composition is the molality (m) which is the number of moles of a solute in a solution containing 1 kg of solvent. If the molecular weight of the solvent is M then 1 kg of solvent contains $1000/M$ moles, hence the mole fraction of a solute in an m molal solution is

$$x = \frac{m}{m + \dfrac{1000}{M}}. \tag{6.3}$$

For dilute solutions $m \ll 1000/M$ and we can use the approximation

$$x \approx \frac{mM}{1000}. \tag{6.4}$$

Miscibility and immiscibility

Let us now discuss in very general terms the question of whether or not two phases will spontaneously mix. For example, if two pure gases are placed in a container but separated by a partition, then when the partition is removed the gases will mix to give a gas which is uniform in composition throughout the container; in other words they give a single phase.

Likewise ethanol and water will form a single phase whatever their relative proportions; we say that the two liquids are completely miscible. In contrast benzene and water when mixed will form two liquid layers (two phases) unless one of the two components is present in a large excess. Benzene has a very small solubility in water and water a very small solubility in benzene but over most of the mole fraction range benzene and water are immiscible.

If two liquids are miscible in all proportions we conclude that the Gibbs free energy of the mixture is less than the sum of the Gibbs free energies of the separate components. Suppose we make a mixture with n_A moles of component A and n_B moles of component B. Before mixing the total Gibbs free energy is

$$n_A G_{A,m} + n_B G_{B,m}. \tag{6.5}$$

We write the free energy after mixing (at constant T and P) as

$$(n_A + n_B)G_m(x), \tag{6.6}$$

where $G_m(x)$ is the molar Gibbs free energy for a mixture with mole fraction

---

†To convert from a volume-based measure to a mass-based measure it is necessary to know the density of the mixture.

of A equal to

$$x = \frac{n_A}{n_A + n_B}.$$ (6.7)

We define the Gibbs free energy of mixing as the difference between 6.6 and 6.5 per mole of mixture

$$\Delta G_{mix}(x) = G_m(x) - \left(\frac{n_A}{n_A + n_B}\right)G_{A,m} - \left(\frac{n_B}{n_A + n_B}\right)G_{B,m},$$

$$= G_m(x) - xG_{A,m} - (1 - x)G_{B,m}.$$ (6.8)

$\Delta G_{mix}(x)$ must be negative for all x if the two liquids are miscible in all proportions. In fact we can make a stronger statement than this as will be seen from the following analysis.

Figure 6.1 shows the typical behaviour of the Gibbs free energy of mixing of two liquids that are completely miscible. Suppose we now take a fraction λ moles ($\lambda < 1$) of a mixture having a mole fraction x_1 of A and $(1 - \lambda)$ of a mixture with mole fraction x_2 of A. Before mixing them the total free energy of mixing is

$$\overline{\Delta G}_{mix}(x) = \lambda \Delta G_{mix}(x_1) + (1 - \lambda)\Delta G_{mix}(x_2)$$ (6.9)

which we note is a linear function of λ. Thus $\overline{\Delta G}_{mix}(x)$ is represented by a point on the straight line joining $\Delta G_{mix}(x_1)$ and $\Delta G_{mix}(x_2)$, whose composition, x, is given by

$$\frac{x - x_1}{x_2 - x} = \frac{1 - \lambda}{\lambda}.$$ (6.10)

When we mix the two solutions of composition x_1 and x_2 we get a single phase

Figure 6.1 ΔG_{mix} for   completely miscible liquids

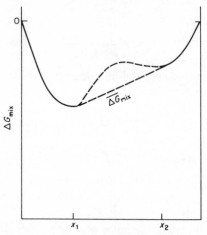

Figure 6.2 ΔG_{mix} for two partially miscible liquids. Only in the regions covered by the solid curves will a single phase occur

so we conclude that $\Delta G_{mix}(x)$ is less than $\overline{\Delta G}_{mix}(x)$. If it were greater, then the two fractions of compositions x_1 and x_2 would not be miscible.

We contrast the situation of Figure 6.1 with that of Figure 6.2. We see that ΔG_{mix} is negative over the whole range but it is greater than $\overline{\Delta G}_{mix}(x)$ over the range $x_1 < x < x_2$ as shown. In other words any mixture that has a composition in this range will spontaneously separate into two liquid phases one of composition x_1 and the other of composition x_2. We conclude that for two liquids to be miscible over the whole composition range not only must $\Delta G_{mix}(x)$ be negative, but it must, in its whole composition range, have a positive curvature.

Other thermodynamic mixing functions can be defined in a similar way to ΔG_{mix}. For mixing at constant temperature and pressure the most important quantities are ΔH_{mix} and ΔS_{mix}, which are related to ΔG_{mix} by

$$\Delta G_{mix}(x) = \Delta H_{mix}(x) - T\Delta S_{mix}(x). \tag{6.11}$$

If ΔH_{mix} is negative and ΔS_{mix} positive the two liquids will be miscible at all temperatures. This conclusion must be qualified by the requirement that $\Delta G_{mix}(x)$ has positive curvature for the liquids to be miscible in all proportions. If both ΔH_{mix} and ΔS_{mix} are positive the liquids may be immiscible at low temperatures but miscible at high temperatures. The minimum temperature at which the liquids are miscible in all proportions is called the upper consolute temperature (UCT).

Figure 6.3 shows an example of this for mixtures of benzene and perfluoroheptane. At temperatures below 386.5 K there will be two liquid phases if the overall composition of the system lies within the two-phase region. As T

Figure 6.3 The miscibility of liquid benzene and perfluoroheptane (atmospheric pressure). The upper consolute temperature (UCT) is 386.5 K. (J. H. Hildebrand, B. B. Fisher and H. A. Benesi, *J. Amer. Chem. Soc.*, **72**, 4348 (1950))

approaches 386.5 K the compositions of these two phases approach one another and at the maximum in the phase boundary curve ($x(C_6H_6) = 0.83$, $T = 386.5$ K), the compositions become equal. This point therefore has similar thermodynamic characteristics to the critical point in the single-component phase diagram where gas–liquid properties become identical, and it is therefore also called a critical point. The UCT is also referred to as the critical solution temperature.

If ΔH_{mix} and ΔS_{mix} are both negative the liquids may be miscible at low temperatures and immiscible at high temperatures. The maximum temperature for which the system shows a single liquid phase is called the lower consolute temperature (LCT). Because ΔH_{mix} and ΔS_{mix} are functions of temperature they may change sign as the temperature is varied and there are systems which exhibit both upper and lower consolute temperatures. In some cases LCT < UCT, i.e. at low temperatures the liquids are miscible in all proportions, this is followed by a region of immiscibility and then at high temperatures they are again miscible: nicotine–water is the classic example. In other cases (e.g. methane–n-hexane) the system has LCT > UCT so that there is a middle temperature range in which the components are completely miscible. In principle all systems showing a LCT should have one higher UCT but only if the pressure is high enough to prevent the liquids boiling before this is reached.

If two liquids of very similar molecular structure are mixed such as benzene and toluene, they will be miscible in all proportions. ΔG_{mix} will be negative for such systems and we can anticipate that there will be a simple mixing law by which ΔG_{mix} can be predicted. This law is embodied in the concept of an ideal mixture, which we shall approach by first examining the mixing of two gases.

6.2 Ideal mixing

Expression 4.25 gives us the chemical potential (molar Gibbs free energy) of a perfect gas as a function of pressure

$$\mu(P) = \mu^{\ominus} \ (P = 1 \text{ atm}) + RT \ln(P/\text{atm}). \tag{6.12}$$

We will now calculate ΔG_{mix} for two gases at a constant pressure.

Figure 6.4 illustrates the situation; we have n_A moles of gas A at pressure P and n_B moles of B also at pressure P. When mixed there will be $n_A + n_B$ moles of gas also at pressure P. By Dalton's law of partial pressures we can say that the partial pressures† of the two gases in the mixture are

$$p_A = \left(\frac{n_A}{n_A + n_B}\right)P, \qquad p_B = \left(\frac{n_B}{n_A + n_B}\right)P. \tag{6.13}$$

Introducing the mole fractions (6.1) these become

$$p_A = x_A P, \qquad p_B = x_B P. \tag{6.14}$$

Before mixing the total Gibbs free energy is

$$G_b = n_A(\mu_A^{\ominus} + RT \ln P) + n_B(\mu_B^{\ominus} + RT \ln P), \tag{6.15}$$

After mixing each gas has a lower pressure, its partial pressure, and hence the Gibbs free energy of the mixture is

$$G_a = n_A(\mu_A^{\ominus} + RT \ln p_A) + n_B(\mu_B^{\ominus} + RT \ln p_B). \tag{6.16}$$

The free energy of mixing is

$$\Delta G_{\text{mix}} = \frac{RT}{n_A + n_B} (n_A \ln(p_A/P) + n_B \ln(p_B/P),$$

$$= RT(x_A \ln x_A + x_B \ln x_B). \tag{6.17}$$

This expression can be generalized in an obvious way for the mixing of any number of non-interacting ideal gases (i) to

$$\Delta G_{\text{mix}} = RT \sum_i x_i \ln x_i. \tag{6.18}$$

Figure 6.4   Mixing of two perfect gases at the same pressure

†See note on pressure symbols on page 3.

An important point to note is that expression 6.18 is independent of pressure. Thus $(\partial \Delta G_{mix}/\partial P) = 0$ and, from 4.3, it follows that there is no volume change on mixing. This is as expected for ideal gases.

We can obtain an expression for the entropy of mixing from expression 4.4.

$$\Delta S_{mix} = -\left(\frac{\partial \Delta G_{mix}}{\partial T}\right)_P = -R \sum_i x_i \ln x_i. \qquad (6.19)$$

From 6.18 and 6.19 we see that

$$\Delta G_{mix} = -T\Delta S_{mix} \qquad (6.20)$$

and conclude that $\Delta H_{mix} = 0$. This is also expected; there is no temperature change on mixing ideal gases providing that no chemical reaction occurs.

As x_i has a value between zero and one, $\ln x_i$ is always negative. It follows that ΔS_{mix} is positive, as expected for a randomizing process, and ΔG_{mix} is negative. Figure 6.5 shows the behaviour of the thermodynamic parameters as a function of mole fraction for two ideal gases. ΔG_{mix} is the type of curve which, from Figure 6.1, we have already seen to be necessary for two components to be miscible in all proportions.

An ideal system in thermodynamics is one whose parameters follow some convenient standard of behaviour. Thus an ideal or perfect gas is one that

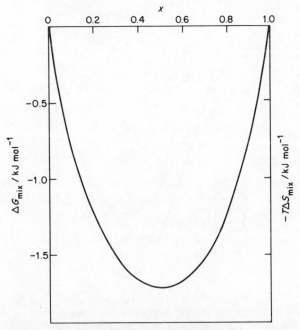

Figure 6.5 The free energy of mixing of two ideal gases as a function of the mole fraction of one component ($T = 300$ K)

obeys the perfect-gas laws and the behaviour of real gases can be measured relative to their ideal behaviour. Likewise, ideal mixtures or ideal solutions are those which follow some standard behaviour, and the model of ideality will differ according to the type of system under study. In this section of the book we are examining mixtures of non-electrolytes, and for these the ideal system is defined as one whose thermodynamic mixing parameters obey the same equations as an ideal gas: the free energy of mixing should obey 6.18, the entropy of mixing should obey 6.19, and ΔH_{mix} should be zero. We shall later examine other standards of ideality, for example for solutions of electrolytes.

Excess functions

Convenient measures of the non-ideality of a liquid mixture are provided by the differences between the thermodynamic mixing parameters and the corresponding values for the ideal mixture. The most important parameters are

$$G^E = \Delta G_{mix} - RT \sum_i x_i \ln x_i,$$
$$S^E = \Delta S_{mix} + R \sum_i x_i \ln x_i,$$
$$H^E = \Delta H_{mix},$$
$$V^E = \Delta V_{mix}. \tag{6.21}$$

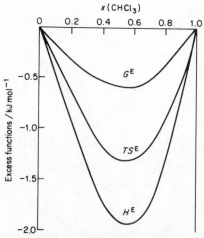

Figure 6.6 The thermodynamic excess mixing functions for acetone and chloroform as a function of the mole fraction of chloroform. (L. A. K. Staveley, W. I. Tupman and K. R. Hart, *Trans. Faraday Soc.*, **51**, 323 (1955))

Each of these functions will be nearly zero for mixtures of liquids which are very similar in their chemical composition.

Figure 6.6 shows the excess functions for mixtures of acetone and chloroform. The negative value of H^E can be attributed to hydrogen bonding between the molecules of the two compounds. ΔS_{mix} will be positive, as mixing is a randomizing process, but S^E is negative because there is more order in the mixture than for an ideal system; again this is due to hydrogen bonding. We shall make further studies of non-ideal mixing later in this chapter.

6.3 Partial molar quantities

In this section we examine some thermodynamic quantities which measure the change in the extensive properties of a mixture with changing composition. We will take the volume of a liquid mixture as an illustrative example because it is relatively easy to see the line of the argument.

A mole of water has a volume of 18 cm^3, one of ethanol a volume of 58.4 cm^3. On mixing one mole of each the total volume is 74.5 cm^3 so that there is a contraction in volume on mixing of 2 cm^3. We shall now define a quantity which can be said to measure the separate volumes of the two components, water and ethanol, in the mixture.

For a two-component mixture (A, B) the total volume is a function of the number of moles of each component. We write this $V(n_A, n_B)$ and think of V as being a surface in three-dimensional space with axes V, n_A, n_B as shown in Figure 6.7. If we make small changes in n_A and n_B the change in volume is given by the complete differential

$$dV(n_A, n_B) = \left(\frac{\partial V}{\partial n_A}\right)_{n_B} dn_A + \left(\frac{\partial V}{\partial n_B}\right)_{n_A} dn_B. \tag{6.22}$$

To obtain the total volume of a mixture from this expression we have to integrate it from $n_A = n_B = 0$ to the values of n_A and n_B appropriate to the mixture. This can be done easily if we note an important property of V, which is that, provided the composition of the mixture is kept constant (i.e., the ratio n_A/n_B is constant), then V is proportional to the number of moles of A (or B). If we return to the water–ethanol example we know that a mixture of 2 moles of water and 2 moles of ethanol will have a volume 2×74.5 cm^3. It is this property that gives the surface $V(n_A, n_B)$ the special feature that along a line of constant ratio (n_A/n_B) the slope of V is a constant. This is indicated in Figure 6.7.

To obtain the total volume of a mixture we therefore integrate 6.22 along a line of constant ratio n_A/n_B that will lead to the required mixture. An alternative way to picture this is that we build up the total V by adding small amounts δV all of which have the same composition $\delta n_A/\delta n_B = n_A/n_B$. By either argument we arrive at the important result that the total volume is given by

$$V = \left(\frac{\partial V}{\partial n_A}\right) n_A + \left(\frac{\partial V}{\partial n_B}\right) n_B. \tag{6.23}$$

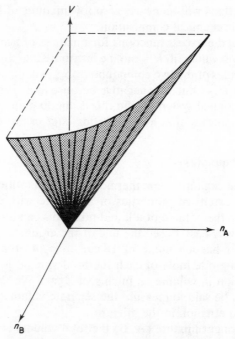

Figure 6.7 A representation of the surface $V(n_A, n_B)$. Lines in the surface of constant composition are shown

The volume of a mixture depends on temperature and pressure as well as composition. As systems are most frequently studied at constant temperature and pressure it is convenient to have a symbol for the change of volume with the concentration of one component, temperature, pressure and the concentrations of all other components being kept constant. This quantity is called the partial molar volume and is given the symbol $\bar{V}$. For the two-component system we have just been discussing we write

$$\bar{V}_A = \left(\frac{\partial V}{\partial n_A}\right)_{T,P,n_B}, \qquad \bar{V}_B = \left(\frac{\partial V}{\partial n_B}\right)_{T,P,n_A}. \qquad (6.24)$$

Thus for constant (T, P) expression 6.23 can be written

$$V = \bar{V}_A n_A + \bar{V}_B n_B, \qquad (6.25)$$

which can be generalized for n components to

$$V = \sum_i \bar{V}_i n_i, \qquad (6.26)$$

where

$$\bar{V}_i = \left(\frac{\partial V}{\partial n_i}\right)_{T,P,n_j}. \qquad (6.27)$$

For a pure substance the partial molar volume is equal to the molar volume.

We can summarize the importance of the partial molar volume in two statements. First, from 6.27, it defines the change in volume on changing the concentration of one component keeping all other components constant. Second, from 6.26, the total volume is equal to the sum of the partial molar volumes of each component multiplied by the number of moles of that component.

The Gibbs–Duhem equation

Figure 6.8 shows the partial molar volumes of ethanol and water as a function of mole fraction in ethanol–water mixtures. We note that the largest contractions in volume occur for the component which is in the mixture only as a trace; the ethanol in almost pure water or the water in almost pure ethanol. Another feature is that there is a maximum in the partial molar volume of water and a minimum in the partial molar volume of ethanol, and these both occur at the same mole fraction. This result follows from a theorem which we shall now prove.

If we differentiate expression 6.25 with respect to n_A keeping n_B constant

Figure 6.8 The partial molar volumes of an ethanol–water mixture as a function of mole fraction of ethanol

we have, at constant T and P:

$$\left(\frac{\partial V}{\partial n_A}\right)_{T,P,n_B} = n_A\left(\frac{\partial \bar{V}_A}{\partial n_A}\right)_{T,P,n_B} + \bar{V}_A + n_B\left(\frac{\partial \bar{V}_B}{\partial n_A}\right)_{T,P,n_B}. \qquad (6.28)$$

However, the left-hand side of this equation is $\bar{V}_A$ so that

$$n_A\left(\frac{\partial \bar{V}_A}{\partial n_A}\right)_{T,P,n_B} + n_B\left(\frac{\partial \bar{V}_B}{\partial n_A}\right)_{T,P,n_B} = 0. \qquad (6.29)$$

Equation 6.29 relates the derivatives of the two partial molar quantities with respect to the number of moles of one component. For more than two components the equation can be generalized to

$$\sum_i n_i\left(\frac{\partial \bar{V}_i}{\partial n_k}\right)_{T,P,n_j} = 0, \qquad (6.30)$$

which is called the Gibbs–Duhem equation for partial molar volumes. It can be seen from 6.29 that if one of the derivatives is zero then the other must be zero also, which explains the simultaneous maximum and minimum in Figure 6.8.

The equations which we have derived in this section for partial molar volumes can be applied to any of the extensive thermodynamic quantities. For example, the partial molar enthalpy is defined by analogy with 6.24 as

$$\bar{H}_i = \left(\frac{\partial H}{\partial n_i}\right)_{T,P,n_j}, \qquad (6.31)$$

hence the total enthalpy is (cf. 6.26)

$$H = \sum_i \bar{H}_i n_i, \qquad (6.32)$$

and the Gibbs–Duhem equation for enthalpies is (cf. 6.30)

$$\sum_i n_i\left(\frac{\partial \bar{H}_i}{\partial n_k}\right)_{T,P,n_j} = 0. \qquad (6.33)$$

The most important partial molar quantity is the partial molar Gibbs free energy and this is given a special name, the chemical potential, and symbol μ.

$$\left(\frac{\partial G}{\partial n_i}\right)_{T,P,n_j} = \bar{G}_i \equiv \mu_i. \qquad (6.34)$$

The chemical potential of a pure substance is equal to the molar Gibbs free energy and was defined as such in section 4.1.

One reason for the importance of the chemical potential is that for two phases in equilibrium which have more than one component the chemical potential *of each component* must be equal in the two phases. We note that this is an extension of the condition (1.4) for a single component that the molar Gibbs free energy must be equal in the two phases, and the proof of the more general result follows the same line.

6.4 The vapour pressure of liquid mixtures

The vapour pressure of a liquid is defined as the pressure exerted by its vapour under conditions of equilibrium. For a single-component liquid the vapour pressure is a function only of the temperature; the liquid–gas boundary line shown in Figure 1.1 represents this functional relationship. For a liquid consisting of more than one component the vapour pressure is a function of composition as well as temperature.

The vapour pressure is an extremely important thermodynamic property of a liquid because it provides a measure of its chemical potential. Expression 4.25, or 4.26 if the vapour is not ideal, gives the chemical potential of the vapour as a function of pressure, and if the vapour is in equilibrium with the liquid then the chemical potentials of vapour and liquid are equal. Thus for a pure liquid (species A) we can write (ideal vapour)

$$\mu_A^*(l) = \mu_A(g) = \mu_A^\circ + RT \ln(p_A^*/atm), \tag{6.35}$$

where the symbol * has been used to indicate a pure component. If several components are present in a mixture then an expression such as 6.35 applies to each component, as follows

$$\mu_A(l) = \mu_A^\circ + RT \ln(p_A/atm), \tag{6.36}$$

where p_A is the partial pressure of species A in the vapour. Subtracting 6.35 from 6.36 eliminates μ°, the standard chemical potential of the gas, with the result

$$\mu_A(l) = \mu_A^*(l) + RT \ln(p_A/p_A^*). \tag{6.37}$$

This expression relates the chemical potential of species A to the chemical potential of the pure liquid and to the ratio of the vapour pressures of A in the mixture and in the pure liquid.

$\mu_A(l)$ must be less than $\mu_A^*(l)$ for any stable liquid phase; if it were not, the liquid mixture would be thermodynamically unstable relative to pure liquid A and a mixture with the other components. It follows that p_A must be less than p_A^*, that is the partial pressure of a component in a single phase mixture is always less than the vapour pressure of the pure component at the same temperature.

Raoult's law and Henry's law

We now ask how the ratio (p_A/p_A^*) depends on the mole fraction of component A. The simplest assumption is embodied in Raoult's law

$$p_A/p_A^* = x_A. \tag{6.38}$$

This law implies that the chance of finding a molecule of A in the vapour, relative to the chance for the pure liquid A, is equal to the fraction of molecules A in the mixture. It is evident that this would be a reasonable assumption if we were dealing with ideal mixtures as defined in section 6.2 (e.g., a

114

mixture of $CHCl_3$ and $CDCl_3$) and in fact Raoult's law can be taken as a definition of ideality, equivalent to that contained in expression 6.18, providing that the vapour is an ideal gas.

Assuming the validity of Raoult's law, expression 6.37 becomes

$$\mu_A(l) = \mu_A^*(l) + RT \ln x_A. \tag{6.39}$$

On mixing n_A moles of A and n_B moles of B the free energy of mixing per mole is

$$\Delta G_{mix} = (n_A + n_B)^{-1}[n_A(\mu_A - \mu_A^*) + n_B(\mu_B - \mu_B^*)] = RT(x_A \ln x_A + x_B \ln x_B), \tag{6.40}$$

which is identical to 6.17.

Figures 6.9(a), (b) and (c) show the vapour pressures of some ideal and non-ideal mixtures. Note in the non-ideal case (c) the total vapour pressure

Figure 6.9 The vapour pressures of the following mixtures: (a) benzene–toluene; (b) acetone–chloroform; (c) carbon disulphide–dimethoxymethane

can be greater than that of either pure component, although we have already noted that the partial vapour pressure cannot be greater than the corresponding pure liquid vapour pressure.

If the vapour pressure of one component obeys Raoult's law then that of the other must also obey this law. This follows from 6.37 and application of the Gibbs–Duhem equation to the chemical potentials. The corresponding expression to 6.30 for two components is

$$\left(\frac{\partial \mu_A}{\partial n_A}\right)n_A + \left(\frac{\partial \mu_B}{\partial n_A}\right)n_B = 0. \tag{6.41}$$

Equation 6.41 can easily be transformed into a similar expression with mole fractions

$$\left(\frac{\partial \mu_A}{\partial x_A}\right)x_A + \left(\frac{\partial \mu_B}{\partial x_A}\right)x_B = 0. \tag{6.42}$$

If we now relate the chemical potential to vapour pressure by 6.36 we obtain

$$\left(\frac{\partial \ln p_A}{\partial x_A}\right)x_A + \left(\frac{\partial \ln p_B}{\partial x_A}\right)x_B = 0, \tag{6.43}$$

or

$$\frac{x_A}{p_A}\left(\frac{\partial p_A}{\partial x_A}\right) + \frac{x_B}{p_B}\left(\frac{\partial p_B}{\partial x_A}\right) = 0. \tag{6.44}$$

Because $x_A + x_B = 1$ we obtain the result

$$\frac{x_A}{p_A}\left(\frac{\partial p_A}{\partial x_A}\right) = \frac{x_B}{p_B}\left(\frac{\partial p_B}{\partial x_B}\right). \tag{6.45}$$

Equations 6.43–6.45 are known as the Duhem–Margules equations; they establish a relationship between the gradients of the vapour pressure–mole fraction curves of the two components. In particular, if $(\partial p_A/\partial x_A)$ is constant then the left-hand side of 6.45 is equal to unity and $(\partial p_B/\partial x_B)$ must also be a constant.

Even for non-ideal mixtures Raoult's law is obeyed for the excess component in a very dilute solution. This is indicated by the partial pressure line becoming asymptotic to the Raoult's law line as $x \to 1$. For dilute solutions the vapour pressure of the component of *low* concentration is also linearly related to mole fraction, but the proportionality constant does not have the Raoult's law value. This result is known as Henry's law and is expressed mathematically as

$$p_A = K_A x_A, \tag{6.46}$$

when $x_A \to 0$. K_A is known as the Henry law constant. The physical basis of Henry's law is that for dilute solutions every solute molecule is completely surrounded by solvent molecules and providing this condition is maintained

116

the vapour pressure of the solute will be proportional to the mole fraction of solute. Deviations from Henry's law will occur when concentrations are reached such that solute molecules have other solute molecules in their vicinity.

Henry's law has special significance for the solubility of gases in liquids. Consider, for example, the solubility of hydrogen (component A) in benzene as a function of the applied pressure P. If P is much greater than the vapour pressure of benzene we can take $P \approx p_A$ whence 6.46 takes the form

$$x_A = P/K_A, \tag{6.47}$$

and if x_A is small we can, from 6.4, give the solubility in molality units

$$m_A = \frac{1000}{M_A K_A} P. \tag{6.48}$$

In our example M_B would be the molecular weight of benzene (78) and K_A the Henry's law constant for hydrogen in benzene, which is 3.62×10^3 atm at 298 K. Thus at a pressure of 10 atm the solubility of hydrogen in benzene is 3.5×10^{-2} mol kg^{-1}.

Figure 6.10 shows the solubility of some common gases in water as a function of applied pressure. The Henry constants are given by the tangents to the curves at the origin and it can be seen that Henry's law applies quite accurately up to gas pressures of 100 atm or greater. At very high pressures

Figure 6.10 The solubility of gases in water as a function of applied pressure ($T = 298$ K)

a correction should be made for non-ideality of the gas and to do this P in 6.47 is replaced by fugacity (f). It has been found empirically that $\log(f/x)$ is a linear function of P, but with the pressure dependence being very small.

Henry's law coefficients increase with increasing temperature so that gases become less soluble in liquids as the temperature is raised. A widely observed relationship is $\log K_A \propto T^{-1}$.

Deviations from the ideal mixing laws can often be explained quantitatively in terms of the interactions between molecules in the pure liquids and in the mixture. For example, the negative deviation from Raoult's law observed for acetone–chloroform mixtures (Figure 6.9(b)) is attributed to hydrogen bonding between these two species in the mixture. This is supported by evidence from the infra-red spectrum of such mixtures, particularly the increase in intensity of the C–H stretching band of chloroform which occurs on addition of acetone. There are also changes in the carbonyl stretching band of the acetone, and these changes have been used to show that a complex with one acetone and two chloroform molecules is present in the mixture.[†]

Positive deviations from Raoult's law are more common than negative deviations, and occur particularly for mixtures of water with a less polar solvent. The reason for this is that water is a strongly associated liquid and a second component will tend to break up this association with a correspondingly unfavourable change in the enthalpy.

A class of solution which can be thought of as intermediate between ideal and non-ideal was defined by Hildebrand and called a regular solution. For such solutions the entropy of mixing obeys the ideal mixing law (6.19), but the enthalpy of mixing is not ideal ($\Delta H_{mix} \neq 0$). The main interest in this class of solution is that it allows for an elegant statistical mechanical treatment of the free energy of mixing.[‡] However, the number of solutions which are exactly regular is too small for us to pursue their theory in this text. A full discussion has been given by Hildebrand and Scott.[§]

6.5 The effect of solute on the boiling and freezing points of a liquid: colligative properties

In this section we shall prove the result that an involatile solute will lower the freezing point and raise the boiling point of a solvent, and we shall find the actual changes as a function of solute concentration on the assumption that the solution is ideal. To calculate the freezing point depression we have to make the additional assumption that the solute does not dissolve in the solid solvent.

The qualitative result is shown very simply. If the solute is involatile and

---

[†]K. B. Whetsel and R. E. Kagarise, *Spectrochim. Acta*, **18**, 329 (1962).
[‡]See for example G. S. Rushbrooke, *Introduction to Statistical Mechanics*, O.U.P., Oxford (1949).
[§]J. H. Hildebrand and R. L. Scott, *Regular Solutions*, Prentice Hall, Englewood Cliffs, New Jersey (1962).

118

does not dissolve in the solid solvent then it will only affect the chemical potential of the solvent in its liquid phase. Moreover, the solute must lower the chemical potential of the liquid solvent (if not it would not be soluble) so that the situation is summarized in Figure 6.11. Lowering the chemical potential of the liquid from $\mu^*(l)$ to $\mu(l)$ lowers T_m to T'_m and raises T_b to T'_b.

An important application of this result that the melting point is an important criterion of purity of a compound because impurities lower the melting point of a substance from its value when pure.

Over a small temperature range the decrease in the liquid solvent chemical potential can be considered to be a constant hence $\mu(l)$ and $\mu^*(l)$ will be parallel lines. From the expanded version of the gas–liquid crossing point in Figure 6.11 it can be seen that, providing the changes brought about by the solute are small,

$$\mu^*(l) - \mu(l) = AC - BC = CD(\tan \theta_1 - \tan \theta_2)$$

$$= \Delta T_b \left[\frac{-d\mu(g)}{dT} + \frac{d\mu^*(l)}{dT} \right] = -\Delta T_b \frac{d}{dT}(\mu(g) - \mu^*(l)), \qquad (6.49)$$

Figure 6.11   Effect of an involatile solute on the melting and boiling points of the solvent

$$\mu^*(l) - \mu(l) = \Delta T_b \Delta S_{vap} = \frac{\Delta T_b \Delta H_{vap}}{T_b},$$ (6.50)

the last step being due to the fact that $\Delta G_{vap} = 0.$[†]

From the expanded version of the solid–liquid crossing point we likewise have

$$\mu^*(l) - \mu(l) = A'C' - A'B' = C'D'(\tan \theta_2' - \tan \theta_1')$$

$$= \Delta T_m \left[-\frac{d\mu^*(l)}{dT} + \frac{d\mu(s)}{dT} \right] = -\Delta T_m \frac{d}{dT} (\mu^*(l) - \mu(s))$$ (6.51)

$$= \Delta T_m \Delta S_{melt} = \frac{\Delta T_m \Delta H_{melt}}{T_m}.$$ (6.52)

For an ideal solution we can write (6.39)

$$\mu^*(l) - \mu(l) = -RT \ln x_1,$$ (6.53)

where x_1 is the mole fraction of the solvent. If x is the mole fraction of solute, then

$$\ln x_1 = \ln(1 - x) = -x - \frac{x^2}{2} \ldots,$$ (6.54)

hence in dilute solution we can take the first term in the expansion and write

$$\mu^*(l) - \mu(l) = RTx.$$ (6.55)

This expression can now be introduced into 6.50 and 6.53, taking T as T_b or T_m as appropriate. We therefore obtain the following expressions for the elevation of boiling point and depression of melting point due to the added solute

$$\Delta T_b = \left(\frac{RT_b^2}{\Delta H_{vap}} \right) x,$$ (6.56)

$$\Delta T_m = \left(\frac{RT_m^2}{\Delta H_{melt}} \right) x.$$ (6.57)

It can be seen from expressions 6.56 and 6.57 that the changes in boiling and melting point depend on specific properties of the solvent (T_b, T_m, ΔH_{vap}, ΔH_{melt}) but only on the mole fraction of the solute; no other feature of the solute is relevant. Solvent properties of this type are called colligative properties.[†] One other colligative property, the osmotic pressure, will be described in a later chapter.

The most important practical use of a colligative property is for the deter-

---

[†] ΔG_{vap} etc. are molar quantities.
[†] From the Latin *colligatus*, bound together. The word can be thought of as having the connotation that these are collective properties of all solutes.

mination of molecular weights in solution. For dilute solutions we can replace the mole fraction by molality according to expression 6.4. Expression 6.57 then becomes

$$\Delta T_m = K_t m, \tag{6.58}$$

where

$$K_t = \frac{MRT_m^2}{1000\Delta H_{melt}}, \tag{6.59}$$

is called the cryoscopic constant of the solvent. The corresponding constant for boiling point elevation is called the ebullioscopic constant. Measuring ΔT_m for a solvent whose cryoscopic constant is known determines m, and if the mass of solute in the solution is known then the molecular weight of the solute can be determined.[†]

The factor M, which is the molecular weight of the solvent, appears in the definition of the cryoscopic constant (6.59) hence it is advantageous to use solvents of high molecular weight for the determination of colligative properties, particularly if the solute is sparingly soluble. For example benzene has a cryoscopic constant of 5.1 K kg mol^{-1}, and camphor has a value 40 K kg mol^{-1}; water has a very low cryoscopic constant, 1.86 K kg mol^{-1}.

Ideal solubility

It is convenient in this section to consider also the question of what is the ideal solubility of a solid in a solvent because the mathematics of the answer is similar to that we have just described. A solid will dissolve in a solvent until the chemical potential of the solute in the solution equals the chemical potential of the pure solid. Starting again with expression 6.39 and taking species A to be the solute we have for a saturated solution (assuming ideality)

$$\mu_A^*(s) = \mu_A(l) = \mu_A^*(l) + RT \ln x_A \tag{6.60}$$

whence (dropping the A for brevity)

$$\ln x = \frac{\mu^*(s) - \mu^*(l)}{RT} = \frac{-\Delta G_{melt}(T)}{RT}. \tag{6.61}$$

We know that the Gibbs free energy of melting is zero at the melting point (T_m) of the solute, but it is not zero at temperature T below T_m. If we add a term of zero value to 6.61 as follows

$$\ln x = -\left\{ \frac{\Delta G_{melt}(T)}{RT} - \frac{\Delta G_{melt}(T_m)}{RT_m} \right\} \tag{6.62}$$

[†]For electrolytes in ionizing solvents each ion will contribute separately to a colligative property so that measuring the depression of freezing point (say) will determine the degree of ionization or, perhaps, the nature of the ionic equilibria if these are uncertain.

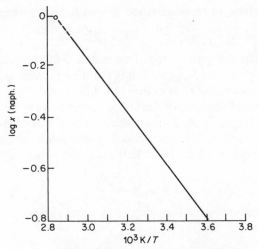

Figure 6.12 The solubility of naphthalene in benzene as a function of temperature. The extrapolation is to the melting temperature

then assuming ΔH_{melt} and ΔS_{melt} do not change appreciably over the temperature range $T \to T_{\text{m}}$ we simplify 6.62 to

$$\ln x = \frac{\Delta H_{\text{melt}}}{R}\left[\frac{1}{T_{\text{m}}} - \frac{1}{T}\right]. \tag{6.63}$$

Close to the melting point ($T \approx T_{\text{m}}$) this can be exponentiated to

$$x \approx \exp\left[\frac{\Delta H_{\text{melt}}(T - T_{\text{m}})}{RT_{\text{m}}^2}\right] \tag{6.64}$$

that is, the solubility, expressed as mole fraction of solute, increases exponentially with temperature becoming unity at $T = T_{\text{m}}$.

Figure 6.12 shows the solubility of naphthalene in benzene as a function of temperature and confirms the functional form of expression 6.63.

6.6 Thermodynamic measures of non-ideal mixing

We have earlier in this chapter introduced two definitions of ideal liquid mixtures and shown them to be equivalent;† the thermodynamic mixing functions should obey equations 6.18 and 6.19 and the vapour pressure should obey Raoult's law, 6.38. Deviations from ideality can likewise be expressed directly in terms of the mixing functions or in terms of the vapour pressure, the link between the two being made through expression 6.37

$$\mu_A(l) = \mu_A^*(l) + RT \ln(p_A/p_A^*). \tag{6.65}$$

For brevity we will drop the suffix indicating a specific component and also

†Assuming that the vapour is ideal.

take the liquid phase to be understood so that 6.65 is written

$$\mu = \mu^* + RT \ln(p/p^*), \qquad (6.66)$$

the star indicating the pure liquid. Expression 6.66 is exact providing the vapour is behaving as an ideal gas. If it is not then the vapour pressures must be replaced by fugacities (f) as defined by 4.26 and 4.27.

For ideal mixtures the ratio of the vapour pressures can be replaced by the mole fraction x, to give 6.39. For non-ideal mixing it is convenient to retain the form of expression 6.39 by introducing a dimensionless quantity, a, called the activity, or more precisely the relative activity, which appears in place of x as follows:

$$\mu = \mu^* + RT \ln a. \qquad (6.67)$$

Providing that the vapour is behaving as an ideal gas, we have

$$a = p/p^*. \qquad (6.68)$$

If we wish to record the chemical potential of a component in a non-ideal mixture we can either have a table of μ values as a function of composition or, what is common practice, a table of the activity as a function of composition, with μ^* being the chemical potential of the reference state. We refer to μ^* as being the chemical potential of the standard state. In this case the standard state is the pure liquid and $\mu = \mu^*$ when $a = x = 1$. We have already noted that the solvent in a dilute solution obeys Raoult's law as infinite dilution is approached so that

$$a \to x \quad \text{as} \quad x \to 1. \qquad (6.69)$$

An important consequence of the mathematical form of equation 6.67 is that μ approaches minus infinity as a approaches zero, because a approaches zero as x approaches zero. In other words the chemical potential of the *solute* in a very dilute solution has a large negative value and this is another reason why a is a more convenient quantity than μ as a measure of non-ideality because it is bounded by the limits zero and one.

The relationship between a and x can be further illuminated by introducing a quantity called the activity coefficient, γ, by the definition (cf. 4.28)

$$a = \gamma x. \qquad (6.70)$$

As a and x are both dimensionless, γ is also dimensionless. For very dilute solutions we have for the solvent, from 6.59, the limit $\gamma \to 1$. However, for the solute in very dilute solutions there is no unique limit to γ because

$$\gamma = a/x \qquad (6.71)$$

is indeterminate when both x and a approach zero. We can make progress by remembering that in dilute solutions the vapour pressure of the solute obeys Henry's law (6.46). Thus introducing 6.68 and 6.46 into 6.71 we have

$$\gamma \to K/p^* \quad \text{as} \quad x \to 0, \qquad (6.72)$$

where K is the Henry's law constant and p^* is the vapour pressure of the pure solute.

Because the solute in a dilute solution is very far from the $x = 1$ limit it is more convenient to take the reference or standard state of the solute as a solution obeying Henry's law. This is particularly true for a solute which is not a liquid (when pure) at the temperature being studied. Introducing Henry's law into 6.66 we have

$$\mu = \mu^* + RT \ln\left(\frac{Kx}{p^*}\right),$$

$$= \mu^* + RT \ln\left(\frac{K}{p^*}\right) + RT \ln x,$$

$$= \mu^{\circ} + RT \ln x, \tag{6.73}$$

where

$$\mu^{\circ} = \mu^* + RT \ln\left(\frac{K}{p^*}\right). \tag{6.74}$$

Expression 6.73 is now the basis for a suitable approach to the chemical potential of the solute in dilute solutions; following our earlier practice we replace x in 6.73 by a and obtain

$$\mu = \mu^{\circ} + RT \ln a = \mu^{\circ} + RT \ln \gamma x. \tag{6.75}$$

This has a similar form to 6.67, but the standard state has the chemical potential μ° and not μ^*. We also note that the Henry's law limit implies

$$a \to x \quad \text{or} \quad \gamma \to 1 \quad \text{as} \quad x \to 0 \tag{6.76}$$

which should be contrasted with 6.69, the limit which is applicable when the pure solvent is taken as standard state.†

It is probably more common to express solute concentrations in molalities than in mole fractions, and when this is done the definitions of activity and activity coefficient are slightly different from those given here. We return to this point in section 9.4.

It cannot be stressed too strongly that values of the activity or activity coefficient have meaning only when the relevant standard state is specified, and failure to note this will make meaningless a comparison between different

---

†Another measure of non-ideality that is frequently used is the osmotic coefficient ϕ defined by

$$\mu = \mu^{\circ} + \phi RT \ln x. \tag{6.76a}$$

Comparison with 6.75 shows that ϕ is related to the activity coefficient by

$$\ln \gamma = (\phi - 1)\ln x. \tag{6.76b}$$

The name stems from the fact that ϕ for the solvent is equal to the ratio of the actual osmotic pressure of a solution to its ideal value. Osmotic pressure, a colligative property, will be discussed in Chapter 11.

systems on the basis of their a or γ values. For example, one cannot even compare a given solute in different solvents without recognizing that the standard state of the solute is solvent dependent (because the Henry's law constant is solvent dependent).

What system actually has the chemical potential μ°? The answer is no real system. We note that $\mu = \mu^\circ$ when $a = 1$ but this is not then a system obeying Henry's law. The standard state is a hypothetical state for which $a = 1$ *and* Henry's law is obeyed. The situation is comparable to that described in section 4.2 for non-ideal gases: the standard state of a real gas is an extrapolated ideal gas at 1 atm.

We shall make a further generalization of the concept of activity in a later chapter when we consider non-ideal behaviour for electrolyte solutions, and we hope that these repeated discussions will help to clarify a very tricky concept in thermodynamics.

Determination of activity

To determine the activity of the solvent in a solution is generally straightforward. One measures the vapour pressure and applies expression 6.68. If the solute is volatile then it is necessary to determine the partial pressure of the solvent. Only for the most accurate work would it be necessary to make a correction for the non-ideal behaviour of the vapour. To determine the activity of a non-volatile solute is much more difficult. For electrolytes activities can be obtained from e.m.f. measurements as will be explained in Chapter 10. For non-electrolytes it is usually necessary to use an indirect method which entails finding the activity of the *solvent* over a range of solute concentrations and then integrating the Gibbs–Duhem equation.

Introducing activities in place of chemical potentials in 6.42, using 6.67, we have for a two-component mixture

$$\left(\frac{\partial \ln a_A}{\partial x_B}\right) x_A + \left(\frac{\partial \ln a_B}{\partial x_B}\right) x_B = 0. \tag{6.77}$$

If A is the solvent for which a_A has been determined by vapour pressure measurement (say) as a function of x_B, the mole fraction of solute, then integrating 6.77 with respect to x_B from some specified value x_B^0 to the concentration of interest we have

$$\int_{x_B^0}^{x_B} \frac{x_A}{x_B} \left(\frac{\partial \ln a_A}{\partial x_B}\right) dx_B + \left| \ln a_B \right|_{x_B^0}^{x_B} = 0. \tag{6.78}$$

Because $x_A = 1 - x_B$ this can be simplified to

$$\ln(a_B(x_B)/a_B(x_B^0)) = -\int_{x_B^0}^{x_B} \left(\frac{1 - x_B}{x_B}\right)\left(\frac{\partial \ln a_A}{\partial x_B}\right) dx_B. \tag{6.79}$$

Hence if we know the activity of the solute at a concentration x_B^0 and the activity of the solvent between x_B^0 and x_B, we can determine $a_B(x_B)$.

There are two situations in which the activity of the solute is known. First, in a saturated solution the chemical potential of the solute is equal to that of the solid and $\mu_B(\text{solid})$ can be obtained by standard thermochemical methods (most can be found in thermodynamic tables). Second, in dilute solutions the solute would satisfy Henry's law and hence expression 6.73 can be applied. Thus if $\mu_B^\ominus$ has been determined, μ_B or a_B can be obtained in more concentrated solutions.

Because a colligative property is (ideally) proportional to the mole fraction of solute it might be thought that measurements of such properties would give directly the solute activity. That is, one can simply replace x by a in an equation such as 6.57. This is unfortunately not the case, the solute mole fraction only appears in these equations by assumptions which imply that the solutions are both dilute and ideal (e.g. terminating the expansion 6.54 at the first term). Colligative properties are in fact direct measures of the activity of the *solvent* and, as for the vapour pressure, it is necessary to use the Gibbs–Duhem equation to deduce the activity of the solute.

The non-ideal form of 6.52 is

$$\ln a_A = \frac{\Delta T_m \Delta H_{\text{melt}}}{RT_m^2}, \tag{6.80}$$

where ΔT_m will be a function of solute concentration. It follows that

$$\frac{d \ln a_A}{dx_B} = \frac{-\Delta H_{\text{melt}}}{RT_m^2}\left(\frac{d\Delta T_m}{dx_B}\right), \tag{6.81}$$

and this can be inserted into 6.79 and the integration performed,

$$\ln(a_B(x_B)/a_B(x_B^0)) = \frac{\Delta H_{\text{melt}}}{RT_m^2} \int \left(\frac{1-x_B}{x_B}\right)\left(\frac{d\Delta T_m}{dx_B}\right) dx_B. \tag{6.82}$$

We will return to a discussion of this formula when we consider electrolyte solutions in Chapter 9.

Chapter 7

Phase diagrams for multicomponent systems

7.1 A general statement of the phase rule

In section 1.2 we discussed the concept of degree of freedom for a single chemical substance and its relevance to the equilibrium between gas, liquid and solid phases. In this chapter we extend this study to multicomponent systems with particular emphasis on three techniques of great practical importance, distillation, crystallization and chromatography.[†]

We first explain how the term component is used in a discussion of the phase rule. The number of components is defined as the minimum number of species whose concentrations can be independently varied. If there is no reaction between the chemical species from which the mixture is constructed then the number of components is just equal to the number of chemical species. If there is a reaction then we have to ask whether there are any equilibria established on the time scale of the experiment which inter-relate the actual species present.

For example, a mixture of hydrogen, oxygen and water is normally a three-component system because the equilibrium

$$2H_2 + O_2 \rightleftharpoons 2H_2O,$$

is established very slowly. In the presence of a catalyst which would establish this equilibrium rapidly it would be a two-component system because the equation

$$K = [H_2O]^2/[H_2]^2[O_2], \tag{7.1}$$

provides a linking condition that allows only two of the three concentrations to be independently varied. By similar reasoning an aqueous solution of sodium chloride is a two-component system although the actual species present are Na^+, Cl^- and H_2O. The reason for this is that the number of

[†]In this chapter we consider only the equilibrium aspects of phase change. Kinetic aspects, such as nucleation, will be dealt with in Chapter 12.

126

anions must be equal to the number of cations to preserve neutrality; in other words they cannot be independently varied. We emphasize that, in the terminology of the phase rule, the number of components is often fewer than the number of chemically distinguishable species which are present.

As explained in section 1.2 the number of degrees of freedom for a system having just one component is two (which can be considered to be temperature and pressure) minus the number of independent linking conditions of equal chemical potential between the phases. If we have c components then the compositions of each phase is specified by $c - 1$ mole fractions (one mole fraction is fixed by specifying all others (6.2)) so that the composition of p phases is described by $p(c - 1)$ mole fractions. However, these cannot be independently varied because of the condition that the chemical potential of any one of the components must be equal in *each* phase. Thus there are $c(p - 1)$ independent restricting equalities between the chemical potentials. The total number of degrees of freedom for a system of c components and p phases is therefore

$$f = 2 + p(c - 1) - c(p - 1),$$

which simplifies to

$$f = 2 + c - p. \tag{7.2}$$

This is Gibbs' phase rule.

We will now consider the equilibria between phases in a two-component system. We remind the reader that the number of degrees of freedom is the number of variables that can be changed without changing the number or type of the phases which are in equilibrium. An equivalent statement is that f is the dimensions of the variable space within which a certain equilibrium set of phases can exist.

For two components we have $f = 4 - p$ and the following situations are of interest.

(1) $p = 1$, $f = 3$. A single phase can exist under changes in P, T and mole fraction, x of a component.

(2) $p = 2$, $f = 2$. Only two of x, P, and T can be independently varied without changing the two phases which are in equilibrium. For example suppose vapour and a single liquid phase are in equilibrium, then for a specified composition of the mixture (x) the vapour pressure is a function of temperature. That is, there is a curve in (P, T)-space along which the two phases can exist for a specified x, just as there is a (P, T)-curve for these two phases for a pure substance (see Figure 1.1).

(3) $p = 3$, $f = 1$. A typical situation might be vapour and two liquid phases (immiscible liquids) or vapour, liquid and solid. If we fix one variable, say take $P = 1$ atm, then the other two are invariant. Three phases could only exist for a specified pressure at fixed values of temperature and composition.

(4) $p = 4$, $f = 0$. This situation is neither important nor easily realized.

For example, there is, in principle, a point in (x, P, T)-space where the immiscible liquids benzene and water are in equilibrium with vapour and one solid phase. It is analogous to the triple point in the one-component case.

We will later in this chapter discuss some of the features of three-component systems which have an additional degree of freedom in each of the situations described above. For the moment we turn to an analysis of the equilibrium between liquid and vapour in a two-component system. This analysis will be based upon the phase rule and the rules governing the vapour pressure of liquid mixtures which were described in section 6.4.

7.2   Vapour–liquid equilibrium with two components

We have seen in case (2) of the previous section that a system having a single liquid phase in equilibrium with vapour has two degrees of freedom. That means that in a three-dimensional axis system (x, P, T) this particular equilibrium can exist on a two-dimensional surface. For example, the pressure will be a function of T and x.

Three-dimensional figures are not easy to construct and analyse, and it is usual practice to describe the behaviour of two-component systems by two-dimensional sections of the (x, P, T)-diagram, either (x, P) or (x, T); we have already used (x, P)-sections in Figure 6.9. Figure 7.1(a) shows the vapour pressure of an ideal two-component liquid at a fixed temperature as a function of mole fraction of the liquid phase. The straight line is a manifestation of Raoult's law. To think of this as a phase diagram we consider a liquid of arbitrary composition x_1 under a pressure P_1. As this pressure is greater than the vapour pressure of a liquid of this composition the system is 100% liquid. If we now reduce the pressure, the first bubbles, indicating boiling, will appear when the pressure reaches P_1'.

For a single-component liquid the pressure would remain at P_1' until all the liquid was evaporated. This is not the case for a mixture because the vapour will be richer than the liquid in the more volatile component; which in this case is B, because B has a higher vapour pressure than A. If we preferentially boil off more B than A the liquid will become progressively richer in A and its composition will change in the direction indicated in the diagram.

Figure 7.1(b) shows the vapour pressure line as a function of the mole fraction in the vapour phase. It is concave upwards for the reason given above: the vapour is richer than the liquid in the more volatile component $(x_B(\text{vap}) > x_B(\text{liq}))$ at a given pressure. Suppose we take the vapour composition x_1 at a pressure P_2. As P_2 is less than the vapour pressure we will have 100% vapour. On increasing the pressure the first drops of liquid will appear when the pressure is P_2' (the dew point or condensation point). The first liquid that condenses out at this pressure is richer in the less volatile component (A), and as this condensation proceeds the vapour becomes richer in B as shown.

Figure 7.1 Representations of the (P, x)
section of a liquid–vapour phase diagram

It is convenient to combine Figures 7.1(a) and 7.1(b) in such a way that x can represent the mole fraction of either the liquid or the vapour phase and this is shown in Figure 7.1(c). It is important to understand that when liquid and vapour are in equilibrium the bubble line gives the liquid composition and the condensation line gives the vapour composition. In other words the

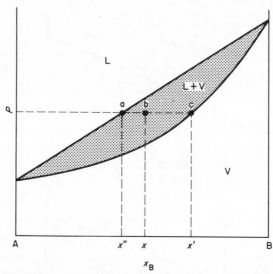

Figure 7.2   Definition of a tie line and representation of the lever rule

shaded region is a two-phase region where the compositions of the two phases are given by the left-hand and right-hand boundaries.

If we now start with liquid at the point (x_1, P_1) and reduce the pressure, we will reach the bubble line at P_1' and the first vapour will have composition x_1'. On reducing the pressure the compositions of liquid and vapour will move as shown by the arrows and when all the liquid has evaporated the vapour must also have composition x_1. Thus the last drops of liquid will have composition x_1'' as shown. Starting with vapour at (x_1, P_2) and reducing the pressure the reverse route will be followed; the first drop of liquid that condenses has composition x_1'' and the last amount of vapour has composition x_1'.

Suppose we have a system whose overall composition and pressure is represented by a point in the two-phase region (x, P) as shown in Figure 7.2. We know that the compositions of the liquid and vapour phases are given by x'' and x' respectively, but we can go further and deduce the relative proportions of liquid and vapour that will be in equilibrium under these conditions.

Let n be the total number of moles of mixture and let n_1 and n_v be the number of moles in the liquid and vapour phases respectively. The total number of moles of B is

$$nx = (n_1 + n_v)x. \tag{7.3}$$

However, summing up the amount of B in the liquid and vapour phases we have

$$nx = n_1 x'' + n_v x', \tag{7.4}$$

and on subtracting 7.3 from 7.4 we have

$$n_1(x'' - x) + n_v(x' - x) = 0, \tag{7.5}$$

whence

$$\frac{n_v}{n_1} = \frac{x - x''}{x' - x}. \tag{7.6}$$

Expression 7.6 can be summarized by what is known as the lever rule. The relative amounts of the phases are in inverse proportions of the distances of the respective phase boundary lines from the point (x, P) of overall composition. Consider the line abc in Figure 7.2 to be a lever with b the fulcrum. If weights are hung at a and c then for a balance the weight at a multiplied by the distance b − a would have to equal the weight at c multiplied by the distance c − b. If 'weight at a' is replaced by 'moles of liquid' and 'weight at c' by 'moles of vapour' then the above statement is in accord with expression 7.6.

Distillation

The above discussion of the (x, P)-section of a two-component liquid–vapour system can be applied to any two-component two-phase system (e.g., solid–liquid) and also to (x, T)-sections. We will now examine such an (x, T)-section for the purpose of analysing the technique of distillation. Figure 7.3

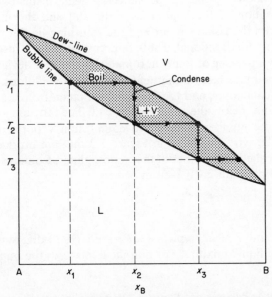

Figure 7.3   The (x, T)-section of a two-component, liquid plus vapour, phase diagram

132

shows a typical (x, T)-section of the phase diagram appropriate to the A–B mixture represented in Figure 7.2. At a fixed pressure, B is more volatile than A and will therefore have the lower boiling point.

The two-phase region has boundary lines which represent the composition of the vapour and liquid. The bubble line gives the temperature at which the liquid starts to boil. The dew line gives the temperature at which the vapour starts to condense. The bubble line gives the liquid composition, and the dew line the vapour composition of any mixture whose overall composition and temperature lie in the two-phase region.

Let us now consider raising the temperature of a liquid of composition x_1. At T_1 it will start to boil and the first vapour that comes from it will have a composition x_2. If this vapour is condensed and the resulting liquid of this new composition is heated, it will start boiling at T_2, and the first vapour that comes from it will have composition x_3. It can be seen that this process of repeated boiling and condensation leads to a distillate which is richer in the more volatile component, and in the limit of an infinite number of steps would lead to pure B, but a negligible amount of B.

Simple distillation is inefficient for the separation of liquids with close boiling points. Young,[†] for example, describes the distillation of a benzene–toluene mixture in which the distillate was first collected in ten fractions or cuts which were then combined and redistilled fourteen times. The process took thirty hours to obtain appreciable amounts of reasonably pure benzene and toluene. Such a separation can be achieved much more efficiently by the process of fractional distillation in which the compositions of the initial fractions are made as distinct as possible. To achieve this one requires the partial condensation of the vapour over the still and the maximum equilibration between the rising vapour and the returning liquid.

The apparatus for fractional distillation consists of an insulated column which has a loose packing of some inert material, or other device for achieving a large gas–liquid interface, under nearly adiabatic conditions.[‡] This column is topped by a condenser, and the fractions are taken from a side-arm at the top of the column, below the condensing head. The efficiency of the column is defined by the number of effective equilibrium vaporizations and condensations of the type illustrated in Figure 7.3 that are produced within the column: this is called the number of theoretical plates. Columns typically have one theoretical plate for each 1–5 cm of height.

Azeotropes

Figures 7.1 and 7.3 are typical (x, P)- and (x, T)-diagrams of an ideal two-component liquid mixture. For non-ideal mixtures the bubble line in the

---

[†]S. Young, *Distillation Principles and Processes*, Macmillan, London (1922).
[‡]F. E. Williams, *Techniques of Organic Chemistry*, Eds. E. S. Perry and A. Weissberger **4**, 299, Wiley, London and New York (1965).

(x, P)-diagram will be curved (i.e. the system will not obey Raoult's law) and the other phase boundary lines will show greater curvature.

Figure 7.4 shows two commonly occurring (x, T)-diagrams for systems with substantial deviation from ideality, but which are still miscible in the liquid phase. Note that in each figure the boundary lines show a coincident turning point so that the two-phase region is divided into two separate parts. The turning points in the phase boundary lines must be coincident to make physical sense. For example, a situation represented by Figure 7.5 would imply that between T_1 and T_2 there would be two immiscible vapours, but we know that vapours are always miscible. If the boundary lines did not touch in Figure 7.4(b) this would imply that there were two liquid phases hence another two-phase region would have to be added to the diagram.

The boiling of a liquid mixture whose composition coincides with the turning point in the phase boundary lines leads to a vapour with the same composition as that of the liquid. In other words, the liquid mixture is

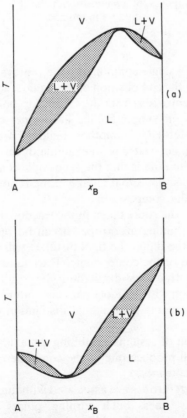

Figure 7.4 (x, T)-diagrams for systems which form an azeotrope

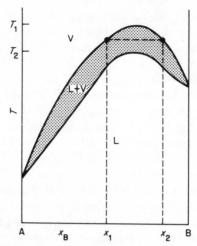

Figure 7.5 An unrealistic (x, T)-diagram which would imply that vapours of composition x_1 and x_2 would be immiscible

behaving as if it were a single component, and removal of the distillate does not lead to a change in the composition of the liquid. Liquid mixtures with this property are called azeotropes (from the Greek for 'boiling without change'). Figure 7.4(a) shows a maximum-boiling azeotrope; chloroform–acetone is such a system and water–HCl is another. Figure 7.4(b) shows a minimum-boiling azeotrope; ethanol–water is an example of this.

An important point to note is that the azeotropic composition is a function of the pressure, and this shows that an azeotrope is not a molecular complex with a specific molecular composition.

Figure 7.6 illustrates the route taken in the fractional distillation of a liquid mixture having a low boiling azeotrope. It can be seen that whatever the initial composition of the liquid the final distillate will be the azeotrope, and the residue will be one of the components. Thus aqueous ethanol cannot be dehydrated directly by fractional distillation; the result will be the azeotrope which has a composition with 10 mole per cent water. If the ethanol is dried beyond this by other means then a final distillation will give a *residue* of absolute ethanol.

Fractional distillation of systems exhibiting a maximum-boiling azeotrope as in Figure 7.4(a) will produce one of the components as distillate and the residue will be the azeotrope.

We have seen that azeotropes are associated with maxima or minima in the (x, T)-phase boundary lines. Such turning points are associated with deviations from ideality, but as should be clear from Figure 7.4 they are also more likely if the two components have rather similar boiling points.

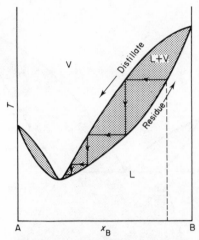

Figure 7.6 The process of fractional distillation of a liquid mixture having a minimum-boiling azeotrope. A path towards the azeotrope is followed for compositions on both sides of the azeotrope composition

Alternatively, if we think of the (x, P)-diagram (Figure 7.1) then an azeotrope is likely at any temperature at which the vapour pressures of the two components are approximately equal.

Partially miscible liquids

The liquid–vapour phase diagram for two components whose liquids are only partially miscible can be of various types. If the liquids are miscible at the boiling point but immiscible at some lower temperature, the phase diagram will be as in Figure 7.3 or 7.4, but with a two-liquid phase region at some lower temperature. If the two liquids are only partially miscible at the boiling point then a phase diagram such as Figure 7.7 is the most common.

There is one point in Figure 7.7 where three phases, vapour and two liquids, are in equilibrium; this is at the cusp in the vapour composition boundary line with $x_B = x_4$. In accordance with the phase rule there will be a line of such points in the full (P, T, x)-diagram. This special point in Figure 7.7 is analogous to the azeotropic point in Figure 7.4(b) but there are two important differences. First, the vapour-composition boundary line has a cusp at this point and not a smooth turning point, and second, the azeotropic liquid consists of two phases whose relative amounts are determined by the appropriate tie line in the liquid plus liquid region.

A mixture of composition x_1 will boil at T_1 and at this temperature the liquid consists of two phases with composition x_2 and x_3. These two liquid phases will

136

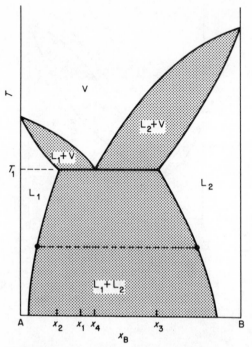

Figure 7.7 The most common (T, x)-diagram
for two liquids which are partially miscible at
their boiling points (e.g. water–isobutanol).
The dashed line in $L_1 + L_2$ is a typical tie line

have definite vapour pressures, the sum of which will be the total pressure
(one atmosphere, say). Thus the boiling point will remain at T_1 (which is lower
than the boiling point of either pure component), and the composition of the
vapour will remain at the azeotropic composition x_4 until one of the two liquids
has disappeared. Because in this example $x_4 - x_2$ is less than $x_3 - x_4$ the
vapour will have a composition closer to that of L_1 than to that of L_2, hence
L_1 will be the first liquid phase to disappear. When this has happened the
composition of the remaining liquid phase L_2 will have become purer in B.

If the two liquids are almost completely immiscible the regions L_1 and L_2
shown in Figure 7.7 will be very narrow. The mixture will boil when the total
vapour pressure equals the external pressure P and this will be at a temperature lower than the boiling point of either pure component. The
composition of the vapour will be given by

$$x_A = \frac{n_A}{n_A + n_B} = \frac{p_A}{p_A + p_B} = \frac{p_A}{P},$$ (7.7)

where p_A and p_B are the partial pressures of the two components at the
boiling point.

This analysis is the basis of the technique known as steam distillation (bubbling steam through a relatively involatile liquid) which allows heat-sensitive materials to be distilled at a lower temperature than their normal boiling point. The technique is widely used for industrial separations, but there are usually alternative separation techniques available for small-scale work (e.g. distillation under reduced pressure).

7.3 Liquid–solid equilibrium with two components

The general form of the vapour–liquid two-component phase diagrams which have been described in the last section apply also to liquid–solid equilibrium. There are, however, a number of important differences. First, liquids and solids have very low compressibilities so that the melting point is a very slowly varying function of pressure. Thus (x, P)-diagrams of the type shown in Figure 7.1 are not very useful for the liquid–solid phase equilibrium because the boundary lines are very steep: if the temperature is fixed at the melting point of one component there is unlikely to be any physically access-ible pressure at which the other component melts at the same temperature. Liquid–solid phase diagrams are, therefore, always considered as (x, T)-sections for a fixed pressure.

A second point is that equilibrium in the solid phase is only attained slowly, in contrast to the fast equilibria of the liquid or vapour phases. Consider, for example, Figure 7.8 which is analogous to Figure 7.3. If liquid of composition

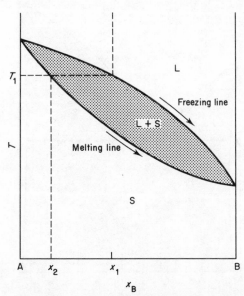

Figure 7.8   A simple two-component liquid–solid phase diagram for which there is a single solid phase (e.g. Ag–Au)

138

x_1 is cooled the first solid will appear at temperature T_1, and this will have the composition x_2. As this solid is richer in component A (the higher melting solid) the liquid composition will move to the right as indicated by the arrow. On further cooling more solid will appear and its composition will also move to the right. The important point to note is that continuous cooling produces a solid which is homogeneous in the sense that it does not consist of aggregations but it is not of uniform composition. The last trace of solid produced may be almost pure B.

Solidification of a multicomponent liquid is therefore not exactly equivalent to condensation of a multicomponent vapour within physically realizable time scales and this difference is used in the important technique for purifying solids known as zone refining. If a rod of impure solid is passed slowly through a local heater the band of melt will be richer than the solid in any lower melting impurities. These impurities will be swept through with the melt to the end of the rod. Repeated passage through the heater will produce a progressively purer solid.

A third difference between liquid–solid and gas–liquid two-component equilibria is that most pairs of solid components are not miscible. Thus Figure 7.8 does not represent a typical situation, and only occurs if A and B have very similar crystal structures. The solid phases of such systems are often called solid solutions. A more typical liquid–solid phase diagram is analogous to Figure 7.7 for partially miscible liquids. However, the single-phase regions

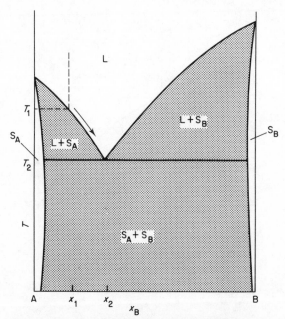

Figure 7.9   The phase diagram for a two-component liquid–solid system with almost immiscible solids (e.g. Ag–Cu)

analogous to L_1 and L_2 of Figure 7.6 can be very narrow and are often omitted altogether. Figure 7.9 shows a typical phase diagram for this situation.

Eutectics

The minimum on the L–S boundary indicates a mixture with a low melting point and one that melts without change in composition. This is called an eutectic (Greek for low melting) and it has a similar role in liquid–solid phase changes to a low boiling azeotrope in gas–liquid phase changes. There are many important eutectics amongst metal alloys. The most common is tinman's solder, a mixture of tin and lead in the approximate ratio 2:1 which melts at 456 K.

Although the eutectic mixture has a definite composition and sharp melting point it is not a single chemical compound. The composition is not exactly represented by a simple integer ratio of the components and separate micro-crystals of the two components can be seen under a microscope. In other words it is an intimate mixture of the two components and not a chemical compound.

Cooling curves

The boundary lines of liquid–solid phase diagrams can be mapped out by carefully following the cooling curves of the liquid. For a single component

Figure 7.10   Cooling curves. (a) Ideal curve for a single component. (b) Single component showing supercooling. (c) A two-component mixture with an eutectic tempera-ture T_2

the ideal form of the cooling curve is shown in Figure 7.10(a). The rate of cooling of the liquid is proportional to the difference between the temperature of the liquid and that of the surroundings. When the melting point T_m is reached the heat of solidification will maintain the system at this temperature until all the solid has formed; after this the solid will cool. If the rate of cooling is too rapid then the temperature of the liquid may fall below the melting point before the first solid appears. This is called supercooling and it will give a cooling curve as in Figure 7.10(b).

If the liquid of composition x_1 in Figure 7.9 is cooled the first solid (almost pure A) will appear at temperature T_1 (subject to possible supercooling). The liquid will become richer in component B and the equilibrium temperature will fall as indicated. When the liquid composition reaches the eutectic point x_2 its temperature will be T_2 and both solids will separate. The temperature will stay at T_2 until all the liquid has solidified. An ideal cooling curve appropriate to this route is shown in Figure 7.10(c).

Complex formation

A final complication which we touch on in this chapter is that in the solid phase the two components may form a complex with definite composition (i.e. a chemical species whose composition is independent of temperature and pressure). One example of this is shown in Figure 7.11. The simplest way of analysing such a diagram is to consider it as two diagrams like Figure 7.9 side-by-side.

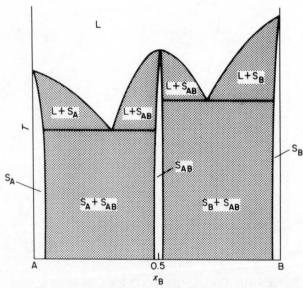

Figure 7.11 Phase diagram for two components which form a solid compound with composition AB (e.g. benzophenone–diphenylamine)

Figure 7.11 shows the phase diagram for a system which forms a solid compound of formula AB. This compound is stable up to its melting point. Whether AB exists in the liquid state or not is irrelevant as far as the phase diagram is concerned because the liquid would have only two components in either case, the amount of AB being dependent on the amounts of A and B originally taken. The single solid phase regions may again be very narrow and are often omitted. However, without them one is likely to be misled about the nature of the two-phase shaded areas, particularly the central hump. A tie line in this connects liquid and solid AB and not two liquid phases.

There are more complicated liquid–solid phase diagrams that we will not discuss in detail. For example one may have immiscible liquids and solids, or compounds formed which become unstable before the melting point is reached. A discussion of these can be found in more detailed texts.[†]

7.4 Three-component liquids

From the phase rule expression 7.2 we see that the number of degrees of freedom of a three-component system is

$$f = 5 - p \tag{7.8}$$

There are clearly many features of such a multidimensional system that could be discussed but we will only look at one situation which is the equilibrium between liquid phases at a constant temperature and pressure. With (P, T) constant there will be $3 - p$ remaining degrees of freedom. A single phase can exist in a two-dimensional variable space and two phases can exist along a line.

The most convenient method of plotting three-component phase diagrams is to use triangular graph paper as this puts each of the three components on the same footing. Figure 7.12 shows this method of plotting the composition of any mixture. Each of the three vertices is identified with one particular component so that a vertex represents 100% of that component and the opposite line 0% of that component. The fraction of component A can therefore be indicated by lines parallel to BC.

Any mixture with fractional composition a, b and c for the three components A, B and C respectively, where $a + b + c = 1$ (these can be mole fractions, volume fractions or mass fractions) is represented by a point whose vertical distances to the sides BC, AC and AB are a, b and c respectively. This method of graphing a function is based on the property of an equilateral triangle that the sum of the vertical distances from a point to the sides of an equilateral triangle is a constant equal to the height of the triangle.

Figure 7.13 shows the phase boundaries for the system chloroform–acetic acid–water at 291 K. Chloroform and water are almost immiscible at this

[†] F. Thomas and I. Pal, *Phase Equilibria Spatial Diagrams*, Iliffe Books, London (1970); A. Findlay, *The Phase Rule and its Application*, Dover, London (1951).

142

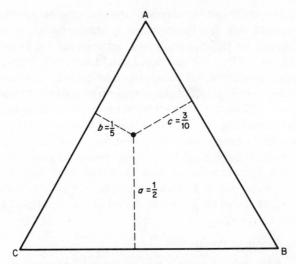

Figure 7.12 Triangular coordinate system. The point indicated has coordinates $(\frac{1}{2}, \frac{1}{5}, \frac{3}{10})$ being the fractional compositions of A, B and C respectively

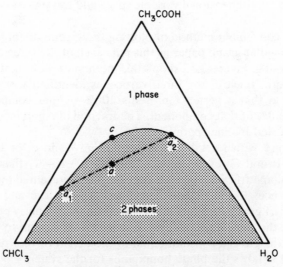

Figure 7.13 Phase diagram for chloroform–acetic acid–water at 291 K. The dotted line indicates a tie line of the two-phase region; a_1 and a_2 indicate the compositions of the two liquid layers in a mixture whose total composition is a

temperature as is indicated by the large two-phase region on the CHCl₃–H₂O line. Acetic acid, on the other hand, is completely miscible with both water and chloroform. On adding acetic acid to a two-phase mixture of chloroform and water the acetic acid will be distributed between the two liquid layers.

For any mixture whose total composition is indicated by a point in the two-phase region the composition of the two layers is indicated by a tie line which is a straight line passing through that point. It must be noted, however, that such a tie line is not parallel to the H₂O–CHCl₃ axis nor are the members of the family of all tie lines parallel to one another. The lever rule (7.6) gives the relative amounts of the two liquid phases. If sufficient acetic acid is added the compositions of the two phases become more similar (i.e. points a_1 and a_2 come together) until they finally coincide at the point indicated by c in the figure. This is called a critical point for the system by analogy with the gas–liquid critical point (when gas and liquid become identical).

The phase boundary in Figure 7.13 can be determined by taking a water–chloroform mixture and titrating with acetic acid until the two layers just disappear (on shaking there is no evidence of turbidity). To find the tie line it is necessary to determine the composition of at least one of the liquid phases.

If one wishes to show the temperature variation of a ternary system then this can be done by taking a vertical stack of diagrams such as Figure 7.13

Figure 7.14   Temperature variation of a ternary system showing an upper critical solution temperature K

Figure 7.15 A ternary system showing
eutectic behaviour. D, E and F are eutectics
for the binary systems AB, BC and CA
respectively. G is the ternary eutectic

with temperature being the vertical axis. With this extra dimension the
boundary between the single-phase and two-phase regions would be a surface
as indicated in Figure 7.14. Under some conditions there may be an upper
critical solution temperature (K in the figure) above which the three components are miscible in all proportions.

Figure 7.15 shows an interesting ternary system showing eutectic
behaviour: KF–LiF–NaF would be one example. Each of the binary systems
shows a binary eutectic. The ternary eutectic, indicated G in the figure, is an
invariant point (at constant pressure) at which three solid and one liquid
phase are in equilibrium. For the above system the ternary eutectic temperature is lower than each of the binary eutectics.

7.5 Partition coefficients and chromatography

Chromatography is an extremely powerful tool for the separation of
complex mixtures into their components. The various methods under this
label depend for their efficiency upon differences in the distribution of the
components between a moving phase and a stationary phase. The different
components pass through the system in a time which depends on this
distribution.

The first techniques to be explored stemmed from the work of Tswett in 1906 who placed a mixture of plant pigments at the top of a powdered chalk column and washed through with petrol. The components were seen as coloured bands moving down the column; hence the name which has stuck to the general technique in spite of the fact that colour has no special relevance. This particular method is known as elution chromatography, a name which is applied whenever the moving phase is not absorbed or adsorbed (Chapter 12) by the stationary phase. In contrast, in the technique known as displacement chromatography the moving phase competes with the mixture to be separated for residence in or on the stationary phase.

A major advance was made in 1941 by Martin and Synge who noted that the laws governing the distribution of a solute between two liquids were simpler than those for the distribution between a liquid and a solid. They showed that with liquid for both the moving and stationary phases sharper component bands could be obtained than with the Tswett technique.

There are three principal methods using packed columns and a moving liquid phase: liquid–solid chromatography involving adsorption of the solute from solution (see Chapter 12) usually with a single-component liquid; liquid–liquid chromatography, usually called partition chromatography; and ion-exchange chromatography. The latter, which will not be discussed further, makes use of groups such as $-SO_3H$ and $-CH_2NR_2$ attached to the backbone of a polymer, itself usually in the form of beads.

Solid supports commonly used include silica, cellulose powder and diatomaceous earths such as kieselguhr and Celite. The use of cellulose powder is analogous to the use of sheets in paper chromatography. The cellulose binds some of the water from the solvent and, in simple terms, the separation can be regarded as being due to the different affinities which the solute has for the bound water phase and the moving mixed-solvent phase. For example, amino acids can be separated from phenol–water, or from butanol–acetic acid–water. In reality adsorption and even ion exchange will also occur in such systems, and the theoretical demarcation between the three types is limited. Paper chromatography can be effective without mixed solvents. Water is drawn into the pores by capillarity (Chapter 12), and adsorption from solution can, for example, separate inorganic ions, or as is often demonstrated, the components of inks.

Martin and Synge also suggested that a gas could be used for the moving phase, as was demonstrated by James and Martin in 1952. In gas–liquid chromatography, g.l.c., the stationary liquid is supported on an inert solid and the sample to be studied is carried through a column of stationary phase by a carrier gas. In addition to the use of g.l.c. for qualitative and quantitative analysis of the constituents of a volatile mixture, and the separation of (and purification of) components as an adjunct to preparative techniques, thermodynamic quantities can be measured. To ellucidate this aspect we must examine the mathematical background to chromatography in more detail.

Partition equations

If a solute A is distributed between two phases α, β, then at equilibrium its chemical potential in the two phases must be equal,

$$\mu_A(\alpha) = \mu_A(\beta). \tag{7.9}$$

If the chemical potential is referred to some standard state according to expression 6.75, we have

$$\mu_A^{\ominus}(\alpha) + RT \ln a_A^{\alpha} = \mu_A^{\ominus}(\beta) + RT \ln a_A^{\beta}, \tag{7.10}$$

whence (dropping the suffix A for brevity)

$$\ln\left(\frac{a^{\alpha}}{a^{\beta}}\right) = -\frac{(\mu^{\ominus}(\alpha) - \mu^{\ominus}(\beta))}{RT}, \tag{7.11}$$

or

$$\frac{a^{\alpha}}{a^{\beta}} = \exp(-\Delta\mu^{\ominus}/RT) \equiv K_a. \tag{7.12}$$

K_a is a constant (an equilibrium constant) whose value depends on the difference in the chemical potentials of the standard states in the two phases.

For the practical application of chromatography we are interested in the ratio of the concentrations (C) of the solute in the two phases rather than the ratio of activities. The ratio

$$\frac{C^{\alpha}}{C^{\beta}} = K \tag{7.13}$$

is called the partition coefficient. For ideal laws of solubility K will be a constant equal to K_a. In practice K is close to being constant for the distribution of most solvents between two liquid phases or between a liquid and a gas phase. However, for the distribution of a solute between a solid and a liquid or a solid and a gas, K is usually far from being constant. This we refer to as a non-linear distribution (a graph of C_{α} against C_{β} is not a straight line) and it leads to broad bands when chromatography is based on such systems (e.g. in the early elution techniques).

We will first consider the partition of a solute between fixed volumes of two immiscible solvents. This is of practical importance in the common extraction technique used in organic chemistry which is carried out in a separating funnel.

We express the compositions arising in 7.13 as mole fractions. A solution of W kg of solute (molecular weight M) in V_{α} dm^3 of liquid α (density ρ_{α}, molecular weight M_{α}) has a mole fraction

$$x(\alpha) = \frac{WM^{-1}}{WM^{-1} + \rho_{\alpha}V_{\alpha}M_{\alpha}^{-1}} \simeq \frac{WM_{\alpha}}{\rho_{\alpha}V_{\alpha}M}, \tag{7.14}$$

the approximation being valid for a dilute solution. We now add V_{β} dm^3 of liquid β (density ρ_β, molecular weight M_β) and establish equilibrium. The equilibrium mole fractions of solution in the two phases are, from 7.14

$$K = \frac{x(\alpha)}{x(\beta)} = \left(\frac{W_\alpha M_\alpha}{M \rho_\alpha V_\alpha}\right)\left(\frac{M \rho_\beta V_\beta}{W_\beta M_\beta}\right),$$ (7.15)

whence

$$\frac{W_\alpha}{W_\beta} = \left(\frac{K \rho_\alpha M_\beta}{\rho_\beta M_\alpha}\right)\left(\frac{V_\alpha}{V_\beta}\right) = \frac{K'V_\alpha}{V_\beta}.$$ (7.16)

Writing $W_\beta = W - W_\alpha$, expression 7.16 can be rearranged to

$$\frac{W_\alpha}{W} = \frac{K'V_\alpha}{V_\beta + K'V_\alpha},$$ (7.17)

which gives the fraction remaining in phase α.

If the layer of liquid β is removed and replaced by fresh liquid, there will be a further extraction and the amount of solute then remaining in phase α, $(W_\alpha)_2$, is obtained from 7.17 by replacing W_α/W by $(W_\alpha)_2/W_\alpha$. If this process is repeated r times, the amount remaining in phase α is given by $(W_\alpha)_r$, where

$$(W_\alpha)_r = W \left(\frac{K'V_\alpha}{V_\beta + K'V_\alpha}\right)^r = W \left(1 + \frac{V_\beta}{K'V_\alpha}\right)^{-r}.$$ (7.18)

It can be seen from 7.17 that for efficient extraction the ratio $V_\beta/K'V_\alpha$ should be as large as possible. A point that is less obvious is that if a fixed total volume, V, of solvent is to be used, then it is better to use n fractions V/n times ($n > 1$), rather than to make a single extraction with the whole volume.

Although apparatus has been developed to carry out automatically the multiple extractions represented by equation 7.18 it is rather cumbersome. However, one can reasonably infer that a continuous process in which the solvent β is replaced by a moving phase which passes down a packed column containing phase α will simulate a multiple extraction with large r. This is the principle behind elution chromatography.

Gas–liquid chromatography

The normal method of carrying out g.l.c. is to take a long narrow tube containing an inert packing material such as silica which is used to support an involatile liquid phase such as squalane ($C_{30}H_{62}$). The mobile phase is usually a constant stream of an inert carrier gas such as nitrogen. The sample is injected by syringe at one end of the column and the time taken to give a signal on a detector at the other end is noted. If the sample contains a mixture of compounds then these will travel down the column at different rates and appear separately at the detector as indicated in Figure 7.16.

The concentration profile of solute that appears at the detector depends on

Figure 7.16 Separation of two components in a g.l.c. column. The curves show the concentration profile of the mixture as it passes down the column

the experimental conditions (e.g. speed of the carrier gas) and a detailed analysis is beyond the scope of this book.[†] In most cases the profile (Y) fits approximately to a gaussian function

$$Y = h \exp(-x^2/2\sigma^2), \tag{7.19}$$

where h is the peak height, x is the distance along the tube measured from the peak centre and σ is the standard deviation of the distribution. The width at half the peak height is 2.35σ. Measured at the outlet σ^2 is approximately proportional to the time taken for the solute to pass down the column.

The chromatogram is generally regarded as the solute concentration–time profile shown by the detector (a device which measures the sample concentration in the gas at the outlet). The retention time t_R is the time taken for a sample injected into the column to appear as a peak at the outlet. This time is inversely proportional to the average flow rate of the carrier gas in the column (f_{av}). Solutes can be differentiated either by their retention time or by the volume of carrier gas that is passed in this time which is called the retention volume and is defined by

$$V_R = t_R f_{av}. \tag{7.20}$$

A marker which is insoluble in the stationary phase will pass down the column in a time t_R^0 and have a retention volume V_R^0. The time for a particular

[†]For a more detailed treatment see: J. H. Purnell, *Gas Chromatography*, Wiley, London and New York (1962); J. R. Conder and C. L. Young, *Physicochemical Measurement by Gas Chromatography*, Wiley–Interscience, Chichester (1979).

solute to appear at the detector will be t_R^0 divided by the fraction of time that the solute molecules spend in the gas phase. If n_g and n_l are the number of moles of solute in the gas and liquid phases then the fraction of time spent in the gas phase is $n_g/(n_g + n_l)$. Although n_g and n_l vary at different places and different times along the tube this fraction will be a constant depending on the partition coefficient for the solute in the two phases. From this argument we have

$$t_R = t_R^0 \left(\frac{n_g + n_l}{n_g} \right). \tag{7.21}$$

It follows that the ratio of molecules in the gas and liquid phases is given by

$$\frac{n_l}{n_g} = \frac{t_R - t_R^0}{t_R^0} = \frac{V_R - V_R^0}{V_R^0} = \frac{V_R'}{V_R^0}. \tag{7.22}$$

V_R' is called the net retention volume of the sample. The relationship between the three retention volumes we have defined is shown in Figure 7.17.

We define the partition coefficient of the solute by the ratio of concentrations expressed as moles per unit volume

$$K = \frac{C_l}{C_g} = \frac{n_l V_g}{n_g V_l}. \tag{7.23}$$

V_l is the volume of liquid in the column and V_g the volume of gas, which can be equated to V_R^0. Thus combining 7.22 and 7.23 we have

$$K = V_R'/V_l, \tag{7.24}$$

hence K can be determined by measuring the net retention volume and knowing the volume of liquid in the column.

Retention volumes are measured by a gas-flow meter external to the g.l.c. column and appropriate corrections for differences in temperature and

Figure 7.17 Definition of the retention volume and net retention volume in a chromatogram. The carrier gas volume is taken at the temperature and the average pressure in the column

pressure between meter and column must be made. An important factor is that the pressure in the column falls between inlet (P_i) and outlet (P_o). The average pressure is approximately the arithmetic mean of P_i and P_o but a more accurate value can be obtained from the expression

$$\frac{P_{av}}{P_o} = \frac{2}{3}\left\{\frac{(P_i/P_o)^3 - 1}{(P_i/P_o)^2 - 1}\right\} \tag{7.25}$$

It has already been said that the partition coefficient is not equal to the equilibrium constant K_a (7.12) unless the gas and liquid phases obey ideal laws. Non-ideality is more pronounced in the liquid phase and can be expressed by the relationship (6.68 and 6.70)

$$p = \gamma p^* x \tag{7.26}$$

where p is the partial pressure of the solute in the gase phase, p^* the vapour pressure of the pure solute, x the mole fraction of solute in the liquid and γ the activity coefficient. It should be recalled that in the limit of x approaching zero γp^* is equal to the Henry law constant (6.72). The limiting value of γ at infinite dilution can, in particular, be accurately measured by g.l.c.

The molar concentration of solute in the gaseous phase is p/RT and that in the liquid phase is $\rho_1 x/M_1$ where ρ_1 and M_1 are the density and molecular weight respectively of the pure liquid stationary phase. It follows from 7.23, 7.24 and 7.26 that

$$\frac{V'_R}{V_1} = \frac{RT\rho_1}{\gamma p^* M_1} \tag{7.27}$$

and introducing the total mass of solvent in the column, m, we have

$$V'_R = \frac{RTm}{\gamma p^* M_1}. \tag{7.28}$$

The net retention volume is proportional to the weight of stationary liquid phase in the column and it is therefore customary to tabulate retention volumes per unit weight of solvent; a quantity called the specific retention volume.

For more accurate work non-ideality in the gaseous phase must be allowed for, and in fact g.l.c. has proved to be an efficient method of measuring second virial coefficients (3.63) of imperfect gases, particularly the contribution to B arising from the interaction of the solute with the carrier gas. The appropriate equations for this analysis can be found in more advanced texts (see footnote on page 148).

It is possible to use g.l.c. for determining a wide range of physical properties. Although the method is not always one of high accuracy it has the great merit of requiring only very small amounts of material and it is not even necessary that the material be pure.

We have already seen that measured retention volumes will allow a

Table 7.1   Infinite dilution activity coefficients for n-alkanes (C_nH_{2n+2})

n-solute \ n-solvent	22	24	28	30	32	34	36
4	0.805	0.739	0.693	0.681	0.639	0.619	0.594
5	0.816	0.753	0.698	0.680	0.654	0.631	0.606
6	0.859	0.801	0.736	0.712	0.689	0.665	0.639
7	0.893	0.831	0.768	0.743	0.721	0.696	0.672
8	0.927	0.854	0.796	0.772	0.753	0.728	0.701
10	0.950	0.895	0.845	0.830	0.817	0.782	0.751

The data are from J. F. Parcher and K. S. Yun, *J. Chromatog.*, **99**, 193 (1974) and are based on measurements for column temperatures between 353 and 393 K.

determination of the activity coefficients of the liquid phase. There have been many studies using homologous series (e.g., n-alkanes) and a constant liquid phase, which show that log V'_R is a linear function of the number of carbon atoms in the molecule. As p^* in 7.28 is a smoothly varying function of the number of carbon atoms it is concluded that γ also varies smoothly in the series. Table 7.1 shows some values for the infinite dilution activity coefficients of n-alkane mixtures that have been obtained in this way. As the n-values for solute and solvent approach one another the mixture becomes more ideal ($\gamma \rightarrow 1$). Several theories of the non-ideality of n-alkane mixtures have been proposed which give quite good agreement with the experimental data.

Chapter 8

Polar liquids

8.1 Dielectric properties

If two charges q_1 and q_2 are separated by a distance R in a vacuum their energy of interaction is given by Coulomb's law

$$E = \frac{q_1 q_2}{4\pi\varepsilon_0 R}, \qquad (8.1)$$

where ε_0 is the vacuum permittivity which has the value 8.854×10^{-12} J^{-1} C^2 m^{-1}. If the charges are not in a vacuum then the electrostatic energy is modified by the dielectric effect of the medium. The molecules of the medium will be oriented and polarized by the two charges and, as we shall see, the energy of interaction is reduced.

If the distance R is large compared with the dimensions of molecules in the medium then the medium can be treated as if it were a uniform material whose electrical properties are characterized by a parameter K_r called the dielectric constant or relative permittivity. In this case the interaction energy of the two charges is given by

$$E = \frac{q_1 q_2}{4\pi\varepsilon_0 K_r R}. \qquad (8.2)$$

Water has one of the highest dielectric constants of all liquids and this is a key factor in its ability to solubilize ionic solids.

The dielectric constant is a macroscopic parameter that has no precise meaning for interactions over distances which are of the order of molecular dimensions. For example, if two charges are separated by a few angstroms so that only one or two water molecules could be accommodated in the space between them, then one cannot calculate their interaction energy by expression 8.2, because the intervening water molecules cannot be modelled by a continuous dielectric. Expression 8.2 will at best give an order of magnitude value for the energy. However, although K_r is a macroscopic parameter its value is, as we shall see, dependent on properties of the molecules which make up the dielectric.

152

Table 8.1 Dielectric constants, K_r, of some liquids,
and dipole moments, μ, of their gaseous molecules

	T/K	K_r	μ/D
Ar	82	1.54	0
CCl_4	298	2.23	0
C_6H_6	298	2.27	0
$C_6H_5NO_2$	298	34.8	4.22
CH_3OH	298	32.6	1.70
$CHONH_2$	293	109	3.73
HF	200	175	1.82
NH_3	195	25	1.47
HCN	293	115	2.92
H_2O	273	87.9	
	298	78.4	1.85
	373	55.6	

Table 8.1 shows the dielectric constants of some common liquids. The most striking conclusion to be drawn from this table is that dipolar molecules give liquids with much higher dielectric constants than non-polar molecules, and that hydrogen-bonded liquids have exceptionally high dielectric constants. It is this relationship between K_r and microscopic properties that we now explore.

The classical theory of dielectric behaviour originated in a suggestion of Faraday that in the presence of an electric field the molecules making up the dielectric suffer a displacement of charge and acquire an induced dipole moment. The mathematical consequences of this were examined by Clausius and Mosotti and their conclusions are embodied in the Clausius–Mosotti law

$$\left(\frac{K_r - 1}{K_r + 2}\right)V_m = P_m = \frac{\alpha \mathcal{N}}{3\varepsilon_0}, \tag{8.3}$$

where V_m is the molar volume, α is the polarizability of the molecule and P_m is a characteristic property of the dielectric called the molar polarization. For molecules of low dielectric constant P_m is found to be approximately constant, independent of pressure and temperature. It has also roughly the same value in the solid, liquid and gaseous states. This is not true for materials of high dielectric constant.

The dielectric constant is determined by measuring the capacitance of a condenser in an alternating current circuit with (C) and without (C_0) the dielectric between the plates, and taking the ratio

$$K_r = C/C_0. \tag{8.4}$$

K_r is a parameter which depends on the frequency of the electric field, but below about 10^6 Hz its value generally changes very little and it is this low-frequency value that is commonly called the static dielectric constant.

154

From the electromagnetic theory of light Maxwell deduced that for a transparent medium the dielectric constant should equal the square of its refractive index

$$K_r = n^2,\tag{8.5}$$

and it was shown by Lorenz and Lorentz that the molar refraction, defined by

$$\left(\frac{n^2 - 1}{n^2 + 2}\right)V_m = R_m,\tag{8.6}$$

was independent of temperature. Refractive index also varies with frequency, and for polar molecules it is only at high frequencies that R_m and P_m become equal, that is, the Maxwell relation holds. For non-polar molecules they are approximately equal over the whole frequency range providing that the wavelength at which n is determined is not close to an absorption band.

The reason for the difference between R_m and P_m is that there are two contributions to P_m, one from the alignment of permanent dipoles in the electric field and the other from the creation of induced dipoles in the molecules. Only the second of these contributes to the refraction. For non-polar molecules there is no dipole alignment, and for polar molecules at high frequency (above $\sim 10^{12}$ Hz) the electric field is alternating too rapidly for the dipoles to reach an aligned position.

In most solids the molecules are not free to rotate and hence there is no dipole alignment contribution to the polarization: plastic crystals are an exception to this rule.

The Debye equation

The two contributions to P_m were first recognized by Debye and encompassed in the Debye equation for the polarization which we shall now derive. The energy of an electric dipole μ in a uniform field $\mathscr{E}$ is

$$E = -\mu \cdot \mathscr{E} = -\mu \mathscr{E} \cos \theta,\tag{8.7}$$

where θ is the angle between the dipole and field vectors. The average value of the dipole moment in the direction of $\mathscr{E}$ can be obtained by weighting the dipole component along $\mathscr{E}$ by the Boltzmann factor, $\exp(-E/kT)$, and averaging over all angles

$$\mu = \frac{\int_0^\pi \mu \cos \theta e^{\mu \mathscr{E} \cos \theta / kT} \sin \theta \, d\theta}{\int_0^\pi e^{\mu \mathscr{E} \cos \theta / kT} \sin \theta \, d\theta}.\tag{8.8}$$

The integrals in 8.8 can be evaluated by making the substitution

$$x = \mu \mathscr{E} \cos \theta / kT,\tag{8.9}$$

which leads to the result

$$\bar{\mu} = \mu \mathscr{L}(x), \tag{8.10}$$

where $\mathscr{L}(x)$ is called the Langevin function

$$\mathscr{L}(x) = \frac{e^x + e^{-x}}{e^x - e^{-x}} - \frac{1}{x}. \tag{8.11}$$

At normal temperatures and field strengths x is very much less than unity and on expanding the exponentials in 8.11 one finds that $\mathscr{L}(x) \approx x/3$. With this approximation the average dipole moment is

$$\bar{\mu} = \mu^2 \mathscr{E}/3kT. \tag{8.12}$$

We must add to this average dipole moment the contribution arising from the polarization of the molecule in the electric field. Expression 2.8 relates the induced dipole moment to the field strength. For non-spherical systems $\alpha.\mathscr{E}$ is a function of the molecular orientation in the field and an appropriate Boltzmann average should be taken. This complication is usually ignored as its effect is small, and hence the average value of the dipole moment of a molecule arising from the permanent and induced moments is

$$\bar{\mu} = \left(\alpha + \frac{\mu^2}{3kT}\right)\mathscr{E}. \tag{8.13}$$

It can be seen from 8.13 that the function $(\alpha + \mu^2/3kT)$ behaves as an effective polarizability for field frequencies which are sufficiently low that the Boltzmann-averaged dipole alignment can be established. This polarizability when multiplied by Avogadro's number can be equated to the molar polarization P_m. Using the Clausius–Mosotti expression, 8.3, we arrive at the Debye equation

$$P_m = \left(\frac{K_r - 1}{K_r + 2}\right)V_m = \frac{\mathscr{N}}{3\varepsilon_0}\left(\alpha + \frac{\mu^2}{3kT}\right). \tag{8.14}$$

The Debye equation holds very well for gases, although the dielectric constants need to be measured very accurately, as they are close to unity, for the equation to be confirmed. Figure 8.1 shows a graph of the molar polarization against T^{-1} for HCl, HBr and HI. The molecular dipole moments and polarizabilities given in Table 8.2 have been obtained from the slopes and intercepts of the lines. Dipole moments can be measured more accurately from the Stark splitting of microwave lines but it can be seen from Table 8.2 that the values obtained by dielectric measurements are quite good.

If one attempts to use the Debye equation to obtain the dipole moment of molecules in a polar liquid the results are generally very unsatisfactory. We will shortly illustrate this for the case of liquid water. The equation can, however, be used for dilute solutions of polar molecules in non-polar solvents.

For a liquid mixture we can write the total molar polarization as a sum of

Figure 8.1 Graph of the molar polarization against T^{-1} for the gaseous hydrogen halides. (Data from C. T. Zahn, *Phys. Rev.* **24**, 400 (1924)

partial molar polarizations of the components multiplied by their mole fractions

$$P_m = \sum_i \bar{P}_i x_i. \tag{8.15}$$

For mixtures of non-polar liquids an ideal mixing law holds quite well, that is, $\bar{P}_i$ can be taken as the molar polarization $P_{i,m}$ of the pure component i. Although the mixing is not ideal when a polar molecule is one of the components it is legitimate to assume that $\bar{P}_i$ for the non-polar component (A) is equal to its pure liquid value when the polar component (B) is in low concentration. Thus the partial molar polarization of the polar component is given by

$$\overline{P_B(x_B)} = (P_m - (1 - x_B)P_{A,m})/x_B, \tag{8.16}$$

and we are interested in the limit of $\overline{P_B(x_B)}$ as x_B approaches zero.

Table 8.2 Values of the dipole moment and polarizability determined from the gas phase dielectric constant (Figure 8.1)

	μ/D	$(4\pi\varepsilon_0)^{-1}\alpha/\text{Å}^3$	$\mu^\dagger/D$
HCl	1.05	3.0	1.08 ± 0.01
HBr	0.81	3.5	0.82 ± 0.02
HI	0.39	5.6	0.44 ± 0.02

†Best literature values.

Figure 8.2 The molar polarization of nitrobenzene in hexane solution (293 K) as calculated from expression 8.16. (Data are taken from V. K. Semenchenko and M. Azimov, *Russ. J. Phys. Chem.*, **30**, 1821, 2228 (1956))

Figure 8.2 shows $\bar{P}$ for nitrobenzene as a function of mole fraction in solution with hexane. It can be seen that the value extrapolated to infinite dilution is more than three times the molar polarization of pure liquid nitrobenzene.

In principle the infinite dilution $\bar{P}$ could be measured as a function of temperature, and dipole moments determined from the Debye equation. In practice this procedure is not often used for two reasons. First, the temperature range over which measurements can be taken for a liquid are often rather small, and there would be a substantial measure of uncertainty in the slope of the Debye graph. Second, the dipole moment of the polar molecule depends to a small extent on its environment; both on the nature of the non-polar solvent and the temperature. Thus P_m may have temperature factors other than those contained in the Debye equation, and these may complicate the situation.

The normal procedure for deducing a dipole moment from infinite dilution partial molar polarization is therefore to obtain an independent measure of

158

the polarizability from refractive index data. Further details of this are given in more advanced texts.† In the case of nitrobenzene the dipolar contribution to P_m is so large that we can get an estimate of μ by ignoring the polarizability contribution. From the value of $\bar{P}(0)$ shown in Figure 8.2 we deduce $\mu = 3.9$ D, which is quite close to the measured gas-phase dipole moment of 4.2 D.

Onsager–Kirkwood equations

If we insert known values of the dipole moment and polarizability of water into the Debye equation (8.14) ($\mu = 1.85$ D, $\alpha/4\pi\varepsilon_0 = 1.48$ Å³) we arrive at the physically impossible value of 4.2 for the factor $(K_r - 1)/(K_r + 2)$. Moreover the temperature dependence of the molar polarization of water is quite unlike the Debye prediction, as can be seen from Figure 8.3. The water

Figure 8.3 The temperature dependence of the molar polarization of liquid water

†J. W. Smith, *Electric Dipole Moments*, Butterworths, London (1955); C. P. Smyth, *Dielectric Behaviour and Structure*, McGraw-Hill, Maidenhead (1955).

Figure 8.4 The Onsager field arising from a polar molecule in a liquid. The reaction field of the dipole is shown as dashed lines

behaviour is not untypical of polar liquids, particularly those whose molecules have high dipole moments.

There are two features of the derivation of the Debye equation that are unsatisfactory. First, no account is taken of the electric field which acts on a molecule due to the polarization of its immediate neighbours. Onsager pointed out that this field, which he called the reaction field, is aligned in the direction of the permanent dipole and is proportional to the permanent dipole moment. Figure 8.4 shows the Onsager field acting on a dipole placed in a spherical cavity. The lines of induction are bent by the field from induced dipoles in the molecules neighbouring the cavity.

The Onsager correction should be applied to dilute solutions of polar molecules in non-polar liquids as well as for pure polar liquids, but in the latter case there is a more important factor to be considered and that is the orientational correlation that exists between the permanent dipole moments of neighbouring molecules. The Boltzmann-averaged alignment factor given by expression 8.12 represents the effect of each dipole acting independently in the field, but if one molecule is aligned in the field, its neighbours will have preferred orientations by virtue of the dipole–dipole electrostatic energy. In the case of water the directional nature of the hydrogen bonds is an additional factor that introduces correlation between the orientations of neighbouring molecules.

There have been several attempts to introduce dipole correlation into the theory of the dielectric constant of polar liquids. The best established theory is that of Kirkwood. He showed that the Onsager field and dipole correlation leads to the expression

$$\left(\frac{(2K_r + 1)(K_r - 1)}{9K_r}\right)V_m = \frac{\mathcal{N}}{3\varepsilon_0}\left(\alpha + \frac{g\mu^2}{3kT}\right). \tag{8.17}$$

A comparison should be made between this and the Debye equation 8.14. The change on the left-hand side is due to the Onsager reaction field. The appearance of the factor g, called the correlation factor, on the right-hand side is due to the dipole correlation. It is defined by

$$g\mu^2 = \boldsymbol{\mu} \cdot \bar{\boldsymbol{\mu}}, \tag{8.18}$$

where $\bar{\boldsymbol{\mu}}$ is the total dipole moment of a molecule and its immediate surrounding molecules.

The Kirkwood theory has been applied to liquid water[†] with $\bar{\boldsymbol{\mu}}$ being calculated from a structure in which each water molecule is hydrogen bonded to four neighbours. Values of g of approximately 2.6 have been obtained with a small decrease as the temperature is raised due to the break-up of the water structure. The value of the dielectric constant obtained from such a calculation is in reasonable agreement with experiment and the dipole moment of a water molecule in the liquid is deduced to be slightly greater than its gasphase value. One estimate is that $\mu = 2.45$ D which is 32% greater than the gas-phase value.[‡]

8.2   Water: the unique liquid?

Water is the only naturally occurring inorganic liquid on earth and as it was abundant before life began it has probably done more than any other chemical substance to shape our biological environment. Water is an essential constituent of animal and plant cells and has a vital influence on the structure of biopolymers. Apart from its role in biochemical reactions, particularly proton transfer, it has a physical role as solvent, lubricant and irrigant.

More chemical and physical studies have been made on water and its solutions than on any other liquid, but the accumulated data have not proved easy to interpret. Water solutions are very far from ideal in the sense that this term has been used for non-electrolyte mixtures. Even H_2O–D_2O mixtures are slightly non-ideal: the heat of mixing for their 1:1 mixture is 1.3 kJ mol^{-1}.

One would expect the properties of water to be most closely paralleled by molecules of similar chemical structure, and the hydrides of the elements neighbouring oxygen in the periodic table obviously bear comparison. NH_3, HF and H_2S are all gases at room temperature due to the fact that the intermolecular energies for these compounds are much weaker than that for water. The binding energies calculated for the dimers of H_2O and HF are quite similar, approximately 24 kJ mol^{-1}, but in the liquid state water molecules can form twice as many hydrogen bonds as can hydrogen fluoride. The hydrogen bond strengths in NH_3 or H_2S are weaker, approximately 16 kJ mol^{-1} and 8 kJ mol^{-1} per bond, respectively, which can be attributed to the fact that nitrogen and sulphur are less electronegative elements than oxygen. Thus the high boiling point of water in comparison with the neighbouring hydrides is due both to the strength of the hydrogen bond and to the number of bonds that can be formed by each molecule.

[†] J. A. Pople, *Proc. Roy. Soc.*, **A205**, 163 (1951).
[‡] C. A. Coulson and D. Eisenberg, *Proc. Roy. Soc.*, **A291**, 445 (1966).

Table 8.3 Properties of water and related liquids

	NH_3	H_2O	HF	H_2S	CH_3OH
m.p./K	195	273	184	187	179
b.p./K	240	373	293	212	338
liq. range/K	44	100	109	25	159
K_r	25(195 K)	79(298 K)	84(273 K)	9(187 K)	33(298 K)

Another molecule that has some features similar to H_2O is CH_3OH. The dimer strengths appear to be very similar for the two species but, as in the case of HF, for CH_3OH there is only one hydrogen atom per molecule that can take part in hydrogen bonding. The relatively high boiling point of methanol in comparison with hydrogen fluoride is certainly due to the fact that CH_3OH gives rise to greater dispersion energies because of its larger size (and hence larger polarizability). A similar fact explains why methylamine has a boiling point 27 K higher than that of ammonia.

As noted in the previous section the dielectric constant of water is very high due to the high degree of spatial correlation between neighbouring dipoles. However, water is not unique as can be seen from Table 8.3. Liquid HF also has a high dielectric constant, and even higher are HCN ($K_r = 158$), and formamide ($K_r = 109$). The dielectric constant is an important parameter for understanding the solvating power of a polar solvent, but it is not the only factor that must be considered. For example, liquid HCN is generally a poorer solvent for ionic solids than is water, yet its dielectric constant is much higher.

In this brief survey of the properties of water we have shown that it is not exceptional in its physical properties but that does not, of course, detract from the important place it holds in the physics and chemistry of liquids.

8.3 The structure of ice

There have been several models of liquid water and aqueous solutions which have invoked some analogy with the structure of ice, and for this reason a brief survey of the solid phases of water is useful.

Whilst the term ice usually refers to the solid phase which is formed when liquid water freezes at atmospheric pressure, an unusually high number of different solid phases of water are known. Figure 8.5 shows the liquid–solid phase diagram deduced by Whalley and co-workers. The solid lines show the measured phase boundaries and the broken lines are estimated boundaries. Some metastable phases are also known and include a phase called IV which has been found within the phase V region.

Normal ice, labelled I or Ih, is also called hexagonal ice, a name which has been taken from its lattice structure, which is shown in Figure 8.6. A cubic modification of ice I is stable below about 153 K. This cannot be prepared by cooling the hexagonal form, but it has been obtained via phases III and II.

Figure 8.5   The phase diagram of ice. (E. Whalley, J. B. R. Heath and D. W. Davidson, *J. Chem. Phys.*, **48**, 2362 (1968))

Several of the phases have been studied by diffraction techniques and they all appear to have the common feature that each oxygen is hydrogen bonded to four neighbouring oxygen atoms with an O . . . O distance of approximately 2.8 Å. In phase I these neighbours are precisely tetrahedral, but in the high-pressure phases the angles are distorted so that some of the distances

Figure 8.6   The lattice structure of ice Ih. Only the positions of the oxygen atoms and the O–H–O hydrogen bonds are shown

between non-bonded oxygen atoms are much reduced from their corresponding phase I distances.

From neutron diffraction studies it has been deduced that the hydrogen atoms lie along or very close to the O . . . O axes. If the water molecules in phase I had the same bond angle as in the gas phase (104.5°) this would imply that the hydrogen atoms were about 2° off the O . . . O axis, but experimental measurements cannot fix their positions to this accuracy.

It can probably be appreciated from Figure 8.6 that normal ice has a rather open lattice structure, and the unusual fact that liquid water at its freezing point is less dense than ice can be attributed more to the low density of ice than to the high density of water. A reasonable interpretation of the fact that at atmospheric pressure water reaches its maximum density at 277 K (4 °C) is that between 273 and 277 K (0 and 4 °C) the structure of liquid water is gradually breaking away from a short-range order similar to that in phase I and moving to a more closely packed structure. Above 277 K the increasing kinetic energy of the molecules will lead to a reduction in density.

Residual entropy

Bernal and Fowler were the first to postulate that all ice structures conformed to the rule that each oxygen was linked to four other oxygen atoms through hydrogen bonds, with two OH distances being short (roughly the same distance as in a free water molecule) and two being long. However, this still leaves the possibility of having a disordered hydrogen atom sublattice as illustrated by the two-dimensional model shown in Figure 8.7. Pauling was the first to calculate the residual entropy arising from this disorder.

In a lattice with N water molecules there are $2N$ O . . . O bonds and in each of these the hydrogen atoms have two possible positions. If we consider the

Figure 8.7 A schematic representation of the hydrogen atom disorder in ice

four hydrogen atoms surrounding any one oxygen there are sixteen distinct arrangements, but only six of these satisfy the Bernal–Fowler rules: others correspond to the structures H_4O^{2+}, H_3O^+, OH^- and O^{2-} which are energetically less favourable. Thus the total number of hydrogen atom configurations for N molecules is

$$W = 2^{2N}(6/16)^N = (3/2)^N. \tag{8.19}$$

The residual entropy per mole is therefore

$$S = k \ln W = R \ln(3/2) = 3.37 \text{ J mol}^{-1}. \tag{8.20}$$

This value agrees closely with that deduced from thermal data, and this agreement confirmed the hypothesis (prior to its confirmation by neutron diffraction) that the hydrogen atoms were not placed at the centres of the O . . . O bonds, but were closer to one oxygen than the other.

One would expect a disordered phase to show a phase change to an ordered phase when the temperature is lowered. However, there is no evidence for a phase equivalent to ice Ih with an ordered hydrogen sublattice. In contrast the high pressure forms VII and VIII do appear to be related in having the same oxygen sublattice (body-centred cubic) but with the hydrogen atoms disordered in VII and ordered in VIII. The transition temperature is approximately 280 K.

8.4 The water intermolecular potential

Because water is such an important and unusual liquid a great deal of effort has been made to explain its properties from the features of its intermolecular potential. Numerous functions to represent the potential can be found in the literature and their development provides an excellent illustration of advances that have occurred in experimental and computational techniques.

Two distinct approaches to the problem of finding the best potential have been taken. The first was aimed at the exact form of the water dimer potential, and the second was aimed at the best empirical dimer potential that would reproduce the properties of liquid and solid water. These two potentials will only be identical if the total potential function for the liquid and solid phases can be accurately represented by a sum of water dimer functions. If in these bulk phases there are significant contributions to the potential from water molecules interacting three or more at a time, then the empirical dimer potential must contain some average contribution of these higher-order terms.

It is to be expected that the many-body contributions to the potential will be more important for liquid water than for a simple atomic liquid such as argon, or even a molecular liquid made up of non-polar molecules such as liquid nitrogen. The reason for this is that the induction and charge-transfer energies are more important for polar than for non-polar molecules and, as stated in Table 2.3, these energies are not pairwise additive.

Whilst the present evidence for the importance of many-body terms in determining the structure and properties of liquid and solid water is not conclusive, the balance lies on the side of believing that for the most accurate picture they cannot be ignored. McDonald and Klein,[†] for example, conclude from their computer simulation of liquid water that there is little hope of reconciling the properties of the liquid and gaseous states on the basis of a single water dimer potential. The radial distribution function in the liquid which is computed from a pair potential derived from gas-phase data is in rather poor agreement with the experimental radial distribution function obtained from X-ray data.

It is possible, in principle, to calculate by quantum mechanics the pair and many-body potentials for small clusters of water molecules and hence to deduce the size of the many-body terms for bulk water. At the present time such calculations cannot be made with sufficient accuracy to give an unambiguous answer. Approximate calculations[‡] which have been made on chains and rings of three or four linked molecules indicate that the pair energy between nearest neighbour water molecules is approximately -15 kJ mol^{-1} and the three-body energy for three molecules in a ring is approximately -5 kJ mol^{-1}. If this estimate proves to be accurate then it is certain that the many-body terms play an important role in determining the structures of the liquid and solid phases.

Evidence for the nature of the exact water dimer potential comes from a variety of sources, particularly measurements on gaseous water. The first such quantity to be seriously employed was the second virial coefficient (3.64). For a monatomic gas the second virial coefficient generally provides useful information about the attractive region of the potential. However, for molecules B values are less useful. Molecular potentials are not just functions of the distance between molecules but they also depend on the relative orientations of the molecules. Second virial coefficients depend only on angular averages of the pair potentials, and hence can give no direct information about the angular features of the potential. Scattering cross-sections measured in low energy molecular beams can in principle provide information on the angular and distance behaviour of the potential but for a system as complicated as the water–water potential such experiments have not as yet given much information.

The most important experimental evidence which exists at present for the intermolecular potentials between small molecules comes from the application of microwave and radio frequency spectroscopy to molecular dimers. These dimers (together with other small clusters) can be formed by expanding a gas through a pinhole nozzle into a vacuum (the so-called supersonic beam). The emerging molecules are characterized by very low rotational and

---

[†] I. R. McDonald and M. L. Klein, *Faraday Disc.*, **66**, 48 (1978). The published discussion of this paper contains several points relevant to this conclusion.
[‡] H. Kistenmacher *et al.*, *J. Chem. Phys.*, **61**, 546 (1974).

Figure 8.8 The geometry of the water dimer. The symmetry axes of each molecule (shown as dashed lines) are lying in the plane of the paper and make angles with the O–O line as shown. The OHO bond is linear within experimental error. The geometry of each water molecule is assumed to be little changed on dimerization. (J. A. Odutola and T. R. Dyke, *J. Chem. Phys.*, **72**, 5062 (1980))

vibrational temperatures (a few degrees kelvin) and as a result the population of clusters held together only by van der Waals bonds is high.

Dyke and co-workers[†] have studied the water dimer in such an experiment. From the rotational energy levels, using isotopic substitution for both the hydrogen and oxygen atoms, it was possible to deduce that the structure of the dimer is a *trans*-linear complex with the geometry shown in Figure 8.8. With further spectroscopic study it should be possible to deduce some of the force constants for this structure and thus enhance our knowledge of the potential energy surface.

There is at present no experimental value for the dissociation energy of the water dimer. Quantum mechanical calculations on the water dimer potential surface give a geometry which agrees closely with the experimental geometry and one, therefore, has grounds for believing that the dissociation energy calculated for this structure, approximately 23 kJ mol^{-1}, is not far from the exact value. In the future such calculations are likely to provide the best route for obtaining a complete picture of the potential energy surface of the water dimer, both its distance and angular features, and one can expect the accuracy of such calculations to improve appreciably in the next few years.

The most important feature of the water–water potential in respect to the structure of the solid and liquid phases is probably the angular behaviour as this accounts for the strong preference for tetrahedral coordination. A model potential which most obviously introduces this behaviour was first suggested by Bjerrum; it is based on the location of four point charges within the molecule at approximately tetrahedral directions from the oxygen as centre as shown in Figure 8.9a. Two of the charges are positive and are placed on the

[†]T. R. Dyke, K. M. Mack and J. S. Muenter, *J. Chem. Phys.*, **66**, 498 (1977).

Figure 8.9   Two point-charge models that have been used to represent the electrostatic part of the water–water potential. (a) F. H. Stillinger and A. Rahman, *J. Chem. Phys.*, **60**, 1545 (1974). (b) H. Popkie *et al.*, *loc. cit.*

hydrogen atoms and the other two are negative and are placed at points which are identified as the centres of density of the lone-pair electrons.

The electrostatic interaction between these point charges on different molecules will lead to tetrahedral coordination with the distance between adjacent molecules being controlled by a repulsive potential which acts either between the centres of the molecules or between individual atoms in the molecules. For example, a potential devised by Ben-Naim and Stillinger[†] combines a Lennard-Jones potential (2.15) acting between the oxygen atoms with the electrostatic interaction between tetrahedral site charges. There have been several calculations of liquid water properties using this potential or variants of it.

The angular feature of the water–water potential can be introduced through other models than the Bjerrum tetrahedral charges. For example, a potential fitted to quantum mechanical calculations of the water dimer surface has for its electrostatic part been represented by only three point charges, all of which are on the same side of the oxygen atom. This electrostatic model shown in Figure 8.9(b) was combined with exponential repulsion terms acting between all pairs of atoms in the system.[‡]

The only attempt to date to use a non-pair-additive potential in the computer simulation of liquid water has been by Barnes and co-workers.[§] The key

[†]A. Ben-Naim and F. H. Stillinger, *Structure and Transport Properties in Water and Aqueous Solutions*, ed. R. A. Horne, Wiley-Interscience, London (1972).
[‡]H. Popkie, H. Kistenmacher and E. Clementi, *J. Chem. Phys.*, **59**, 1325 (1973).
[§]P. Barnes, J. L. Finney and J. E. Quin, *Nature*, **282**, 459 (1979).

feature of this potential is that the electrostatic interaction is introduced by placing point dipole and quadrupole moments at the centre of the molecule, and the magnitude of the dipole moment is allowed to be dependent on the total electric field of all the surrounding molecules. It has been claimed that with this approach both gas-phase and liquid-phase properties can be reproduced satisfactorily, and further studies may well show that this is a good way of allowing for many-body terms in the potential.

8.5 Structural models of liquid water

Because of its importance as a solvent and its interesting properties there have been many attempts to establish structural models of liquid water. The properties that have engaged most attention are its anomalous density, its X-ray and neutron diffraction patterns, its dielectric constant and its infra-red and Raman spectra.

All models invoke a high degree of ice-like order to cold water at low pressures and attempt to explain the disappearance of this as either temperature or pressure is raised. The models fall roughly into three classes. The first are mixture models and the simplest of these assumes water to consist of ice-like regions and fluid regions. These regions are not permanent, but move around the liquid through breaking and forming of hydrogen bonds. The relative proportions of the two regions will be a function of temperature and pressure.

In the second class of model, water is considered to be uniform in structure but the hydrogen bonds are distorted in varying degrees from the ideal geometry which exists in ice I. The average degree of bond distortion is a function of temperature and pressure.

The third class of model is based on the view that the bulk of water is ice-like, albeit with distorted hydrogen bonds, but individual water molecules occupy some of the empty space in the ice lattice as interstitial molecules. It is this filling of spaces that is used to explain the anomalous density of water.

Vibrational spectra

The infra-red and Raman spectra of H_2O, D_2O and their mixtures tend to support either the mixture or the interstitial models. The vibrational frequencies associated with hydrogen motion in liquid water occur in the region of 3500 cm^{-1} for O–H stretch (2500 cm^{-1} for D_2O), 1600 cm^{-1} for HOH bend and between 1000 cm^{-1} and 300 cm^{-1} for libration. The latter can be thought of as a mixture of hindered rotation of the water molecules and hydrogen bond bending.

If the Raman spectrum of a 1% mixture of H_2O in D_2O is examined (almost all the hydrogen is then in HDO species) the OH stretching band appears to have two components as shown in Figure 8.10. A dilute mixture of D_2O in H_2O shows, less prominently, a similar two-component profile for the OD

Figure 8.10 Argon-ion-laser Raman spectrum of (a) 1% H_2O in D_2O; (b) 1% D_2O in H_2O at 298 K. The sharp lines marked with a cross are argon lines. The arrows show the weak second components. (G. E. Walraten, *Water, a Comprehensive Treatise*, Vol. 1, Chapter 5, ed. F. Franks, Plenum Press, London and New York (1972))

stretching band. These experiments suggest that there are two types of environment for the dilute isotope.

The relative intensities of the two components in the Raman bands change as expected with a rise in temperature and only the high-frequency component is evident in high density supercritical water. The corresponding isotopically mixed ices also show only a single band which in this case is the low-frequency component shown in Figure 8.11.

Both the mixture and interstitial models involve two types of environment for a water molecule and hence are consistent with the Raman results. The uniform model has a continuous range of environments for the hydrogen

Figure 8.11 High temperature, high pressure Raman spectra from 11 mole % D_2O in H_2O. A, 293 K, 100 atm; B, 373 K, 1000 atm; C, 473 K, 2800 atm; D, 573 K, 4700 atm; E, 673 K, 3900 atm. (Data of H. Lindner reported in G. E. Walraten, *loc. cit.*)

atoms and appears to be inconsistent with the results. However, a uniform model may still possess a bimodal distribution of environments (i.e. two peaks of probability amongst a broad distribution) and hence cannot be ruled out.

Diffraction

The most important experimental data for judging the validity of any model of liquid water are those from X-ray and neutron diffraction experiments. It is therefore not surprising that a great deal of effort has been made to collect such data for a range of temperatures and pressures, and to analyse them to obtain radial distribution functions. An important conclusion from this work is that there is no evidence for large ice-like regions in liquid water. These would be expected to possess long-range order and would give rise to oscillations in the small angle X-ray scattering intensities. No variation has been found in the parameter s (defined by 1.9) in the region $0.04 \, \text{Å}^{-1} < s < 0.5 \, \text{Å}^{-1}$ for Mo K_α radiation ($\lambda = 0.7107 \, \text{Å}$) and this rules out any order existing over more than about 10 Å. A mixture model, if taken to imply large ice-like regions, is therefore untenable.

Figure 8.12 shows the radial distribution function $g(r)$ (defined in section 1.3) which has been obtained from the Oak Ridge X-ray data. This radial distribution function includes positional correlation for both the oxygen and hydrogen atoms. The X-ray scattering is predominantly from oxygen atoms but the contributions from $O \cdots H$ (12%) and $H \cdots H$ (2%) are not negligible.

The prominent peak which is seen in $g(r)$ at all temperatures at approximately 1 Å must be due to the intramolecular O–H distance. The second prominent peak at about 2.9 Å will be due to the nearest O–O distance. It can be seen that this increases from 2.84 Å at 4 °C to 2.94 Å at 200 °C.

The peak in $g(r)$ at 2.9 Å is flanked on both sides by ripples which are thought to be an artefact of the analysis due to termination of the Fourier integral (1.13) at a finite value of s. However, the broad maxima at approximately 4.5 Å and 7.0 Å are physically real and represent average second and third neighbour distances. These peaks gradually disappear as the temperature is raised.

In ice I the shortest O–O distance is 2.76 Å and the second and third O–O neighbours are separated by 4.75 Å and 5.2 Å respectively. The second neighbour distances in ice I and liquid water are therefore very similar and we conclude that the average O$\hat{\text{O}}$O angle made by an oxygen atom and its first and second neighbours is close to the tetrahedral value (109°) which occurs in ice I. At third neighbours, however, the difference between ice I and liquid water is considerable.

To obtain from experiment the separate radial distribution functions for the different types of atom in water, g_{OO}, g_{OH} and g_{HH}, it is necessary to have data from other scattering experiments in which the ratio of the scattering factors (the parameter A in expression 1.10) for hydrogen and oxygen is different from that pertaining for X-rays. There has been some analysis of electron

Figure 8.12 The radial distribution frunction $g(r)$ for water determined from the Oak Ridge data. The figure is taken from A. H. Narten and H. A. Levy, *Water, a Comprehensive Treatise*, vol. 1, ed. F. Franks, Plenum Press, London and New York (1972)

scattering from thin films of water, but the results are controversial and in any case it is not clear that the internal structure of a thin film is the same as that of bulk water.

Neutron scattering is the obvious technique to use. It has the advantage over X-ray scattering that different isotopes have different scattering factors.

Figure 8.13 The dominant structure in water which was assumed by Narten in order to separate the total radial distribution function into g_{OO}, g_{OH} and g_{HH}

Unfortunately normal hydrogen gives a large amount of incoherent scattering due to its large nuclear spin and as yet neutron scattering on H_2O has given no structural information. In addition all the oxygen isotopes have about the same scattering factor and hence using a rare oxygen isotope leads to no new information. Thus only D_2O provides useful neutron diffraction data.

To provide a third condition on the radial distribution functions and thus allow all three to be determined, Narten assumed that the dominant structure in liquid water was a molecule surrounded tetrahedrally by four other molecules as shown in Figure 8.13. With such a model if g_{OO} and g_{OH} are known g_{HH} can be determined. The resulting distribution functions for water at 298 K are shown in Figure 8.14. (The intramolecular O–H correlation has been subtracted from g_{OH}.)

Computer simulation

Figure 8.13 also shows the radial distribution functions calculated by Lie and Clementi by the Monte Carlo method, using a water–water pair potential based upon molecular orbital calculations of the water dimer with additional terms to represent the dispersion energy. The agreement between the diffraction experiment and the computer experiment is very good when one considers that neither is made without assumptions: the diffraction results include the Narten assumption about the dominant water structure and the computer results assume that a pair-additive potential is adequate for liquid water.

A recent careful analysis[†] of the slow neutron scattering for liquid D_2O has

[†]J. G. Powles, *Molec. Phys.*, **42**, 757 (1981).

Figure 8.14 The radial distribution functions for water at 298 K determined from X-ray and neutron diffraction data (A. H. Narten, *J. Chem. Phys.*, **56**, 5681 (1972)). The results are compared with those from a Monte Carlo computer simulation (G. C. Lie and E. Clementi, *J. Chem. Phys.*, **62**, 2195 (1976))

Table 8.4   Analysis of hydrogen bond structure in liquid water from molecular dynamics computer simulation

E_{HB}/kJ mol^{-1}	>8.87	>12.80	>16.47	>20.27
$\bar{b}$	3.88	3.14	2.26	1.18
N_0	0	0.003	0.041	0.249
N_1	0.003	0.029	0.180	0.415

A. Rahman and F. H. Stillinger, *J. Amer. Chem. Soc.*, **95**, 7943 (1973).

led to the conclusion that the intramolecular O–D distance is 0.983 ± 0.008 Å. This is larger than the value appropriate to an isolated molecule (0.958 Å), but smaller than the distance in ice I, which is generally taken as 1.01 Å although shorter distances have been proposed.

The results of computer simulation suggest that it is naive to adopt any structural model of water in which there is a sharp distinction between molecules which are hydrogen bonded and those which are not. There appears to be a wide range of O–H⋯O interactions with no clear demarcation between hydrogen bonding and non-hydrogen bonding situations.

Rahman and Stillinger analysed their molecular dynamics results by counting the number of hydrogen bonds that fell within different energy limits. Their results are shown in Table 8.4: E_{HB} is the minimum energy required for a bond to be classified as a hydrogen bond: $\bar{b}$ is the average number of hydrogen bonds terminating at an oxygen atom; N_0 is the fraction of molecules without hydrogen bonds; and N_1 is the fraction of molecules having only one hydrogen bond. It can be seen that if a very low limit is chosen for the hydrogen bond energy then $\bar{b}$ is almost four and there are no free molecules. However, if the highest limit is chosen for the hydrogen bond energy then there is only, on average, one hydrogen bond per molecule and less than half of the molecules have the two hydrogen bonds per molecule found in ice-like structures.

Although these results give no simple answer to the question of how many hydrogen bonds there are in liquid water they give one unambiguous result. Whatever lower limit is placed on the hydrogen bond energy the distribution function for the number of hydrogen bonds per molecule is always singly peaked as shown in Figure 8.15. Any mixture model for liquid water would probably give a bimodal distribution for hydrogen bonds arising from two different types of environment.

In reviewing the evidence for the structural models of water in 1972, H. S. Frank came down marginally in favour of the interstitial model.† The uniform models he thought to be contrary to the infra-red and Raman data that we have already referred to. Since that date the evidence of computer simulation

†H. S. Frank, *Water, a Comprehensive Treatise*, Vol. 1, chapter 14, Ed. F. Franks, Plenum Press, London and New York (1972).

Figure 8.15 Distribution of molecules according to the number of hydrogen bonds N_r in which they engage. The inset numbers are the minimum energies (kJ mol^{-1}) required to count as hydrogen bond. These numbers were obtained using a slightly different potential to that which produced the results of Table 8.3. (A. Rahman and F. H. Stillinger, *J. Chem. Phys.*, **55**, 3336 (1971))

has come down strongly in favour of the uniform model with no evidence for two distinct types of molecule in the liquid. The question of whether this conclusion conflicts with the vibrational behaviour remains to be answered.

There are, of course, other properties of water which provide a test of structural models or computer simulation. Dielectric constants are referred to in section 8.1. Transport properties, heat capacity, nuclear magnetic resonance and many others have received attention. Readers are directed elsewhere for more information, and in particular to the volumes titled *Water, a Comprehensive Treatise*, edited by F. Franks, which have already been referred to.

8.6 Non-aqueous polar solvents

Polar solvents are important because they solubilize polar molecules to produce electrolyte solutions. The physical and chemical properties of ions can therefore be studied in a homogeneous medium. Water is, of course, by far the most important polar solvent and, in respect to the range of compounds which will dissolve in it, is one of the strongest solvating liquids.

Table 8.5   Properties of common polar organic solvents

	m.p./K	b.p./K	K_r (K)	μ/D
1,4-Dioxane	285.0	374.5	2.21 (298)	0.45
Diethylether	156.9	307.8	4.43 (293)	1.15
Pyridine	231.6	388.5	12.4 (294)	2.37
Acetone	178.5	329.5	20.7 (298)	2.69
Ethanol	159.1	351.5	24.6 (298)	1.66
Nitromethane	244.6	374.4	35.9 (303)	3.56
Sulpholane	301.7	560.5	43.3 (303)	4.81
Dimethylsulphoxide	291.7	462.2	46.7 (298)	3.9

Data from J. A. Riddick and W. B. Bunger, *Techniques of Chemistry*, 3rd edn, vol. II, Organic Solvents, Wiley–Interscience, London (1970).

However, there are many salts which are virtually insoluble in water, AgCl for example, yet other solvents can be found to solubilize them.

A comprehensive theory of ion solvation in a polar medium must recognize that there are at least two contributions to the solvation energy. The first is the electrostatic energy which may be interpreted macroscopically through the dielectric constant or microscopically through the interaction of the ion charge and the dipole moments of the solvent molecules. The second contribution is from covalent bonding between ion and solvent molecules, which is most simply described in terms of charge-transfer forces. These were discussed briefly in Chapter 2.

The importance of the two effects is most clearly seen by comparing the solubilities of alkali metal and transition metal salts in water and liquid ammonia. Water has a larger dipole moment and dielectric constant than ammonia and will therefore give a larger electrostatic binding. On the other hand, ammonia gives stronger covalent bonds to cations because its ionization potential is lower (easier electron transfer from solvent to cation), and because its lone-pair electrons are spatially more suitable for overlapping cation acceptor orbitals.

Table 8.6   Properties of common inorganic polar solvents

	m.p./K	b.p./K	K_r (K)	μ/D	$-\log K_i$
HF	189.8	292.7	80 (273)	1.83	9.7
H_2O	273.16	373.16	78.3 (298)	1.85	14.0
NH_3	195.5	239.8	22.7 (223)	1.47	~30
H_2SO_4	283.6	543 (with decomp.)	~110	—	3.6
SO_2	197.7	263.1	20 (233)	1.62	—

Most data from *Chemistry of Nonaqueous Solvents*, Ed. J. J. Lagowski, Academic Press, London and New York (1966–).

For alkali metal cations and for anions the electrostatic energies are more important than covalent energies, but for transition metal ions and other heavy metal cations like Ag^+ the covalent energies are probably dominant. Thus Na_2SO_4 is soluble in water but insoluble in liquid ammonia, whereas AgCl is insoluble in water but soluble in liquid ammonia.[†]

There are several reasons, apart from solubility, for using a polar solvent other than water in solution studies. First, a different temperature range for the liquid state may be required. For example, HF, SO_2 and NH_3 all have melting points around 190 K and are valuable liquids for handling compounds which are unstable at room temperature. In contrast, molten salts can have temperatures above 1000 K and will dissolve metals and normally insoluble solids such as SiO_2.

Further interest in non-aqueous polar solvents arises from the variation that can be obtained in the chemical stability of solutes. For example, alkali metals react with water but in liquid ammonia they form stable solutions with strong reducing properties. In Chapter 10 we shall examine chemical equilibria in solution and, in particular, see how acid–base and redox equilibria depend on the nature of the solvent.

Molten salts

Molten salts are extremely important in metallurgical processes because most methods of extracting metals from their ores by chemical or electrolytic reduction are carried out in the molten state. In addition, there has been a growing interest in preparative inorganic chemistry in molten salt media.

The melting points of pure salts range from about 500 K to well over 1500 K. $LiNO_3$, for example, melts at 527 K, and K_2SO_4 at 1342 K. Many organic salts have even lower melting points (e.g. Bu_4NI, m.p. = 417 K) and with eutectic mixtures values below 400 K can be obtained (e.g. an $AlCl_3$–NaCl–KCl eutectic melts at 362 K).

The liquid range is typically 500–1000° although some salts with oxyanions or organic cations will decompose before the boiling point is reached.

Most molten salts have a high electrical conductivity and obey Faraday's laws of electrolysis. It can be deduced from this that in the molten state they are largely composed of ions. There are exceptions; $HgCl_2$, for example, has a low conductivity and a very small liquid range (26 K) indicating that the melt is composed mainly of uncharged species.

From X-ray or neutron diffraction experiments it is possible to deduce a radial distribution function for the ions in the melt. If one makes use of isotopic enrichment of samples then it is possible to obtain separately the distribution functions for distinct pairs in the mixture. Figure 8.16 shows the results of such an analysis on molten NaCl. The coordination numbers deduced by integrating the first peaks are 5.8 ± 0.1 for unlike ions and

[†]A more detailed discussion of the solvation of ions in water will be given in section 9.1.

Figure 8.16 The radial distribution functions for NaCl at 1123 K, as determined by neutron diffraction. (F. G. Edwards, J. E. Enderby, R. A. Howe and D. I. Page, *J. Phys.* C,**8**, 3483 (1975)) Solid, Na–Cl; dashed, Na–Na; dotted, Cl–Cl.

13.0 ± 0.5 for like ions. These numbers are quite close to those pertaining to the solid phase, 6 and 12 respectively. Early X-ray measurements had suggested that the unlike ion coordination number was as low as 4, which would explain the large increase in molar volume on melting, but this is now thought to be incorrect.

The computer simulation of ionic melts using the Monte Carlo or molecular dynamics techniques described in Chapter 3 is difficult because of the long-range nature of the Coulomb force. The Coulomb potential of an ion decreases as $1/r$, r being the distance from the centre and for a uniform density the number of interacting ions at distance r is proportional to r^2. Thus the Coulomb energy of an ion with all others of the same charge at distance r is a divergent function.

There is, of course, a divergent interaction also between ions of opposite sign and there is a cancellation between the two at large distances, but how best to introduce this cancellation has been a controversial matter. Moreover, whatever technique is adopted, one cannot get around the fact that the length of the cell considered in the computer simulation (see Figure 3.4) should be greater than the distance over which pair correlation persists and, as Figure 8.16 shows, this is rather large. In other words one cannot make a satisfactory computer simulation of an ionic melt without considering a large number of ions in the cell, preferably above 10^3.

The melting of an ionic solid is generally accompanied by a large volume increase, typically about 20%. This has been attributed to the presence of holes in the melt, which in turn would explain the generally high ionic mobility. However, computer simulation does not support the concept of holes in the sense of missing ions in a nearly regular lattice into which neighbouring ions can jump. Instead the concept of 'voids' with a short lifetime

($\sim 10^{-12}$ s) which collapse by the concerted motion of all neighbouring ions, is preferable.

Complex ions

The phase diagrams of salt mixtures show a variety of patterns. Solid solutions can be obtained if the salts have similar cation and anion sizes (e.g. LiBr and NaBr). In other cases there is the formation of a simple eutectic (LiF–KF) or compound formation (LiF + CsF → LiCsF$_2$). Complex ions are frequently present in melts of mixed salts, particularly when transition metals are involved, and these can be identified by spectroscopy. For example, the Raman spectrum of KCl–ZnCl$_2$ shows the presence of ZnCl$_3^-$ and ZnCl$_4^{2-}$; the electronic spectrum of VCl$_3$ in a LiCl–KCl eutectic shows the presence of VCl$_4^-$ and VCl$_6^{3-}$.

Complex ion formation can also be deduced from cryoscopic measurements on mixed salts. Because the freezing point depression is a colligative property, it depends on the number of distinct molecules or ions of solute. Thus expression (6.57) for a solute that dissociates is

$$\Delta T_m = \left(\frac{RT_m^2}{\Delta H_{\text{melt}}}\right) ix \tag{8.21}$$

where x is the mole fraction of solute and i is the number of independent particles per formula unit of solute which differ from those present in the solvent. Thus for KCl in AgNO$_3$, $i = 2$ but for KNO$_3$ in AgNO$_3$, $i = 1$. HgCl$_2$ in AgNO$_3$ gives a value $i = 2$ at infinite dilution and not $i = 3$ which would be obtained for complete dissociation. One possible explanation is that the ions present are HgCl$^+$ and Cl$^-$. Another possibility is that there is a high proportion of undissociated molecules present in the melt, a point already noted for pure HgCl$_2$. Experience suggests that a great deal of care is needed in interpreting the cryoscopic behaviour of ionic melts as there are large deviations from ideal behaviour even in very dilute conditions.

Mixtures of ionic salts and metals show interesting behaviour. Such mixtures fall roughly into two classes. The first, typified by K in KBr, have a high solubility of the metal in the salt and the conductivity of the mixture is almost entirely electronic as opposed to ionic. It can be concluded that the metal is ionized in the salt medium with the electrons being more or less freely delocalized on the halide anions. The second class, e.g. Ni + NiCl$_2$, has a rather low metal solubility and little increase in conductivity from that of the pure salt. In these systems the metal will reduce the salt to a subhalide, e.g. forming the Ni(I) oxidation state. Ionic melts have in consequence proved valuable for the synthesis of some normally unstable low oxidation states.

Chapter 9

Aqueous solutions of electrolytes

9.1 The hydration of ions

One of the most puzzling facts to emerge from a student's first contact with chemistry must be why some inorganic salts are soluble in water and others insoluble. For example, silver fluoride is very soluble, silver iodide is almost insoluble; calcium fluoride has a low solubility but calcium iodide is very soluble.

As a general rule like dissolves like. Polar or ionic solids are more soluble in a polar solvent such as water than in a non-polar solvent such as benzene. A non-polar solid such as naphthalene is more soluble in benzene than in water. In crude terms we can say that if A is a solvent and B a solute then B will dissolve in A only if A–B interactions are energetically more favourable than the average of A–A and B–B interactions.

Naphthalene is insoluble in water but soluble in benzene, not because water–naphthalene interactions are less stabilizing than benzene–naphthalene, but because water–water interactions are very much more stabilizing than benzene–benzene. A water molecule would much prefer to be adjacent to

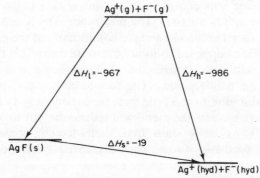

Figure 9.1 Relationship between enthalpies of the lattice, of hydration and of solution for AgF (kJ mol^{-1})

180

Table 9.1 Lattice enthalpies and solubilities (in cold water) of some ionic solids

	$-\Delta H_1/\text{kJ mol}^{-1}$	Sol./g kg(water)$^{-1}$
AgF	967	1820
AgI	889	1.6×10^{-6}
CaF$_2$	2630	0.016
CaI$_2$	2074	2090

another water molecule than to a naphthalene molecule. Likewise, most salts do not dissolve in benzene because the salt–benzene interaction is much less stabilizing than the salt–salt interaction.

The solubility of an ionic solid in water is, therefore, a balance between the hydration energies of its ions on the one hand the lattice energy and water internal energy on the other.

The lattice energy (cohesive energy) of an ionic solid is the energy liberated when one mole of solid is formed from its component ions in the gaseous state. This energy is primarily due to the electrostatic interaction amongst the ions, which in turn depends on the absolute and relative sizes of the anions and cations. Figure 9.1 shows the enthalpy relationship between an ionic solid, its free gaseous ions and the ions in solution. ΔH_1 is the lattice enthalpy, ΔH_h the hydration enthalpy and ΔH_s the enthalpy of solution (all negative in Figure 9.1). A similar relationship exists for other thermodynamic quantities such as entropy and free energy.

Table 9.1 shows the lattice enthalpies and solubilities in water of AgF, AgI, CaF$_2$ and CaI$_2$. Because the lattice enthalpy of AgF is greater than that of AgI, yet AgF is the more soluble, we can conclude that the enthalpy of hydration of F$^-$ is greater than that of I$^-$. Because the lattice enthalpy of CaI$_2$ is greater than that of AgI, yet CaI$_2$ is the more soluble, we deduce that the enthalpy of hydration of Ca^{2+} is greater (much greater) than that of Ag$^+$. However, the hydration enthalpies of Ca^{2+} and F$^-$ are not sufficiently negative to make CaF$_2$ soluble in water.

For a solid to be appreciably soluble in water ΔG_s must be negative. A more detailed discussion of the equilibrium between a solid and its ions in solution will be given in section 10.3. For most salts ΔH_s is also negative, although there are many examples (e.g. NaCl) where it has a small positive value. In this case there is a lowering of the temperature when the salt is dissolved in water.

Most salts dissolve in water with complete dissociation to ions. This is shown by the fact that the conductivity of their solutions per mole of dissolved salt is almost independent of the salt concentration (see Figure 9.3). These salts are referred to as strong electrolytes.† In contrast, a compound like acetic

† Further evidence, first supplied by Bjerrum, is that the visible and u.v. absorption spectra of strong electrolyte solutions is the sum of spectra associated with cations and anions. Only at high concentrations do bands appear which are attributed to ion pairing.

acid is a weak electrolyte. It dissolves in water to give a mixture of ions and undissociated molecules and the molar conductivity increases rapidly with increasing dilution.

For strong electrolytes it is a natural assumption that the thermodynamic parameters for their dilute aqueous solutions can be expressed as a sum of contributions from each of the ions. The formal basis of this assumption will be examined in section 9.3, particularly the effect that ions have on one another. At this point we just discuss the problem of how the separate ion contributions can be determined.

The enthalpy of hydration of NaCl is -780 kJ mol^{-1}, but as there is always an equal number of Na$^+$ and Cl$^-$ ions in solution we have no unique way of dividing the total enthalpy into the separate enthalpies of hydration of the two ions. If the hydration enthalpy is known for any one ion then all others can be found by reference to it. The ion which has received most attention as a standard is H$^+$. As early as 1919 Fajans proposed the value of -1100 kJ mol^{-1} for its enthalpy of hydration at 298 K and this has stood well against later investigations which have given values between approximately -1000 and -1250 kJ mol^{-1}: -1125 kJ mol^{-1} is now commonly accepted as the best value.[†]

The Born equation

One of the earliest attempts to establish a model for ion hydration energies was by Born. Taking the ion as a uniformly charged hard sphere of radius r embedded in a fluid of dielectric constant K_r he obtained the free energy of hydration, per mole, as

$$\Delta G_h = \mathcal{N} \frac{Z^2 e^2}{8\pi\varepsilon_0 r}\left[1 - \frac{1}{K_r}\right]. \tag{9.1}$$

Ions are not, of course, hard spheres with definite radii, but effective ionic radii can be deduced from the lattice spacings in ionic crystals. The radius of Na$^+$, for example, is approximately 0.95 Å; inserting the appropriate parameters into the Born equation gives the result $\Delta G_h(\text{Na}^+) = -720$ kJ mol^{-1}. However, the generally accepted value is -410 kJ mol^{-1} so that the Born model is, in absolute terms, not very good.

The deficiencies in the Born equation lie not only in the assumption of a hard-sphere ion, but also in treating the solvent as a continuous dielectric. The hydration free energies of positive and negative ions of the same radius would be the same in the Born model yet we know that the arrangement of water molecules around the ions is quite different in the two cases. The equation also leads to the prediction that the solubility of an ionic compound will increase with increasing solvent dielectric constant and this is not always

[†]L. G. Hepler and E. M. Wooley, *Water, a Comprehensive Treatise*, vol. 3, p. 163, Ed. F. Franks, Plenum Press, London and New York (1973).

true. However, most developments of the Born model, and there have been several, have been to add just a correction factor to the ionic radius of expression 9.1. Latimer, for example, showed that if 0.85 Å was added to the cation radius and 0.10 Å to the anion radius then the Born prediction that $\Delta G_h \propto r^{-1}$ is held more accurately.

The main impact of the Born equation on the problem of separating the total hydration energy into ionic parts is its implication that there is a correlation between ionic radius and hydration energy. This led Bernal and Fowler to argue that since K^+ and F^- have almost equal radii the enthalpy of hydration of KF, -820 kJ mol^{-1}, should divide into equal contributions for the two ions. A similar suggestion has been made that the large ions $AsPh_4^+$ and BPh_4^- would have approximately equal sizes and hence equal hydration enthalpies.

Probably the minimal conclusion that one can draw from the Born equation, and developments of it, is that the hydration enthalpies of ions in the same periodic groups tend monotonically to zero as the ionic radius approaches

Figure 9.2   Relationships between the enthalpy of hydration and the ionic radius (data from Friedman and Krishnan, *loc. cit.* Table 9.2). Gas phase enthalpies for the formation of the hexahydrate are shown as separate points: + = alkali metals, ● = halides. Data from Table 9.3

Table 9.2 Enthalpies, entropies and free energies of hydration at 298 K (units kJ mol^{-1} for ΔH_h and ΔG_h and J mol^{-1} K^{-1} for ΔS_h)

	$-\Delta H_h$	$-\Delta S_h$	$-\Delta G_h$		$-\Delta H_h$	$-\Delta S_h$	$-\Delta G_h$
H$^+$	1129	131	1090	Ga^{3+}	4799	577	4628
Li$^+$	559	141	517	In^{3+}	4223	493	4072
Na$^+$	444	110	411	F$^-$	474	133	434
K$^+$	360	74	338	Cl$^-$	340	76	317
Be^{2+}	2563	425	2436	Br$^-$	326	61	303
Mg^{2+}	1998	311	1906	I$^-$	268	38	257
Ca^{2+}	1669	254	1593	OH$^-$	423	149	379
Al^{3+}	4774	530	4616	S^{2-}	1296	86	1270

Values selected by H. L. Friedman and C. V. Krishnan, *Water, a Comprehensive Treatise*, vol. 3, ch. 1, Ed. F. Franks, Plenum Press, London and New York (1973).

infinity. In general, the hydration enthalpies that have been deduced from models having their origin in the Born equation satisfy this criterion, as can be seen from Figure 9.2 where some of the 'best' single ion enthalpies collected by Friedman and Krishnan are shown as a function of the Pauling ionic radius.

The trivalent cations that are included in Figure 9.1 do not all fall on a single smooth curve. In the case of the transition metals it is known that there are variations in the hydration enthalpies arising from the ligand field stabilization of the d electrons. For example, Fe^{3+}, a d^5 system, has a smaller hydration enthalpy than would be expected from a smooth varation within the period. A detailed explanation of this can be found elsewhere.†

It can be seen from Table 9.2 that the enthalpies and free energies of hydration are very similar in magnitude because the entropy of hydration is rather small. The entropies show a correlation with ionic radius which is not too dissimilar from 9.1. Hydration entropies are always negative which means that the water molecules surrounding an ion have a greater degree of order than they do in the pure liquid.

Gas-phase hydration

An experimental technique which sheds light on the hydration of individual ions has been developed by Kebarle and co-workers. Ions are produced in the gas phase either by thermionic emission from a filament painted with a suitable salt or, for negative ions, by reactive electron transfer with O$_2^-$. For example, F$^-$ can be produced by

$$O_2^- + NF_3 = O_2 + F^- + NF_2. \tag{9.2}$$

†For example, J. N. Murrell, S. F. A. Kettle and J. M. Tedder, *Valence Theory*, 2nd edn, Wiley, London and New York (1965).

The ions are produced in a reaction chamber containing water vapour and they stay there a sufficient time for equilibrium to be reached in the following general reaction scheme

$$M^{\pm}(H_2O)_{n-1} + H_2O \rightleftharpoons M^{\pm}(H_2O)_n. \qquad (9.3)$$

The equilibrium concentrations of hydrated ions can be determined by mass spectrometry and, following the principles to be described in Section 10.1, the standard free energy changes can be determined. By varying the temperature in the reaction chamber the enthalpies and entropies of the reactions can be found (Table 9.3).

Clusters with up to six water molecules per ion have been detected, and if the total enthalpy change for the reaction

$$M^{\pm} + 6H_2O \rightarrow M^{\pm}(H_2O)_6 \qquad (9.4)$$

is calculated (with extrapolation to $n = 6$ where necessary), then it can be seen from Figure 9.1 that these values show a good correlation with the enthalpies of hydration in solution. From this we can infer that there are probably six water molecules in the first coordination shell around these ions in aqueous solutions.

The hydrated proton has also been studied in the gas phase by Kebarle and

Table 9.3 Enthalpies of the reactions 9.3 $(-\Delta H_m/\text{kJ mol}^{-1})$ for alkali metal and halide ions

n	Li^+	Na^+	K^+	Rb^+	Cs^+
1	142	100	75	67	57
2	108	83	67	57	52
3	87	66	55	51	47
4	69	58	49	47	44
5	58	51	45	44	—
6	51	45	42	—	—
Σ $n=1,6$	515	403	333	306	282

n	F^-	Cl^-	Br^-	I^-
1	97	55	53	43
2	69	53	51	41
3	57	49	48	39
4	56	46	46	—
5	55	—	—	—
Σ $n=1,6$	389	287	280	228

The summations are the enthalpies for the addition of six water molecules to the ion (extrapolation where necessary). Data from I. Dzidic and P. Kebarle, *J. Phys. Chem.*, **74**, 1466 (1970); M. Ashardi, R. Yamdagni and P. Kebarle, *J. Phys. Chem.*, **74**, 1475 (1970).

Table 9.4 Gas phase enthalpies (300 K, 1 atm) for the reaction 9.5 and accumulated enthalpies for the addition of n water molecules to H^+

n	1	2	3	4	5	6	7	8
$-\Delta H_h(n)/kJ\ mol^{-1}$	690	151	93	71	64	54	49	43
$-\sum_{i=1}^{n} \Delta H_h(i)/kJ\ mol^{-1}$	690	841	934	1005	1069	1123	1172	1215

P. Kebarle, S. K. Searles, A. Zolla, J. Scarborough and M. Arshadi, *J. Amer. Chem. Soc.*, **89**, 6393 (1967).

co-workers. Table 9.4 gives $\Delta H_h(n)$ the enthalpies of hydration for the reaction

$$H^+(H_2O)_{n-1} + H_2O \rightarrow H^+(H_2O)_n \tag{9.5}$$

and the accumulated enthalpies for the addition of n water molecules. It appears that $-\Delta H_h(n)$ approaches a value of 30–40 kJ mol^{-1} as n approaches infinity and this is quite close to the enthalpy of evaporation of liquid water which is 44 kJ mol^{-1}. The best estimate of the hydration enthalpy of the proton can be seen from Table 9.2 to be -1129 kJ mol^{-1}, which is broadly consistent with the values given in Table 9.4.

Standard states

The enthalpy change for a chemical reaction is equal to the difference between the enthalpies of formation of the reactants and the enthalpies of formation of the products. For pure compounds enthalpies of formation are by convention referred to a scale in which the enthalpy of every element at its standard state is zero. The standard state is the most stable form of the element at 1 atm and the temperature under consideration; most tabulated values refer to a temperature of 298 K.

For example, if we require the enthalpy change for the reaction

$$CH_4 + 2O_2 \rightarrow CO_2 + 2H_2O(1), \tag{9.6}$$

in which all components are gases except for water, then

$$\Delta H^\circ = \Delta H_f^\circ(CO_2) + 2\Delta H_f^\circ(H_2O, 1) - \Delta H_f^\circ(CH_4) - 2\Delta H_f^\circ(O_2), \tag{9.7}$$

and from available tables†

$$\Delta H^\circ(298\ K, 1\ atom) = [-393.5 - 2 \times 285.8 + 74.8 + 0]\ kJ\ mol^{-1},$$
$$= -890.3\ kJ\ mol^{-1}.$$

Free energies of formation are defined with respect to the same zero scale

†JANAF thermochemical tables. NSRDS technical note, 2nd edn (1971) and later supplements.

as enthalpies but entropies are by custom always referred to a value of zero for a perfect crystal at absolute zero (the third law of thermodyanics). Thus for the reaction 9.6

$$\Delta S^\circ = S^\circ(CO_2) + 2S^\circ(H_2O, 1) - S^\circ(CH_4) - 2S^\circ(O_2) \qquad (9.8)$$

and

$$\Delta S^\circ(298 \text{ K, 1 atm}) = [213.6 + 2 \times 69.9 - 186.2 - 2 \times 205.1]$$
$$= -243.0 \text{ J K}^{-1} \text{ mol}^{-1}$$

However, for the sole objective of calculating entropy changes for a reaction, it would have been possible to have adopted the same procedure as for enthalpy and free energy, and taken as zero the entropies of formation of the elements in their standard states.

We only have to specify the thermodynamic parameters for one ion in solution to enable tables for all ions to be constructed which have the correct relationship to the thermodynamic tables for gaseous ions. By convention ΔH_f°, ΔG_f° and S° are taken as zero for the hydrated proton. Note that entropies are still indicated as absolute quantities although they have no connection with the third-law scale. Third-law entropies for pure substances are always positive, but S° values for ions in solution may be positive or negative.

The enthalpy of solution of HCl gas is -75 kJ mol^{-1} and the enthalpy of formation of HCl gas is -92 kJ mol^{-1}. We therefore have for the process

$$HCl(g) \rightarrow H^+(aq) + Cl^-(aq), \qquad (9.9)$$

$$-75 \text{ kJ mol}^{-1} = \Delta H_f^\circ(H^+, aq) + \Delta H_f^\circ(Cl^-, aq) - \Delta H_f^\circ(HCl, g)$$
$$= [0 + \Delta H_f^\circ(Cl^-, aq) + 92] \text{ kJ mol}^{-1}$$

whence

$$\Delta H_f^\circ(Cl^- \text{ aq}) = -167 \text{ kJ mol}^{-1}.$$

By successive consideration of such reactions a ΔH_f° table can be constructed for all ions which is based upon the standard $\Delta H_f^\circ(H^+, aq) = 0$. It is important to note that the relative values for cations and anions in this scale have no direct physical significance. If $\Delta H_f^\circ(H^+, aq)$ had been given some other value, A (say) then $\Delta H_f^\circ(Cl^-, aq)$ would have been reduced by A, so that the *difference* between the ΔH_f° values for the two ions would be $2A$.

There is an inconsistency in the convention that for the reaction

$$\tfrac{1}{2}H_2(g) \rightarrow H^+(aq), \qquad (9.10)$$

ΔG° and ΔH° are zero but ΔS° is not zero (because S° for H$_2$ is not zero). However, this inconsistency has no practical effect for reactions in which a charge balance is retained. For example, for

$$\tfrac{1}{2}H_2(g) + \tfrac{1}{2}Cl_2(g) \rightarrow H^+(aq) + Cl^-(aq)$$

the values of ΔG°, ΔH° and ΔS° which are calculated from standard tables satisfy the requirement that $\Delta G = \Delta H - T\Delta S$.

9.2 Ionic transport and hydration numbers

Much of our present knowledge of the nature of electrolyte solutions stems from the study of their electrical conductivity in the nineteenth century by such scientists as Faraday, Kohlrausch and Arrhenius. Kohlrausch, for example, showed that the conductivity per mole of electrolyte when extrapolated to infinite dilution could be expressed as the sum of contributions from individual ions. He published his results in 1855 as the law of independent migration of ions.

The resistance R of a material is proportional to its length l and inversely proportional to its cross-section area A. The proportionality factor is called the resistivity, ρ,

$$R = \rho l/A \qquad (9.11)$$

and the inverse of ρ is the conductivity κ. The conductivity of pure water is very low, $\kappa \approx 1 \times 10^{-8} \ \Omega^{-1} \mathrm{cm}^{-1}$ (Ω = ohm) at 273 K, so that even for electrolyte solutions of low concentration all the conductivity can be attributed to the ions, and for strong electrolytes the conductivity is roughly proportional to the concentration of the salt.

Figure 9.3 Molar conductivities as a function of concentration for some electrolyte solutions at 298 K. (Data from C. W. Davies, *Electrochemistry*, Newnes, London (1967))

Table 9.5 Values of Λ_m^0 for some electrolyte solutions in water at 298 K and their differences

System		Λ_m^0	$\begin{array}{c}2-1\\4-3\end{array}$	$\begin{array}{c}3-1\\4-2\end{array}$
1	LiCl	115		
2	NaCl	126	11	122
3	LiOH	237		122
4	NaOH	248	11	

Units: $\Omega^{-1}\,mol^{-1}\,cm^2$.

As a measure of the conductivity for unit concentration of salt we use the molar conductivity defined by

$$\Lambda_m = \kappa/c \qquad (9.12)$$

where c is the molarity. Because ions carry different charges a better measure of the speed at which ions travel through the solution is given by the equivalent conductance. This is obtained from Λ_m by dividing by the number of Faradays carried by a mole of salt; the divisor is one for NaCl, two for Na_2SO_4, six for $Fe_2(SO_4)_3$, etc.

Figure 9.3 shows the molar conductivities of some strong electrolytes in dilute solutions. As mentioned earlier the conductivities are not rapidly varying functions of concentration, but what variation there is follows the relationship

$$\Lambda_m = \Lambda_m^0 + ac^{1/2} \qquad (9.13)$$

where Λ_m^0 is the conductivity at infinite dilution. This empirical relationship was first noted by Kohlrausch. We note in addition that all the 1:1 electrolytes have approximately the same values of a. There is in fact a theory of ion transport by Onsager which is more advanced than the level we reach in this book, which shows that a has the form $A + B\Lambda_m^0$, where both A and B depend on the charges carried by the ions as well as on bulk properties of the solution such as dielectric constant and viscosity.[†]

Kohlrausch noted that the difference in Λ_m^0 values for pairs of salts having a common ion were independent of that ion, as is illustrated by the values given in Table 9.5. This behaviour can be attributed to the independent mobility of the two ions and stimulated Kohlrausch to write

$$\Lambda_m^0 = \Lambda_m^{0+} + \Lambda_m^{0-} \qquad (9.14)$$

where $\Lambda_m^{0\pm}$ are the molar ionic conductances at infinite dilution.

We have already seen that to write some property as the sum of separate ion contributions does not necessarily mean that there is an unambiguous

[†]H. S. Harned and B. B. Owen, *The Physical Chemistry of Electrolyte Solutions*, Reinhold, New York (1958).

method of obtaining the separate ion values; hydration energy is a case where the separation can only be made with certain assumptions. However, for ionic mobilities it is possible to determine the separate ion values directly by experiment. The technique involves measuring changes in the concentration of the ions arising from the passage of an electric current through the solution.

The fraction of the current carried by an ion in solution is called its transport or transference number. These are related to the ionic conductance by the expressions

$$t_0^+ = \frac{\Lambda_m^{0+}}{\Lambda_m^{0+} + \Lambda_m^{0-}}, t_0^- = \frac{\Lambda_m^{0-}}{\Lambda_m^{0+} + \Lambda_m^{0-}}. \qquad (9.15)$$

It should be noted that these transport numbers are not parameters characteristic of the individual ions, but of the electrolyte as a whole because both ion conductances are involved in their definition.

If v^+ and v^- are the velocities of the two ions in solution in the direction of the applied field then

$$\frac{t_0^+}{t_0^-} = \frac{|Z^+v^+|}{|Z^-v^-|} \qquad (9.16)$$

where Z^+ and Z^- are the ion charges. It follows that if we measure the ratio v^+/v^- we also have a measure of $\Lambda_m^{0+}/\Lambda_m^{0-}$. One method of measuring this ratio was developed by Hittorf and the principles of the method are shown in Figure 9.4.

To carry out the Hittorf experiment one requires an electrochemical cell with three compartments; an anode compartment, a cathode compartment and a central connecting compartment. It is important that there is no mixing

Figure 9.4 The changes in concentration of electrolyte near the electrodes which arise from different transport numbers of the ions (Hittorf experiment)

Table 9.6 Ionic conductances at infinite dilution in water at 298 K ($\Lambda_m^{0\pm}/\Omega^{-1}$ mol^{-1} cm^2) and for Na$^+$ and Cl$^-$ at other temperatures

	Λ_m^{0+}		Λ_m^{0-}			$\Lambda_m^{0\pm}$
H$^+$	350	OH$^-$	192	NH$_4^+$		40
Li$^+$	39	F$^-$	55	Me$_4$N$^+$		44
Na$^+$	51	Cl$^-$	76	^{n}Bu$_4$N$^+$		19
K$^+$	74	Br$^-$	78	NO$_3^-$		71
Ca^{2+}	120	I$^-$	77	SO$_4^{2-}$		158
Ba^{2+}	130					
T/K	273	298	323	348		373
Na$^+$	26	51	82	116		155
Cl$^-$	41	76	116	160		207

The equivalent conductances of doubly charged species are half the above values. Data from *Handbook of Chemistry and Physics*, 59th edn, Chem. Rubber Publ. Co. (1979) and R. L. Kay and D. F. Evans, *J. Phys. Chem.*, **70**, 2325 (1966).

of solutions between these three compartments by convection, so that changes in concentration are entirely due to the migration of ions under the influence of the electric field.

If the cations are three times as mobile as the anions then it can be seen from Figure 9.4 that in the anode compartment three times more cations will leave in a given time than anions enter. In the cation compartment three times more cations enter than anions leave. The potential excess charge in each compartment which would be produced in these compartments by such movements is neutralized by discharge of the ions at the electrode, and it can be seen (Figure 9.4(c)) that this produces a build-up of electrolyte concentration in the cathode compartment. The ratio of the changes in concentration of electrolyte, $\Delta n_c/\Delta n_a$, in the cathode and anode compartments is equal to the ratio of the velocities of anion and cation, and hence by 9.15 and 9.16 the ratios of the ionic conductances can be obtained.

Other techniques for measuring transport numbers are described in more comprehensive texts on electrolyte solutions.[†]

Table 9.6 gives some values of ionic conductances in water at 298 K and shows the temperature dependence for Na$^+$ and Cl$^-$. One of the most interesting points concerning these values is that they do not show the expected correlation with ionic radius. The radius increases down a group in the periodic table (see Figure 9.2) yet the conductances, and hence mobilities, of both the alkali metal and halide ions also increase down the group. The reason for this behaviour is that the species being carried along in an electric field is not the bare ion but the hydrated ion. Because the hydration energies

[†]H. S. Harned and B. B. Owen, *loc. cit.*

decrease from Li^+ to Cs^+ and from F^- to I^- so the effective size of the hydrated ion also decreases.

The effect of temperature on the ionic conductance can also be explained by hydration. As the temperature is increased so the average number of water molecules bound to the ion decreases. However, although the ions carry a hydration shell with them as they move through the solution, it must not be thought that this shell is permanently attached to the ion. A more realistic picture is that the hydration shell continuously evolves as the ion passes through the solution, water molecules dropping off and others taking their place. We can in fact place some limits on the average time a water molecule spends within a hydration shell by nuclear magnetic resonance spectroscopy.

N.m.r. spectroscopy is by the time scale of molecular motion rather a slow experiment. If a magnetic nucleus has two environments whose n.m.r. frequencies, v_1 and v_2, differ by Δv, then these will appear as separate lines in the spectrum only if the average time for exchange between the sites is appreciably greater than Δv^{-1}. If the exchange time is appreciably less than Δv^{-1} the system will show only a single line in the spectrum whose frequency is a population average of v_1 and v_2.

Typical frequency differences (chemical shifts) in proton n.m.r. are 10^2–10^3 Hz so that exchange times faster than 10^{-3}–10^{-2} s will lead to frequency averaging. Other nuclei can give a much bigger spread of chemical shift. For water O^{17} has proved particularly useful: in the presence of paramagnetic ions chemical shift differences of 10^5 Hz can be obtained between water molecules in a solvation shell and water in the bulk.

At room temperature aqueous solutions of electrolytes containing only diamagnetic ions show frequency-averaged proton n.m.r. spectra but on cooling to around 223 K separate frequencies for the solvation shell and free molecules can be seen for many multicharged cations. For Al^{3+}, for example, two frequencies separated by approximately 270 Hz have been observed[†] showing that at these temperatures the exchange time between water in the solvation shell and in the bulk is greater than about 10^{-3} s. However, for the alkali metal ions, or for all anions, only exchange-averaged spectra are observed even at low temperatures.

Because the intensity of a line in an n.m.r. spectrum is proportional to the number of nuclei which contribute to that line, it is possible by measuring the relative intensities of the two lines in the non-exchanged spectra, to deduce the relative number of solvation shell and bulk water molecules. In the case of Al^{3+} solutions it was found from this technique that there were six water molecules in the hydration shell. This number has been found to be remarkably constant for the cations studied by n.m.r. With pure water as a solvent only Be^{2+} has been found to have a different hydration number, approximately four, although other low numbers have been found for mixed solvent systems.

†R. E. Schuster and A. Fratiello, *J. Chem. Phys.,* **47**, 1554 (1967).

Figure 9.5 The radial correlation function $\overline{G(r)}$ for $NiCl_2/D_2O$ based on isotopic substitution of Ni. (J. E. Enderby and G. W. Neilson, *loc. cit.*)

Several review articles[†] provide a more detailed discussion of the application of n.m.r. to solvation studies. To summarize the most important result: for multicharged cations at room temperature the exchange of water molecules between the solvation shell and the bulk takes about 10^{-5} s, and for monovalent cations and anions it is considerably faster.

The concept of hydration number has often been abused in the past. If it is taken to mean the number of water molecules around an ion whose properties can be distinguished from those of water in the bulk, then the number depends on what property is being measured. Hydration numbers of the order of 20 have been derived from the analysis of some experiments. N.m.r. undoubtedly indicates the number of water molecules which are directly in contact with the ion. If there are second shells of molecules which are significantly influenced by the electrostatic field of the ion, then they exchange too quickly with bulk water to be studied by n.m.r.

X-ray and neutron scattering from aqueous electrolyte solutions confirm the n.m.r. result that six is the most common hydration number for monatomic ions, and gives some structural information about the hydration shell. Of the two techniques neutron diffraction appears to have more promise for the future because by using isotopic substitution some of the complicating features such as incoherent scattering and inelastic scattering (energy transfer in the scattering process) can be eliminated.

Figure 9.5 shows a radial distribution function $\overline{G(r)}$ that has been obtained by taking the Fourier transform of the difference in scattering factors for naturally occurring $NiCl_2$ in D_2O and for $^{62}NiCl_2/D_2O$. For details of the analysis the reader is referred to the original papers;[‡] it is sufficient for our purposes to think of $\overline{G(r)}$ as a function like $g(r)$ (equation 1.13) which gives the radial correlation between Ni^{2+} and surrounding nuclei.

[†]For example: A. Fratiello, *Prog. Inorg. Chem.*, **17**, 57 (1972).
[‡]For a review see J. E. Enderby and G. W. Neilson, *Water, a Comprehensive Treatise*, Ed. F. Franks, vol. **7**, 1, Plenum Press, London and New York (1979).

194

The two peaks in Figure 9.5 at 2.07 Å and 2.67 Å are identified with Ni–O and Ni–D correlations respectively. The areas beneath them when weighted by r^2 are almost exactly in the ratio 1:2 as required. The integral over $4\pi r^2 \overline{G(r)}$ between 1.8 and 3.0 Å yields a total of 5.8 ± 0.2 water molecules in the first coordination shell. The low value of $\overline{G(r)}$ between 3 and 4 Å suggests that the first hydration shell is very tight.

If it is assumed that the geometry of the water molecules in the solvation shell is the same as in the bulk then from the Ni–O and Ni–D peak distances it is concluded that the water-twofold axis makes an angle of approximately 40° to the Ni–O line as shown in Figure 9.6.

Similar studies of $CaCl_2$ and NaCl solutions using chlorine isotopes show that the Cl^- ions also have approximately six water molecules in the hydration shell but in this case one Cl–D distance is less than the Cl–O distance. Figure 9.6 shows the anion–water structure that has been deduced from these data.

It can be seen from Figures 9.5 and 9.6 that neutron diffraction is giving very interesting results on the structure of electrolyte solutions. This now extends to the nature of ion–ion distribution functions, a topic which we cover in section 9.3.

The structure of the hydrated proton and hydroxyl anion are very important for understanding the properties of aqueous solutions of acids and bases. It can be seen from Table 9.2 that the enthalpy of hydration of the proton is

Figure 9.6 Geometries of the solvating water molecules around Ni^{2+} and Cl^- that have been deduced by neutron diffraction. The Ni^{2+}–H_2O geometry applies to solutions more concentrated than 1.46 molar. In more dilute solutions θ decreases and possibly becomes zero

Figure 9.7   Calculated structures of the trihy-
drates of H_3O^+ and OH^-

much more negative than that of any other singly charged cation, and from Table 9.4 that much of this stabilization comes by adding the first water molecule. The convention of writing the proton in water as the species H_3O^+ is consistent with these values, but gives no indication of how the H_3O^+ ion is hydrated.

Quantum mechanical calculations on H_3O^+ show that it is pyramidal with bond angles of about 114°: neutron diffraction studies of some solid acid hydrates give a value a little less than this, approximately 110°. As the hydrogen atoms in H_3O^+ carry a substantial net positive charge they would be expected to form three strong hydrogen bonds to other water molecules in aqueous solution. Calculations confirm this and predict the equilibrium structure for $H_9O_4^+$ shown in Figure 9.7.[†] This is a structure first postulated by Eigen as the best representation of the hydrated proton.

An interesting question is whether the oxygen atom in H_3O^+ can be involved in hydrogen bonding. Calculations show that if another water mole-

†M. D. Newton and S. Ehrenson, J. Amer. Chem. Soc., 93, 4971 (1971); M. D. Newton, J. Chem. Phys., 67, 5535 (1977).

Figure 9.8   The mechanism of proton conduction in water

cule is added to $H_9O_4^+$ it goes preferably to one of the external H_2O fragments and not to the central H_3O^+.

In contrast to H_3O^+ the species OH^- hydrogen bonds only through its oxygen atom. Three strong bonds are formed with water molecules to give the species $H_7O_4^-$ whose structure is shown in Figure 9.7.

From Table 9.6 it can be seen that the molar conductivities of H^+ and OH^- are much larger than those of the other ions listed. From their enthalpies of hydration we know that they have a tightly bound solvent shell, and one might expect H^+ to be less mobile than Li^+ and OH^- to have a comparable mobility to F^-. As no rationalization of the data can be made on the basis of ion size, or hydration enthalpy, we anticipate that the mechanism of conduction for these ions in water is different from that of other ions.

Figure 9.8 illustrates schematically the mechanism of conduction for the proton (there is not, of course, such perfect alignment in real water). A proton from OH_3^+ passes to one of the H_2O molecules to which it is hydrogen bonded and this molecule then passes on one of its other protons to one of its neighbours: the proton received is not the proton passed on. The mechanism for OH^- mobility is similar; in this case a proton is transferred from H_2O to OH^- and another proton comes in to replace it along a different hydrogen bond direction.

The question remains as to why the molar conductivity of OH^- is only about half the value for H^+ when the mechanisms for conduction appear to be so similar. There is evidence from the rates of acid–base reactions that the transfer of protons between molecular species depends to a considerable extent on quantum mechanical tunnelling through potential energy barriers.[†] This is evident from the deuterium isotope effect on such rates. We therefore expect the proton migration involved in H^+ and OH^- transport to be sensitive to small details of the hydrogen bonding of water to H_3O^+ and OH^-. The binding energy of three water molecules to H_3O^+ in $H_9O_4^+$ is slightly greater than to OH^- in $H_7O_4^+$ and we infer that such differences have a large effect on the proton mobility in the two cases.

9.3   The ionic atmosphere

Electrolyte solutions depart strongly from ideality. The evidence for this is extensive; from colligative properties such as the depression of freezing point,

[†]See R. P. Bell, *The Proton in Chemistry*, ch. 11, Methuen, London (1959).

from the molar conductivity, as shown in Figure 9.3, and from many other sources.

For many years this non-ideal behaviour was attributed to ion pairing and, following the Arrhenius treatment of weak electrolytes, the concentration of ions in solution was calculated by assuming that an equilibrium existed between free ions and undissociated salt molecules. However, the degree of dissociation that had to be assumed to account for, say, the molar conductivity, was in conflict with other evidence, particularly spectroscopic, that the dissociation was almost complete.

By 1910 it was becoming clear that strong electrolytes were completely dissociated in solution, and that their non-ideality was due to the Coulomb interaction between ions which was effective over large distances. In 1912 Milner proposed a mathematical formulation of the problem which was subsequently shown to be essentially correct, but it was not until 1923 that a satisfactory solution of the equations describing this long-range interaction was produced by Debye and Hückel. The delay is remarkable in view of the fact that in 1910 Gouy and Chapman produced a mathematically similar theory of the distribution of ions outside a charged electrode (Chapter 13).

Although there are contentious steps in the Debye–Hückel theory it has proved to be very successful in predicting the non-ideal behaviour of very dilute solutions of strong electrolytes. The mathematical details of their solution are, we feel, less important than the underlying physical principles. For that reason we concentrate here on these principles and leave the most difficult part of the mathematics to an appendix at the end of this chapter.

Because like charges repel and unlike charges attract one another there will, in electrolyte solutions, be a preference for an anion to have cations in its vicinity and for a cation to have anions in its vicinity. This situation also occurs in ionic solids where an ion is surrounded by alternating shells of anions and cations at discrete radial distances. This is illustrated in Figure 9.9(a) for the NaCl crystal. However, in dilute solutions we expect the average charge distribution arising from the surrounding ions to be a smoothly decaying function of r as shown qualitatively in Figure 9.9(b). An unresolved question is whether in concentrated electrolyte solutions the charge density function has oscillatory features suggestive of the solid state.

The time-averaged distribution of charge surrounding an ion is called its ionic atmosphere. The Debye–Hückel theory is concerned with finding the functional form of this atmosphere and deducing its effect on the chemical potentials of the ions.

The electrostatic potential ϕ at distance r from a single ion of charge Ze in a solvent of dielectric constant K_r is

$$\phi = \frac{Ze}{4\pi\varepsilon_0 K_r}\left(\frac{1}{r}\right). \tag{9.17}$$

The ionic atmosphere surrounding this ion will partly shield this Coulomb potential at short distances. To preserve electrical neutrality for the system as

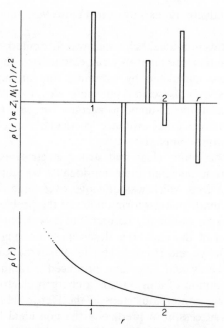

Figure 9.9 (a) A representation of the charge distribution around an anion in the NaCl crystal. The ions are treated as point charges; N_i ions of charge $Z_i e$ at distance r (measured in lattice units). (b) A representation of the charge distribution around an anion in dilute solution. Arbitrary units for $\rho(r)$ in both figures

a whole the integral of the electrical charge in the ionic atmosphere from $r = 0$ to infinity must be equal and opposite to the charge on the ion. It follows that at a large distance the ionic atmosphere will completely screen the potential of the ion. We can therefore write the potential of the ion and its atmosphere as

$$\phi = \frac{Ze}{4\pi\varepsilon_0 K_r}\left(\frac{F(r)}{r}\right),$$ (9.18)

where

$$\underset{r \to \infty}{\text{Limit}} F(r) = 0.$$ (9.19)

It will be shown in Appendix 9 that the Debye–Hückel theory in its simplest form leads to the result

$$F(r) = \exp(-r/r_D),$$ (9.20)

where r_D, called the Debye length, can be thought of as the effective radius of the ionic atmosphere.

We shall see that r_D depends on various parameters of the solution and in qualitative terms this dependence can be deduced by physical arguments. For example, an increase in temperature will tend to break up any ordered structure in the solution, hence we expect r_D also to increase. Similarly the dielectric constant reduces the electrostatic energy between ions so we expect r_D to increase with increasing K_r.

The most important factors determining r_D are the charges and concentrations of the ions. The Coulomb interaction between two ions is proportional to the product of their charges hence we expect r_D to decrease if the charges are increased. With increasing concentration the ions will, on average, be closer together and hence r_D will again decrease.

The relationship between the non-ideality of electrolyte solutions and the charge and concentration of ions was first discovered empirically by Lewis and Randall. To describe their findings they defined a quantity called the ionic strength by

$$I = \tfrac{1}{2} \sum_i m_i Z_i^2, \tag{9.21}$$

where m_i is the molality of the ion of charge $Z_i e$, and they arrived at the following conclusion.[†] 'Aside from the specific characters of individual ions there is unquestionably a factor depending upon the concentration of the ions and upon their charge, which largely determines the properties of any electrolyte solution; and we feel confident that this factor is the ionic strength.' Their confidence has proved justified for the ionic strength is the most important factor controlling the deviation from ideality of dilute electrolyte solutions.

It can be seen from the definition, 9.21, that the ionic strength is proportional to the electrolyte concentration, but the proportionality factor depends on the ion charges. For a 1:1 electrolyte like NaCl, $I = m$. For a 1:2 electrolyte like Na_2SO_4 of molality m we have

$$m(Na^+) = 2m, \; m(SO_4^{2-}) = m,$$

and hence

$$I = \tfrac{1}{2}(2m.1^2 + m.2^2) = 3m. \tag{9.22}$$

For a 2:2 electrolyte $I = 4m$, and so on.

We show in the appendix to this chapter that the simplest solution of the equations governing the ionic atmosphere gives the following expression for the Debye length (equation A9.12)

$$r_D = \left[\frac{\varepsilon_0 K_r RT}{2d \mathcal{N}^2 e^2 I} \right]^{1/2}. \tag{9.23}$$

where d is the density of the solvent in kg m^{-3}. This expression satisfies the

[†]G. N. Lewis and M. Randall, *Thermodynamics*, McGraw-Hill, Toronto and New York (1923).

qualitative statements made above regarding the relationship between r_D and T, K_r and I. For water at 298 K

$$r_D = 3.04I^{-1/2}\ \text{Å}, \tag{9.24}$$

where I is measured in mol kg^{-1}.

To derive 9.23 it has to be assumed that the solvent can be treated as a continuous dielectric and the ions can be approximated as point charges. These assumptions can only be valid for solutions which are sufficiently dilute that the average separation of the ions is large compared with the size of solvent molecules and the ions themselves. If r_D is only a few ångströms the assumptions are clearly invalid because the ions would overlap each other. If we take a rather generous limit of validity of $r_D \approx 10$ Å this gives an upper limit to the concentration of a 1:1 electrolyte in water at 298 K of 0.1 mol kg^{-1} and for a 2:2 electrolyte of only 0.025 mol kg^{-1}.

9.4 The activities of ions in solution

We follow the practice already established for non-electrolyte solutions (6.67) and refer the chemical potential to a convenient standard state using an expression of the form

$$\mu = \mu^\ominus + RT \ln a, \tag{9.25}$$

where a is the activity. Ideal behaviour of the solute in a non-electrolyte solution was defined as a system obeying Henry's law for which we could write (6.73)

$$\mu = \mu^\ominus + RT \ln x. \tag{9.26}$$

For electrolytes it is more common to express solute concentrations as molality, so that ideal behaviour can be represented by

$$\mu = \mu^\ominus + RT \ln(m/\text{mol kg}^{-1}). \tag{9.27}$$

Note, from 6.4, that in dilute solutions x is proportional to m, so that 9.27 is equivalent to 9.26 except for a redefinition of $\mu^\ominus$; this is now the chemical potential of the solute in an ideal system at unit molality. Moreover as electrolytes are usually involatile, the connection between ideality and Henry's law is now purely formal.

For the chemical potential of the solute in real solutions we therefore adopt expression 9.25 with the activity being a dimensionless quantity that approaches the numerical value of m as m approaches zero,

$$\underset{m\to 0}{\text{Limit}}\ a = m/\text{mol kg}^{-1}. \tag{9.28}$$

Further, if we introduce an activity coefficient γ (also dimensionless) as in 6.65 by

$$a = \gamma m/\text{mol kg}^{-1}, \tag{9.29}$$

then

$$\underset{m\to 0}{\text{Limit}}\ \gamma = 1. \tag{9.30}$$

The chemical potential is equal to its standard-state value when $a = 1$. If the system were ideal we could write $a = m = 1$ but for real systems this is not true. When $a = 1$ the solutions are far from ideal. Following the same policy as for the perfect gas and for the solute in non-electrolyte solutions we therefore note that the standard state is not a real state that can be achieved for the system. The value of $\mu^\ominus$ assigned to it can, however, be obtained by extrapolating the value of $\mu - RT \ln m$ to the ideal limit of $m = 0$.

If we adopt expression 9.25 for each type of ion in solution then the chemical potential for a strong electrolyte that ionizes as follows

$$A_p B_q \rightleftharpoons p A^{q+} + q B^{p-}, \tag{9.31}$$

is given by

$$\begin{aligned} \mu &= p\mu_+ + q\mu_- = p\mu_+^\ominus + q\mu_-^\ominus + RT \ln a_+^p a_-^q, \\ &= p\mu_+^\ominus + q\mu_-^\ominus + RT \ln m_+^p m_-^q + RT \ln \gamma_+^p \gamma_-^q. \end{aligned} \tag{9.32}$$

However, we have seen in section 9.1 that there is no absolute way of separating the thermodynamic properties of electrolytes into separate ion values and hence no way of deducing separate values for γ_+ and γ_-. Moreover the deviation from ideality arises from the electrostatic interaction between ions and it is not at all obvious that separate and different ion activity coefficients would have any meaning. For this reason only the average ionic activity coefficient is a measurable quantity and it is defined as the geometric mean of γ_+ and γ_- as follows:

$$\gamma_\pm = (\gamma_+^p \gamma_-^q)^{1/i}, \tag{9.33}$$

where $i = p + q$ is the number of ions produced by the electrolyte. For a 1:1 electrolyte $\gamma_\pm = (\gamma_+ \gamma_-)^{1/2}$.

Introducing 9.33 into 9.32 gives

$$\mu = p\mu_+^\ominus + q\mu_-^\ominus + RT \ln m_+^p m_-^q + iRT \ln \gamma_\pm, \tag{9.34}$$

and the separate ion chemical potentials are defined by

$$\mu_+ = \mu_+ + RT \ln m_+ + RT \ln \gamma_\pm, \tag{9.35}$$

$$\mu_- = \mu_-^\ominus + RT \ln m_- + RT \ln \gamma_\pm. \tag{9.36}$$

The strategy adopted by Debye and Hückel to relate $\gamma_\pm$ to the Debye length r_D was to assume that all the non-ideal behaviour of strong electrolyte solutions arises from the electrostatic interaction between the ions. Although solvents which are non-electrolytes exhibit some non-ideal behaviour the departure from ideality is generally much smaller than for electrolytes so that the above assumption is expected to be valid.

The model for an ideal solution is one in which the ions *have the same distri-*

bution as in the real solution but in which the electrostatic interaction between an ion and its atmosphere is ignored (but not the ion–solvent interaction). The chemical potential of an ion under these conditions, μ^*, is

$$\mu^* = \mu^\circ + RT \ln m, \tag{9.37}$$

with a $+$ or $-$ suffix as appropriate. Taking the difference between this and 9.35 (or 9.36) gives

$$\mu - \mu^* = RT \ln \gamma_\pm. \tag{9.38}$$

The difference $\mu - \mu^*$ can now be equated to the change in chemical potential, or work done, on raising the ion charge from zero to its final value Ze in the potential produced by its ionic atmosphere.

Expression 9.18 gives the potential due to the ion and its atmosphere, hence the potential due to the atmosphere alone is

$$\phi'(r) = \frac{Ze}{4\pi\varepsilon_0 K_r r} (e^{-r/r_D} - 1) \tag{9.39}$$

We can obtain the value of this at $r = 0$ by expanding the exponential and taking the leading term; this gives the result

$$\phi'(0) = -\frac{Ze}{4\pi\varepsilon_0 K_r r_D}. \tag{9.40}$$

On building up the charge of the ion from zero to Ze the work done per mole is[†]

$$W = \mathcal{N} \int_0^{Ze} \phi'(0) \mathrm{d}(Ze) = -\frac{Z^2 e^2 \mathcal{N}}{8\pi\varepsilon_0 K_r r_D}, \tag{9.41}$$

and equating this to the change in the chemical potential we have

$$\ln \gamma = \frac{-Z^2 e^2}{8\pi\varepsilon_0 K_r RT r_D}. \tag{9.42}$$

There will be an expression like 9.42 for each ion in solution. For an $A_p B_q$ electrolyte (9.31) we have, from 9.33

$$\ln \gamma_\pm = i^{-1}(p \ln \gamma_+ + q \ln \gamma_-), \tag{9.43}$$

and introducing the appropriate expression from 9.42

$$\ln \gamma_\pm = -i^{-1}(p Z_+^2 + q Z_-^2) \frac{e^2 \mathcal{N}}{8\pi\varepsilon_0 K_r RT r_D}. \tag{9.44}$$

This can be simplified by noting that for electrical neutrality

$$p Z_+ + q Z_- = 0, \tag{9.45}$$

[†]As r_D is a function of the ionic charge it might be thought that this factor should be allowed as a variable when evaluating the integral. This is not so because the work done is being calculated for charging the ion in an ionic atmosphere whose Debye length is fixed.

whence

$$pZ_+^2 + qZ_-^2 + (p + q)Z_+Z_- = 0, \qquad (9.46)$$

and

$$i^{-1}(pZ_+^2 + qZ_-^2) = -Z_+Z_-. \qquad (9.47)$$

It follows that expression 9.44 becomes

$$\ln \gamma_\pm = -|Z_+Z_-| \frac{e^2 \mathcal{N}}{8\pi\varepsilon_0 K_r R T r_D}, \qquad (9.48)$$

where, as is customary, the positive value of the product Z_+Z_- has been introduced. If we substitute expression 9.23 for r_D we have

$$\ln \gamma_\pm = -\frac{|Z_+Z_-|e^3 \mathcal{N}^2 (2dI)^{1/2}}{8\pi(\varepsilon_0 K_r R T)^{3/2}} \qquad (9.49)$$

which is known as the Debye–Hückel limiting law (limiting meaning applicable to dilute solutions). A working expression for water at 298 K is

$$\ln \gamma_\pm = -1.172 |Z_+Z_-| (I/\text{mol kg}^{-1})^{1/2}. \qquad (9.50)$$

The chemical potentials or activities of strong electrolytes in solution can be determined by a wide variety of techniques. One can establish an equilibrium between the solution of interest and another phase which either can be treated as ideal (e.g. the dilute gas or solid), or is one whose chemical potentials have been previously determined. Most electrolytes are involatile and hence measuring the solute vapour pressure is impractical.

The indirect methods, already described for non-electrolytes, require the determination of solvent activities either by vapour pressure measurements or from a colligative property, followed by application of the Gibbs–Duhem equation. Freezing point measurements have been extensively used in this way although care is required in both measurement and analysis to obtain accurate results.

The expression relating the solute activity to the freezing point depression ΔT_m was given in 6.82. The only change we make to it is to use the molality of the solute as variable instead of mole fraction. The two are related by 6.3 and we note in particular

$$\frac{1 + x}{x} = \frac{1000}{mM}, \qquad (9.51)$$

thus expression 6.82 becomes

$$\ln(a(m)/a(m^\circ)) = \frac{1000 \, \Delta H_{\text{melt}}}{R T_m^2 M} \int_{m^\circ}^{m} \frac{1}{m} \left(\frac{d\Delta T_m}{dm}\right) dm,$$

$$= \frac{1}{K_t} \int_{m^\circ}^{m} \frac{1}{m} \left(\frac{d\Delta T_m}{dm}\right) dm, \qquad (9.52)$$

where K_t is the cryoscopic constant (6.59).

For an A_pB_q electrolyte we have from 9.32 and 9.33

$$a = a_+^p a_-^q = (m\gamma_\pm)^i,$$ (9.53)

whence

$$\ln a = i(\ln m + \ln \gamma_\pm),$$ (9.54)

expression 9.52 therefore becomes

$$\ln(m/m^\circ) + \ln(\gamma_\pm/\gamma_\pm^\circ) = \frac{1}{iK_t}\int_{m^\circ}^m \frac{1}{m}\left(\frac{d\Delta T_m}{dm}\right)dm.$$ (9.55)

If we let the lower limit of the integral m° approach zero then $\gamma_\pm^\circ$ approaches unity. However, there are difficulties in evaluating the integral by graphical means because $m^{-1} \to \infty$ and on the left-hand side of 9.55 $\ln m^\circ \to -\infty$. The solution is best obtained by introducing a new variable

$$j = 1 - \frac{\Delta T_m}{iK_t m},$$ (9.56)

from which we have

$$dj = (1 - j)\frac{dm}{m} - \frac{1}{iK_t m}\left(\frac{d\Delta T_m}{dm}\right)dm,$$ (9.57)

and

$$\int_{j^\circ}^j dj = \ln(m/m^\circ) - \int_{m^\circ}^m \frac{j}{m}dm - \frac{1}{iK_t}\int_{m^\circ}^m \frac{1}{m}\left(\frac{d\Delta T_m}{dm}\right)dm.$$ (9.58)

It can be seen that on combining 9.56 and 9.58 the terms which become infinite as $m^\circ \to 0$ will cancel. There is now no difficulty in taking the lower limit of integration to be $m^\circ = 0$, and we note that as the solution is ideal in this limit $(\Delta T_m/iK_t m) = 1$, hence $j^\circ = 0$. We, therefore, arrive at the expression

$$\ln \gamma_\pm = -j - \int_0^m \frac{j}{m}dm,$$ (9.59)

which poses no problems for a graphical solution. Moreover, G. N. Lewis showed empirically that j was related to m by the expression

$$j = \beta m^\alpha,$$ (9.60)

where α and β are constant parameters of the system, so that once α and β have been determined the integral in 9.55 can be evaluated to give

$$\ln \gamma_\pm = -(\beta + \beta/\alpha)m^\alpha.$$ (9.61)

The most direct method of measuring the activity coefficients of electrolytes is by e.m.f. measurements, but as this topic is to be covered in the next chapter we will give no details here. It should be emphasized that where tests

Figure 9.10   The mean ionic activity coefficient of H_2SO_4 in water at 298 K as determined by freezing point, vapour pressure and e.m.f. measurements. (G. N. Lewis and M. Randall, *Thermodynamics*, McGraw-Hill, Maidenhead (1923))

have been made there is excellent agreement between activity coefficients obtained from colligative and e.m.f. measurements, and this is surely one of the most satisfying results of applied thermodynamics. Figure 9.10 shows some early data collected by Lewis and Randall for the activity coefficient of sulphuric acid at 298 K.

Table 9.7 gives the values of some activity coefficients in water at 298 K. The Debye–Hückel limiting law values, shown in parenthesis, are reasonably accurate for 1:1 electrolytes up to concentrations of 0.01 mol kg^{-1}. For higher valence electrolytes, however, there are significant errors even at 0.001 mol kg^{-1}.

One of the most satisfactory aspects of the Debye–Hückel theory is that it treats the solvent as a continuous dielectric, but requires no adjustable parameters to get agreement with experiment in the dilute solution limit. Confirmation of this part of the model can be obtained from measurements of the activity coefficient in non-aqueous solvents. Figure 9.11 shows data for HCl in methanol; there is excellent agreement with the limiting law below 0.1 mol kg^{-1}.

The first correction to the Debye–Hückel limiting law that is usually made

Table 9.7   Mean ionic activity coefficients $\gamma_{\pm}$ in water at 298 K

$m/\mathrm{mol\ kg}^{-1}$	HCl	NaCl	H_2SO_4	Na_2SO_4
0.001	0.966	0.964	0.830	
	(0.963)	(0.963)	(0.880)	
0.005	0.929	0.927	0.639	
0.01	0.905	0.902	0.544	
	(0.889)	(0.889)	(0.666)	
0.05	0.830	0.820	0.340	
0.1	0.796	0.778	0.266	0.452
	(0.690)	(0.690)	(0.277)	(0.277)
0.5	0.757	0.681	0.156	0.270
1.0	0.809	0.657	0.132	0.204
2.0	1.009	0.668	0.128	0.154
4.0	1.762	0.783	0.170	0.138

Data from R. A. Robinson and R. H. Stokes, *Electrolyte Solutions*, 2nd edn revised, Butterworths, London (1970). The values in parenthesis are from the Debye–Hückel limiting law, equation 9.50.

is to allow for the finite size of the ions. It is shown in Appendix 9 (A9.11 and A9.16) that if a is the mean radius of the ions then there is an additional factor $r_D \exp(a/r_D)/(a + r_D)$ in the expression for the potential due to the ion and its atmosphere. This factor multiplies only the exponential term in the expression for the potential of the ionic atmosphere (9.39) and evaluating this potential at $r = a$ we have

$$\phi'(a) = \frac{-Ze}{4\pi\varepsilon_0 K_r}\left(\frac{1}{a + r_D}\right). \tag{9.62}$$

Figure 9.11   The mean ionic activity coefficient for HCl in methanol (298 K). The straight line shows the Debye–Hückel limiting law. (Data from B. E. Conway, *Electrochemical Data*, Elsevier, London and Amsterdam (1952))

Moreover, as the potential anywhere inside a spherical shell of charge is a constant this expression for ϕ' applies for $0 \leq r \leq a$.

If we now carry through the charging procedure as in 9.41 the expressions 9.42 and 9.48 are changed only by replacing r_D in the denominator by $(a + r_D)$. For $r_D \gg a$ this is equivalent to multiplying 9.49 by the factor $(1 - a/r_D)$. As r_D is proportional to $I^{-1/2}$ this gives a correction factor to the Debye–Hückel limiting law proportional to $I^{1/2}$ and to a. Although values of a have been determined by comparing this theory with experimental deviations from the limiting law, there are many other factors which contribute to such deviations, and it is probably best to consider the effect of ion size as an illustration that the activity coefficient should obey an expression[†]

$$\ln \gamma_{\pm} = -|Z_+ Z_-|(PI^{1/2} - QI), \tag{9.63}$$

where P is given by the limiting law and Q is an empirical constant for the system under study. This expression gives a good representation of the initial deviation from the limiting law; say for concentrations of 1:1 electrolytes up to 1 mol kg^{-1}.

There is a vast literature dealing with the theory of electrolyte solutions beyond the Debye–Hückel model. Some of these are concerned with mathematics alone, that is they retain the same model as Debye and Hückel and attempt solutions of the equations valid over a greater range of electrolyte concentration. Others extend the range by allowing for ion pairing as well as the Debye–Hückel generalized ion interaction; the best known of such approaches is by Bjerrum and Fuoss.[‡]

The statistical–mechanical theories of liquids by virial expansions and integral equations (see Chapter 3) have also been applied to electrolyte solutions. The long-range nature of the Coulomb potential is a particular difficulty in this work and also in computer simulations.

Monte Carlo computer simulations have been carried out with the Debye–Hückel assumptions that the ions are hard spheres and the solvent is a continuous dielectric.[§] Figure 9.12 shows the activity coefficients obtained from these computer experiments for a 1:1 electrolyte in water at 298 K and an ionic radius of 4.25 Å. The results extend to concentrations far beyond the Debye–Hückel limit, and a comparison with Figure 9.10 shows that they are in general agreement with experimental observations. In addition they confirm that the solutions obtained from integral equations with the same model are generally satisfactory, particularly from the so-called hyper-netted-chain equations.

From the Monte Carlo calculations it is possible to determine radial

---

[†]H. S. Harned and B. B. Owen, *The Physical Chemistry of Electrolyte Solutions*, Van Nostrand–Reinhold, New York (1958). R. M. Fuoss, *Chem. Rev.*, **17**, 27 (1935).

[‡]See, for example, E. A. Guggenheim and R. H. Stokes, *Equilibrium Properties of Aqueous Solutions of Single Strong Electrolytes*, Pergamon Press, Oxford (1969).

[§]D. N. Card and J. P. Valleau, *J. Chem. Phys.*, **52**, 6232 (1970); J. C. Rasaiah, D. N. Card and J. P. Valleau, *J. Chem. Phys.*, **56**, 248 (1972).

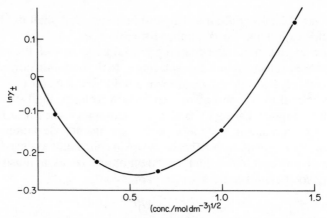

Figure 9.12 Monte Carlo calculations of the mean ionic activity coefficient. A simulation of hard-sphere ions in water at 298 K§

distribution functions for both like and unlike ion correlation. Figure 9.13 shows the results for a fairly concentrated solution of 1.968 mol dm^{-3} with agreement again with the integral equation results. A point of particular interest is that in the region beyond 10 Å there is a crossing of the g_{++} and g_{+-} curves showing that there is a long-range charge oscillation in the ionic atmosphere. This is expected for concentrated solutions, as explained in the discussion centred around Figure 9.9, but is not predicted by Debye–Hückel theory.

Oscillations in g_{++} have been determined from neutron diffraction studies

Figure 9.13 Pair correlation functions for like and unlike ions calculated by a Monte Carlo computer simulation. Error bars are for ±1 standard deviation. The lines show the results obtained by solving an integral equation§

§Ref. page 208.

of concentrated $NiCl_2$ solutions,[†] but these arise from the hydration shell structure which has been mentioned earlier. Oscillations of this kind could not arise from any theory of electrolytes which assumes that the solvent is a continuous dielectric. There have been a few attempts to simulate the structure of electrolyte solutions with an assembly of ions and water molecules but this approach is in its early days.[‡]

Appendix 9

In this appendix we derive an expression for the functional form of the potential due to an ion and its ionic atmosphere.

The electrostatic potential $\phi(r)$ due to a continuous charge distribution $\rho(r)$ is given by Poisson's equation

$$\nabla^2 \phi(r) = -\rho(r)/\varepsilon_0 K_r, \tag{A9.1}$$

where

$$\nabla^2 = \partial^2/\partial x^2 + \partial^2/\partial y^2 + \partial^2/\partial z^2. \tag{A9.2}$$

If $\rho(r)$ is spherically symmetrical $\phi(r)$ is just a function of the radial distance r and satisfies the equation

$$\frac{1}{r^2} \frac{d}{dr} \left(r^2 \frac{d\phi}{dr} \right) = -\rho/\varepsilon_0 K_r. \tag{A9.3}$$

To solve this we need another relationship between ϕ and ρ. Debye and Hückel proposed that the charge density at any point should be governed by the Boltzmann distribution law so that $n_j(r)$, the number of ions of type j per unit volume, is given by

$$n_j(r) = \bar{n}_j \exp(-Z_j e\phi/kT), \tag{A9.4}$$

where $\bar{n}_j$ is the average number of ions of type j per unit volume. The charge density is then equal to the concentration of ions multiplied by the charge each one carries. If the solution contains only two types of ion we have

$$\begin{aligned} \rho(r) &= n_+(r)Z_+e + n_-(r)Z_-e, \\ &= \bar{n}_+ Z_+ e \exp(-Z_+ e\phi/kT) + \bar{n}_- Z_- e \exp(-Z_- e\phi/kT) \end{aligned} \tag{A9.5}$$

Z_+ is a positive number, Z_- is negative. The average concentration of ions can be expressed in terms of their molality by

$$n_j = m_j \mathcal{N}d, \tag{A9.6}$$

where d is the density of the solvent and $\mathcal{N}$ is Avogadro's number.

Substituting A9.5 into A9.3 gives the so-called Poisson–Boltzmann (P–B)

[†] J. E. Enderby and G. W. Neilson, *Water, a Comprehensive Treatise*, ch. 1, vol. 6, Ed. F. Franks, Plenum Press, London (1979).

[‡] See for example J. Fromm, E. Clementi and R. O. Watts, *J. Chem. Phys.*, **78**, 1509 (1974).

equation

$$\frac{1}{r^2}\frac{d}{dr}\left(r^2\frac{d\phi}{dr}\right) = -\frac{\mathcal{N}de}{\varepsilon_0 K_r}(m_+ Z_+ \exp(-Z_+ e\phi/kT)$$
$$+ m_- Z_- \exp(-Z_- e\phi/kT)). \tag{A9.7}$$

For a 1:1 electrolyte, $Z_+ = -Z_- = 1$, $m_+ = m_- = m$, and A9.7 becomes

$$\frac{1}{r^2}\frac{d}{dr}\left(r^2\frac{d\phi}{dr}\right) = \frac{\mathcal{N}dem}{\varepsilon_0 K_r}\sinh(e\phi/kT). \tag{A9.8}$$

Debye and Hückel solved A9.7 by expanding the exponentials and taking the first non-zero term. Because of electrical neutrality

$$m_+ Z_+ + m_- Z_- = 0, \tag{A9.9}$$

hence A9.7 becomes

$$\frac{1}{r^2}\frac{d}{dr}\left(r^2\frac{d\phi}{dr}\right) = \frac{\mathcal{N}de^2\phi}{\varepsilon_0 K_r kT}(m_+ Z_+^2 + m_- Z_-^2) = \left(\frac{2\mathcal{N}^2 de^2 I}{\varepsilon_0 K_r RT}\right)\phi, \tag{A9.10}$$

where I is the ionic strength (9.21). A9.10 is referred to as the linearized P–B equation; it is a second-order differential equation whose general solution is

$$\phi = \frac{A}{r}e^{-r/r_D} + \frac{B}{r}e^{r/r_D}. \tag{A9.11}$$

This can be confirmed by differentiating A9.11 and substituting the result back into A9.10. When this is done one can equate coefficients of ϕ on both sides of the equation to give the result

$$r_D = \left[\frac{\varepsilon_0 K_r RT}{2d\mathcal{N}^2 e^2 I}\right]^{1/2}, \tag{A9.12}$$

which was previously quoted at 9.23.

The constants A and B in A9.11 are determined by boundary conditions on ϕ. First, ϕ must become zero at $r = \infty$ hence $B = 0$. Second, the total charge in the ionic atmosphere must be equal but opposite in sign to the charge on the central ion. If the ions are taken to be rigid spheres of mean radius a (only the close approach of ions of opposite charge is important, hence a can be taken as half their distance of closest approach) then on integrating the spherical shell of charge, $4\pi r^2\rho$, from a to infinity we have

$$\int_a^\infty 4\pi r^2\rho(r)\,dr = -Ze. \tag{A9.13}$$

Substituting for $\rho(r)$ from A9.3 gives

$$4\pi\varepsilon_0 K_r\int_a^\infty \frac{d}{dr}\left(r^2\frac{d\phi}{dr}\right)dr = Ze, \tag{A9.14}$$

which on integration leads to

$$\left| r^2 \frac{d\phi}{dr} \right|_a^\infty = \frac{Ze}{4\pi\varepsilon_0 K_r} .$$ (A9.15)

Introducing the expression for $d\phi/dr$ from A9.11 ($B = 0$) leads to the result

$$A = \frac{Ze}{4\pi\varepsilon_0 K_r} \left(\frac{r_D}{a + r_D} \right) \exp(a/r_D).$$ (A9.16)

If a is small compared with r_D the term in brackets can be replaced by unity to give the result

$$\phi = \frac{Ze}{4\pi\varepsilon_0 K_r} \frac{e^{-r/r_D}}{r} ,$$ (A9.17)

which was quoted in 9.18 and 9.20.

There has been a great deal of discussion of the validity of the linear approximation to the P–B equation A9.10. For the exponents in A9.7 to be less than unity implies that the electrostatic energy $Ze\phi$ is less than the thermal energy, kT. This will be true at large distances from the central ion but the linearized equation is to be solved over the whole range of r from a to infinity and at the short end of the range the assumption will not be valid.

A numerical solution of A9.7 or A9.8 is quite straightforward using the same boundary conditions as for the linearized solution. This was first obtained by Müller in 1927 and extended later by Guggenheim.[†] However, it has also been argued that the faults lie earlier in the P–B equation itself. Onsager was the first to point out that the chance of finding ions i and j a distance r apart would be given by the Boltzmann distribution law either as proportional to $\exp(-Z_i e\phi_j/kT)$ or as proportional to $\exp(-Z_j e\phi_i/kT)$. This implies that

$$\frac{\phi_i(r)}{Z_i} = \frac{\phi_j(r)}{Z_j} ,$$ (A9.18)

a condition which is satisfied by the Debye–Hückel approximate solution, but not by exact solutions of the P–B equation.

†E. A. Guggenheim, *Disc. Faraday Soc.*, **24**, 53 (1957).

Chapter 10

Chemical equilibria in solution

10.1 Principles of chemical equilibria

In sections 4.1 and 6.1 we discussed the criteria for the equilibrium between phases. In this chapter we deal with chemical equilibria in solution with particular emphasis on the solubility of electrolytes and the strengths of acids and bases. The criterion for chemical equilibrium is the same as that for phase equilibrium, namely, the Gibbs free energy of the system shall be a minimum. For phase equilibria this can be specialized to the important result that the chemical potential of a chemical species must be the same in each phase. For chemical equilibria there is a further specialization which relates concentrations of each chemical species to differences in their chemical potentials in their standard states.

We consider a general stoichiometric chemical reaction

$$a\mathrm{A} + b\mathrm{B} + \ldots \to m\mathrm{M} + n\mathrm{N} + \ldots. \qquad (10.1)$$

If it proceeds from left to right by a small amount, insufficient to change the concentrations of reactants and products, then the free energy change per mole of reaction is

$$\Delta G_\mathrm{m} = m\mu_m + n\mu_n + \ldots -a\mu_a - b\mu_b \ldots = \sum_\mathrm{p} k_\mathrm{p}\mu_\mathrm{p} - \sum_\mathrm{r} k_\mathrm{r}\mu_\mathrm{r}, \qquad (10.2)$$

where k_p and k_r are the stoichiometric numbers of products and reactants respectively.

The chemical potential is a function of temperature, pressure and the concentrations of other species in the phase. We have earlier met expressions for the chemical potential of a perfect gas (4.25), an imperfect gas (4.26); for the components of an ideal liquid mixture (6.39), for the solvent and solute in non-ideal liquids, (6.67) and (6.75), and for electrolytes (9.25). These expressions all have the same form which we shall generalize to

$$\mu = \mu^\ominus + RT \ln a, \qquad (10.3)$$

where μ is the chemical potential of a standard state and a is the activity.

It should be recalled that to complete the definition of activity it is necessary to specify the relationship between a and some measure of the composition of the system. In an ideal system a will be identical to pressure measured in atmospheres, or mole-fraction, or molality measured in moles per kg of solvent, and in non-ideal systems it will approach these numbers as ideality is approached (e.g. at infinite dilution).

On substituting 10.3 into 10.2 we have

$$\Delta G_m = \left(\sum_p k_p \mu_p^{\ominus} - \sum_r k_r \mu_r^{\ominus}\right) + RT\left(\sum_p k_p \ln a_p - \sum_r k_r \ln a_r\right), \quad (10.4)$$

which can be simplified to

$$\Delta G_m = \Delta G_m^{\ominus} + RT\ln\left[\frac{\Pi a_p^{k_p}}{\Pi a_r^{k_r}}\right], \quad (10.5)$$

where Π represents the product of the activities raised to powers of their stoichiometric numbers. $\Delta G_m^{\ominus}$ is the free energy change per mole of reaction with all species in their standard states.

$$\Delta G_m^{\ominus} = \sum_p k_p \mu_p^{\ominus} - \sum_r k_r \mu_r^{\ominus} \quad (10.6)$$

Expression 10.5 is known as the van't Hoff isotherm, or general reaction isotherm.

If the reaction is run to equilibrium then for any further infinitesimal change ΔG_m will be zero. In this case we have from 10.5

$$\Delta G_m^{\ominus} = -RT\ln\left[\frac{\Pi a_p^{k_p}}{\Pi a_r^{k_r}}\right]. \quad (10.7)$$

The ratio of products of activities at equilibrium which appears on the right-hand side of this equation is called the thermodynamic equilibrium constant. We write

$$K_a = \frac{\Pi a_p^{k_p}}{\Pi a_r^{k_r}}, \quad (10.8)$$

where

$$\Delta G_m^{\ominus} = -RT\ln K_a. \quad (10.9)$$

K_a is a constant at constant T because $\Delta G_m^{\ominus}$ is an energy defined with respect to all species being in their standard states. $\Delta G_m^{\ominus}$ for the reaction can be calculated by reference to standard thermodynamic tables which record free energies of formation of chemical species (generally at 298 K).

Chemists are interested in knowing the ratios of concentrations of species present at equilibrium so that expressions 10.8 and 10.9 are not very useful for non-ideal systems unless we have a method of relating activities to concentrations. For this reason one chooses to define the composition of a chemical system in units such that the activity coefficients shall be most nearly equal to unity. For example, for gases the most suitable unit is the numerical value of the pressure in atmospheres because for non-ideal gases pressure is almost equal to fugacity and the activity is fugacity measured in atmospheres. As a result K_p defined by

$$K_p = \frac{\Pi(P_p/\text{atm})^{k_p}}{\Pi(P_r/\text{atm})^{k_r}},$$ (10.10)

will be a number which is almost independent of total pressure for most gases.

For non-electrolyte liquid mixtures the mole fraction is the best concentration unit because activity is approximately equal to mole fraction and the ratio

$$K_x = \frac{\Pi x_p^{k_p}}{\Pi x_r^{k_r}},$$ (10.11)

is approximately independent of composition. For dilute solutions of electrolytes molality is the most widely adopted unit and

$$K_m = \frac{\Pi(m_p/\text{mol kg}^{-1})^{k_p}}{\Pi(m_r/\text{mol kg}^{-1})^{k_r}},$$ (10.12)

is approximately constant. However, deviations from ideality are much greater for electrolyte solutions than for non-electrolytes as we have explained in Chapter 9.

We will illustrate the use of the above equilibrium constants by considering the equilibrium

$$N_2O_4 \rightleftharpoons 2NO_2,$$ (10.13)

in the gas phase and in solution. From standard thermodynamic tables we find the following free energies of formation at 298 K:

$NO_2(g)$ $\Delta G_f^{\ominus} = -38.4$ kJ mol^{-1}
$N_2O_4(g)$ $\Delta G_f^{\ominus} = -81.6$ kJ mol^{-1}
$N_2O_4(l)$ $\Delta G_f^{\ominus} = -81.9$ kJ mol^{-1}

Thus in the gas phase at 298 K

$$K_p = e^{-\Delta G_m^{\ominus}/RT} = e^{+(2\times38.4-81.6)/2.48} = 0.14.$$ (10.14)

In the pure liquid there is very little NO_2 and no accurate measurements of the equilibrium constant have been made. However, in CCl_4 at 298 K experiment has shown that the solution is quite close to ideal and a value of the equilibrium constant has been obtained

$$K_x = 6.4 \times 10^{-5}.$$ (10.15)

The two equilibrium constants 10.14 and 10.15 have very different values but we are not yet in a position to compare the ratios of NO_2 and N_2O_4 in the two phases as this depends on the mole fractions or total pressures. If gas and solution are in equilibrium we can write

$$\mu_{N_2O_4}(\text{sol}) = \mu_{N_2O_4}(g). \tag{10.16}$$

Assuming ideality in both phases we have

$$\mu^{\ominus}_{N_2O_4}(l) + RT \ln x = \mu^{\ominus}_{N_2O_4}(P = 1) + RT \ln(P_{N_2O_4}/\text{atm}). \tag{10.17}$$

If the mole fraction of N_2O_4 in CCl_4 solution is 0.1 then the relevant numbers in 10.17 are

$$-81.9 + 2.48 \ln 0.1 = -81.6 + 2.48 \ln(P_{N_2O_4}/\text{atm}), \tag{10.18}$$

whence

$$P_{N_2O_4} = 0.089 \text{ atm}. \tag{10.19}$$

In this case we have in solution

$$\frac{x_{NO_2}^2}{0.1} = 6.4 \times 10^{-5}, \quad \therefore x_{NO_2} = 2.5 \times 10^{-3}, \tag{10.20}$$

and

$$\frac{x_{NO_2}}{x_{N_2O_4}} \approx \frac{[NO_2]}{[N_2O_4]} = 2.5 \times 10^{-2}. \tag{10.21}$$

In the gas phase

$$\frac{P_{NO_2}^2}{0.089} = 0.14, \quad \therefore P_{NO_2} = 0.11 \text{ atm}, \tag{10.22}$$

and

$$\frac{P_{NO_2}}{P_{N_2O_4}} = \frac{[NO_2]}{[N_2O_4]} = 1.24. \tag{10.23}$$

It can be seen from the above figures that the ratio of NO_2 to N_2O_4 is much greater in the gas phase than in solution. This can be explained from the fact that the decomposition of N_2O_4 in the gas phase is favoured by the extra translational entropy of the NO_2.

In the gas phase there is usually no difficulty in defining what are the chemical species. In the above example we have considered an equilibrium between NO_2 and N_2O_4; at higher temperatures we might have to include NO and O_2 arising from the reaction

$$2NO_2 \rightleftharpoons 2NO + O_2. \tag{10.24}$$

All of these species can be identified unambiguously and their concentrations determined by spectroscopic or other means.

In the liquid phase the identification of chemical species is less easy. For example, there might be spectroscopic evidence to show that the NO_2 is strongly solvated. If this is so should we distinguish between free NO_2 in solution and solvated NO_2; is there more than one type of solvation complex? In aqueous solutions the situation is often more complex because of the strong hydrogen bonding capability of water and its cooperative effect. Thus a species A could be hydrated to a multiplicity of forms $A(H_2O)_n$ which would generally be in rapid equilibrium.

It is unlikely that all feasible species that could be present in solution can be identified by physical or chemical means. If this is so there is no chance of determining the multiplicity of equilibrium constants that would fully describe the equilibrium system. Accepting this, the empirical approach is to treat the system as a simple equilibrium between NO_2 and N_2O_4 at the expense of having a large deviation from ideality. In short, large deviations from ideality are a reflection of the fact that other equilibria arising from solvation, hydrogen bonding etc. are occurring in the solution.

10.2 Equilibrium electrochemistry

The field of electrochemistry, particularly non-equilibrium electrochemistry, is too wide to be contained within the format of this book. A brief introduction to equilibrium electrochemistry is, however, required for its relevance to the determination of the activities of ions in polar, mainly aqueous, solvents.

The chemical reaction represented by

$$Zn + Cu^{2+}(aq) \rightarrow Zn^{2+}(aq) + Cu, \qquad (10.25)$$

can be carried out in two contrasting ways. The first is to add powdered zinc to copper sulphate solution. The zinc will dissolve and copper will be precipitated. The reaction is being carried out irreversibly and heat will be evolved equal to $-\Delta H = 217$ kJ mol^{-1} per mole of reactant.

A second method is to take a cell, called the Daniell cell, one electrode of which is a zinc rod dipped in an aqueous solution of $ZnSO_4$ and the other is a copper rod dipped in an aqueous solution of $CuSO_4$. The two solutions are connected by an electrically conducting bridge which prevents the diffusion of Cu^{2+} and Zn^{2+} between the two cell compartments: this is typically a concentrated solution of K_2SO_4 in an agar gel. The cell is represented in a simplified form in Figure 10.1.

If the two electrodes are short circuited then the reaction represented by 10.25 will occur, the zinc electrode will dissolve and copper will be deposited on the copper electrode. Electrons will flow between the electrodes in the direction indicated.

The cell can also be run reversibly by applying an external e.m.f. $\mathscr{E}$, across the two electrodes which just balances the natural e.m.f. of the cell reaction. By changing this external e.m.f. slightly, either increasing or decreasing $\mathscr{E}$, current will dribble through the cell in one direction or the other. The chemical reaction can in this way be made to proceed forwards or backwards in a thermodynamically reversible manner.

The electric current extracted from a cell working reversibly can be directly

Figure 10.1 Simple representation of the Daniell cell. The direction of electron flow under short circuit is shown

converted to work through an electric motor and as the system is at constant pressure and temperature this work is measured by the Gibbs free energy of the reaction. One mole of reaction produces nF Coulombs of charge through the circuit, n being the number of moles of electrons per mole of reaction ($n = 2$ for reaction 10.25) and F is the Faraday, $F = 96,487$ Coulombs. This charge passes against an external e.m.f. $\mathscr{E}$ and produces an amount of work $nF\,\mathscr{E}$. As ΔG_m is the work done on the system in a reversible process at constant T and P, we have

$$\Delta G_m = -nF\,\mathscr{E}. \tag{10.26}$$

The sign of ΔG_m for reaction 10.25 is given by convention as

$$\Delta G_m = G_{products} - G_{reactants}, \tag{10.27}$$

and by virtue of the relationship 10.26 we require a consistent convention for the sign of the cell e.m.f. The cell which carries out the reaction 10.25 is written symbolically as

$$Zn\,|\,Zn^{2+}\,\|\,Cu^{2+}\,|\,Cu, \tag{10.28}$$

which we can read from left to right as Zn losing electrons to give Zn^{2+} and Cu^{2+} gaining electrons to give Cu. Exactly the same words can be applied to equation 10.25 as written. The double bar in the middle of 10.28 indicates that there is no contribution to the e.m.f. arising from contact between the two solutions: the salt bridge eliminates what is called the liquid junction potential which is a source of irreversibility.[†]

The e.m.f. of the cell 10.28 is determined by the balance between the tendency of Zn to pass into solution as Zn^{2+} and Cu to pass into solution as Cu^{2+}. These tendencies are measured by the e.m.f.s of the so-called half cells

$$Zn^{2+}\,|\,Zn \qquad \mathscr{E}_L \tag{10.29}$$

[†]The single vertical lines indicate phase boundaries at the electrodes.

$$Cu^{2+} | Cu \qquad \mathscr{E}_R \qquad\qquad (10.30)$$

for which the appropriate chemical reactions and free energies are

$$Zn^{2+} + 2e \rightarrow Zn \qquad \Delta G_L \qquad\qquad (10.31)$$

$$Cu^{2+} + 2e \rightarrow Cu \qquad \Delta G_R \qquad\qquad (10.32)$$

The chemical reaction 10.25 can be constructed by taking $10.32 - 10.31$, hence ΔG_m for this reaction is given by

$$\Delta G_m = \Delta G_R - \Delta G_L. \qquad\qquad (10.33)$$

Likewise the cell 10.28 can be obtained by combining the two half cells $10.30 - 10.29$ so that we deduce the e.m.f. of the cell to be related to the half cell e.m.f.s by

$$\mathscr{E} = \mathscr{E}_R - \mathscr{E}_L. \qquad\qquad (10.34)$$

We emphasize that the sign of the e.m.f. of a cell refers to the symbolic representation such as 10.28 rather than to the actual cell as set up on the laboratory bench. Thus the e.m.f. of

$$Cu | Cu^{2+} \parallel Zn^{2+} | Zn, \qquad\qquad (10.35)$$

has the opposite sign to 10.28 although it is the same laboratory cell.

Standard reduction potentials

Expression 10.5 gives the dependence of the Gibbs free energy on the activities of reactants and products. Because of the proportionality between $\mathscr{E}$ and ΔG_m the e.m.f. of the cell must also depend on the activities of the cell components. By substituting 10.26 into 10.5 we obtain the Nernst equation

$$\mathscr{E} = \mathscr{E}^{\ominus} - \frac{RT}{nF} \ln \left[\frac{\Pi a_p^{k_p}}{\Pi a_r^{k_r}} \right] \qquad\qquad (10.36)$$

where $\mathscr{E}^{\ominus}$ is the e.m.f. of the cell with unit activities. In the example under consideration this is the cell

$$Zn | Zn^{2+}(a = 1) \parallel Cu^{2+}(a = 1) | Cu, \qquad\qquad (10.37)$$

the free energy of the cell reaction being

$$\Delta G_m^{\ominus} = -2F \, \mathscr{E}^{\ominus}. \qquad\qquad (10.38)$$

We have seen from 10.34 that the e.m.f. of a cell is equal to the difference in the e.m.f.s of two half cells. If the half cells have ions of unit activity then this difference gives $\mathscr{E}^{\ominus}$

$$\mathscr{E}^{\ominus} = \mathscr{E}_R^{\ominus} - \mathscr{E}_L^{\ominus}. \qquad\qquad (10.39)$$

A table of standard half-cell potentials can therefore be constructed provided a suitable zero is chosen; absolute values of half-cell potentials have no meaning because one requires two half cells to obtain a practical cell with a measurable e.m.f.

The zero half-cell potential is chosen to be consistent with the zero Gibbs free energy of ions in solution which, as described in Chapter 9, is $\Delta G_m(H^+(a = 1)) = 0$. Thus the standard half cell with zero e.m.f. is

$$Pt \,|\, H_2(1\text{ atm}) \,|\, H^+(a = 1), \qquad \mathscr{E}^{\ominus} = 0. \tag{10.40}$$

To be precise, the hydrogen gas should also be at unit activity which is roughly one atmosphere pressure. This standard electrode can be constructed by bubbling H_2 at 1 atm around a platinized platinum electrode dipped in acid with unit hydrogen ion activity. The platinum acts as a catalyst for the ionization of the hydrogen, which is normally a slow process.

Table 10.1 lists a few standard electrode potentials. In principle these can all be taken directly as the e.m.f. of a cell whose left-hand electrode is the standard hydrogen electrode. For example,

$$Pt \,|\, H_2(1\text{ atm}) \,|\, HCl\,(a = 1) \,|\, AgCl\,(s) \,|\, Ag \tag{10.41}$$

is a cell with a silver–silver chloride electrode (Ag with a coating of AgCl dipped in HCl) on the right. The e.m.f. of this cell is, from Table 10.1

$$\mathscr{E}^{\ominus} = 0.2223 \text{ V}. \tag{10.42}$$

The reaction associated with this cell is

$$H_2 + AgCl \rightleftharpoons 2H^+ + 2Cl^- + Ag,$$

Table 10.1 Standard reduction potentials in acid solution at 298 K

Cell reaction	$\mathscr{E}^{\ominus}/V$
$Li^+ + e \rightleftharpoons Li$	-3.045
$Na^+ + e \rightleftharpoons Na$	-2.7109
$\frac{1}{2}Mg^{2+} + e \rightleftharpoons \frac{1}{2}Mg$	-2.375
$\frac{1}{3}Al^{3+} + e \rightleftharpoons \frac{1}{3}Al$	-1.706
$\frac{1}{2}V^{2+} + e \rightleftharpoons \frac{1}{2}V$	-1.2
$\frac{1}{2}Fe^{2+} + e \rightleftharpoons \frac{1}{2}Fe$	-0.409
$D^+ + e \rightleftharpoons \frac{1}{2}D_2(g)$	-0.0034
$H^+ + e \rightleftharpoons \frac{1}{2}H_2(g)$	0
$Cu^{2+} + e \rightleftharpoons Cu^+$	0.158
$AgCl + e \rightleftharpoons Ag + Cl^-$	0.2223
$\frac{1}{2}Cu^{2+} + e \rightleftharpoons \frac{1}{2}Cu^+$	0.3402
$Fe^{3+} + e \rightleftharpoons Fe^{2+}$	0.770
$Ag^+ + e \rightleftharpoons Ag$	0.7996
$\frac{1}{2}Br_2(1) + e \rightleftharpoons Br^-$	1.065
$H^+ + \frac{1}{4}O_2(g) + e \rightleftharpoons \frac{1}{2}H_2O(1)$	1.229
$Ce^{4+} + e \rightleftharpoons Ce^{3+}$	1.61
$\frac{1}{2}S_2O_8^{2-} + e \rightleftharpoons SO_4^{2-}$	2.0

Data from CRC *Handbook of Chemistry and Physics*, 59th edition, 1978–79.

and as this is a two-electron process the standard Gibbs free energy change is

$$\Delta G_m^\ominus = -2F \mathscr{E}^\ominus. \tag{10.43}$$

Table 10.1 has been written with all reactions being one-electron reductions. This has the advantage that there is linear relationship between $\mathscr{E}^\ominus$ and $\Delta G_m^\ominus$. If the reader keeps in mind the fact that $-F\mathscr{E}^\ominus$ is a free energy scale the difficulties frequently met in keeping track of signs should be alleviated.

One of the most useful features of the table of standard reduction potentials is to decide which way a redox reaction will go. For example, will Cu reduce Fe^{3+} to Fe^{2+} or will Fe^{2+} reduce Cu^{2+} to Cu? The half-cell reactions in Table 10.1 have been written with oxidizing agents on the left increasing in strength down the page, and reducing agents on the right increasing in strength up the page. The strongest reducing agent has the most negative $\mathscr{E}^\ominus$ and the strongest oxidizing agent the most positive $\mathscr{E}^\ominus$.

If we compare any pair of reactions in the table then the one above will move to the left and the one below to the right. Thus Cu will reduce Fe^{3+} to Fe^{2+}. The standard free energy change for the reaction

$$Fe^{3+} + \tfrac{1}{2}Cu \rightarrow Fe^{2+} + \tfrac{1}{2}Cu^{2+}, \tag{10.44}$$

will be obtained from $\mathscr{E}^\ominus$ for the cell[†]

$$Cu\,|\,Cu^{2+}\,\|\,Fe^{3+},\,Fe^{2+}\,|\,Pt \tag{10.45}$$

$$\mathscr{E}^\ominus = \mathscr{E}_R^\ominus - \mathscr{E}_L^\ominus = 0.770 - 0.340 = 0.430\ \text{V}$$

$$\Delta G_m^\ominus = -F\mathscr{E}^\ominus = -41.5\ \text{kJ mol}^{-1} \tag{10.46}$$

Standard reduction potentials refer to half cells with all species in their standard states and, as has been emphasized in Chapter 9, for ionic species these are hypothetical states extrapolated from ideal (dilute) solutions. Thus $\mathscr{E}^\ominus$ cannot be obtained directly by measuring a cell e.m.f. but must be obtained by extrapolation. We will illustrate this from some data on the cell

$$Pt\,|\,H_2(1\ \text{atm})\,|\,HCl(m)\,|\,AgCl\,|\,Ag, \tag{10.47}$$

which was studied by Harned and Ehlers in great detail. Their measured e.m.f.s at 298 K are given in Table 10.2.

The cell reaction is

$$\tfrac{1}{2}H_2(1\ \text{atm}) + AgCl \rightarrow Ag + H^+ + Cl^-, \tag{10.48}$$

and from the Nernst equation 10.36 we can write the e.m.f.

$$\mathscr{E} = \mathscr{E}^\ominus - \frac{RT}{F}\ln(a_{H^+}\,a_{Cl^-}), \tag{10.49}$$

the activities of all other species being unity. The mean ionic activity co-

---

[†]The electrode on the right is called an oxidation–reduction electrode and consists of an inert metal collector, usually bright platinum, immersed in a solution which contains two ions of the same element in different oxidation states.

Table 10.2   Measured e.m.f. of the cell 10.47 at 298 K
as a function of HCl molality

$m(HCl)$	$\mathscr{E}/V$	$m(HCl)$	$\mathscr{E}/V$
0.005	0.4984	0.04	0.3967
0.006	0.4894	0.05	0.3859
0.007	0.4818	0.06	0.3771
0.008	0.4752	0.07	0.3697
0.009	0.4694	0.08	0.3632
0.01	0.4642	0.09	0.3575
0.02	0.4302	0.1	0.3524
0.03	0.4106		

Data from H. S. Harned and R. W. Ehlers, *J. Am. Chem. Soc.*,
54, 1350 (1932); **55**, 2179 (1933).

efficient is defined by

$$a_{H^+} a_{Cl^-} = m^2 \gamma_{\pm}^2, \tag{10.50}$$

and substituting this into 10.49 gives

$$\mathscr{E} = \mathscr{E}^{\ominus} - \frac{2RT}{F} \ln m - \frac{2RT}{F} \ln \gamma_{\pm}. \tag{10.51}$$

As we approach infinite dilution $\gamma_{\pm}$ approaches zero but as in this limit $\ln m$ approaches minus infinity it is difficult to obtain an accurate measure of $\mathscr{E}^{\ominus}$ without taking into account the dependence of $\gamma_{\pm}$ on m. This can be done using the Debye–Hückel limiting law. For a 1:1 electrolyte in water at 298 K we have, from 9.50

$$\ln \gamma_{\pm} = -1.172 \, m^{1/2}. \tag{10.52}$$

A graph of $\mathscr{E} + 2(RT/F)\ln m$ against $m^{1/2}$ is shown in Figure 10.2. The extra-polated value of $\mathscr{E}^{\ominus}$ is equal to the standard reduction potential for the AgCl/Ag, Cl$^-$ half cell because the left cell in 10.47 is the hydrogen electrode whose $\mathscr{E}^{\ominus}$ is zero. Once $\mathscr{E}^{\ominus}$ is known a measurement of $\mathscr{E}$ gives the activity coefficient for HCl; such values were discussed in Chapter 9.

10.3   Solubility of salts

In dilute aqueous solutions most salts are completely dissociated to ions and this is true whether the salts are very soluble like NaCl or very insoluble like AgCl. The solubility of a sparingly soluble salt M_pX_q can therefore be analysed through the equilibrium

$$M_pX_q(s) \rightleftharpoons p\,M^{q+}(aq) + q\,X^{p-}(aq). \tag{10.53}$$

The activity of the solid is unity hence the equilibrium constant (10.8) is a function only of the activities of the ions. This equilibrium constant is called

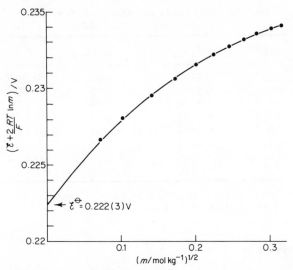

Figure 10.2 Graphical extrapolation to find $\mathcal{E}^{\ominus}$ for the Cl$^-$/AgCl/Ag half cell

the solubility product and is written

$$K_{sp} = a_{M^+}^p\, a_{X^-}^q = \gamma_{\pm}^{p+q} m_{M^+}^p\, m_{X^-}^q \, . \qquad (10.54)$$

An approximate value of the solubility of the salt can be obtained by taking $\gamma_{\pm} = 1$. If S is the solubility in moles per kg, then

$$m_{M^+} = pS, m_{X^-} = qS, \qquad (10.55)$$

and from 10.54

$$K_{sp} \approx (pS)^p(qS)^q \qquad (10.56)$$

whence

$$S \approx \left(\frac{K_{sp}}{p^p q^q}\right)^{\frac{1}{p+q}} \qquad (10.57)$$

To obtain a more accurate value of the solubility one must either determine $\gamma_{\pm}$ from experiment or calculate it from the Debye–Hückel limiting law. Alternatively if K_{sp} can be determined by e.m.f. measurements, as we shall describe, and S determined by independent means (e.g. spectroscopic measurements) then $\gamma_{\pm}$ can be calculated.

The solubility product can be calculated from the standard free energies of formation of the solid and the ions, or from the e.m.f. of an appropriate cell. For example, the cell

$$Ag\,|\,Ag^+\,\|\,Cl^-\,|\,AgCl\,|\,Ag, \qquad (10.58)$$

has at the right-hand electrode the reaction

$$AgCl + e \rightleftharpoons Ag + Cl^-, \tag{10.59}$$

and at the left-hand electrode

$$Ag^+ + e \rightleftharpoons Ag. \tag{10.60}$$

The overall cell reaction is

$$AgCl \rightleftharpoons Ag^+ + Cl^-, \tag{10.61}$$

and the e.m.f. of the cell will be given by the Nernst equation

$$\mathscr{E} = \mathscr{E}^{\ominus} - \frac{RT}{F} \ln a_{Ag^+} a_{Cl^-} = \mathscr{E}^{\ominus} - \frac{RT}{F} \ln K_{sp}, \tag{10.62}$$

where, from Table 10.1

$$\mathscr{E}^{\ominus} = \mathscr{E}_R^{\ominus} - \mathscr{E}_L^{\ominus} = 0.2223 - 0.7996 = -0.5773 \text{ V}. \tag{10.63}$$

At equilibrium the cell e.m.f. is zero hence from 10.62 we have

$$\ln K_{sp} = \frac{-0.5773 \times 9.648 \times 10^4}{8.314 \times 298} = -22.48 \tag{10.64}$$

from which

$$K_{sp}(298 \text{ K}) = 1.72 \times 10^{-10}. \tag{10.65}$$

From expression 10.57 ($p = q = 1$) this gives the solubility of AgCl in water at 298 K as

$$1.31 \times 10^{-5} \text{ mol kg}^{-1}.$$

If the concentration of either Ag^+ or Cl^- is increased by adding a soluble salt with a common ion, such as $AgNO_3$ or NaCl, then the concentration of the other ion must decrease in order to maintain the constancy of K_{sp}. For example, if sufficient NaCl is added to give a $0.1\,m$ solution then, if the solubility of AgCl is S, the concentration of Ag^+ will be S and of Cl^- ($S + 0.1$). Thus from 10.65

$$S(S + 0.1) = 1.72 \times 10^{-10}, \tag{10.66}$$

and as S is much less than 0.1 this has the solution $S = 1.72 \times 10^{-9}$ mol kg^{-1}. In other words $0.1\,m$ NaCl decreases the solubility of AgCl by a factor 10^{-4}. This is known as the 'salting-out' effect arising from the presence of a common ion.

A 'salting-in' effect can be achieved by adding a salt without a common ion as this will reduce the activity coefficient below unity. For example, a $0.1\,m$ solution of $AgNO_3$ has, from 10.52, an activity coefficient of

$$\ln \gamma_\pm = -0.1172, \therefore \gamma_\pm = 0.89, \tag{10.67}$$

hence, from 10.54 and 10.65

$$S = K_{sp}^{1/2}/\gamma = 1.47 \times 10^{-5} \tag{10.68}$$

so that the solubility has been increased by 6%.

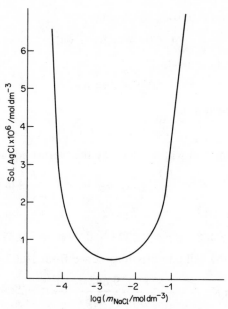

Figure 10.3 Dependence of AgCl solubility on the concentration of added NaCl. (Data for 298 K from F. W. Linke, *Solubilities of Inorganic and Metal Organic Compounds*, D. Van Nostrand, New York (1958))

This is a much smaller change (in the opposite direction) than can be achieved by the common ion effect and although higher concentrations of added salt can be used the solution will then be in a concentration range where the Debye–Hückel limiting law breaks down. Indeed at high salt concentrations there are no universal rules. For example, the solubility of AgCl decreases with added chloride ion up to about $10^{-3} m$ but then undergoes an increase as shown in Figure 10.3. This has been attributed to the formation of complex ions $[AgCl_{n+1}]^{n-}$.

10.4 Acid and base strengths

In 1925 Brönsted defined an acid as a species having a tendency to lose a proton and a base as a species having a tendency to gain a proton. The deprotonated form of an acid is a base and the protonated form of a base is an acid. Thus acids (A) and bases (B) are linked in conjugate acid–base pairs connected schematically by the equilibrium

$$A \rightleftharpoons B + H^+. \tag{10.69}$$

For example, CH_3COOH is the acid and CH_3COO^- the base; NH_4^+ the acid,

NH_3 the base. The free proton does not exist in the liquid state and hence the equilibrium 10.69 has only schematic significance. In practice an equilibrium is established between two conjugate pairs, (A_1, B_1) and (A_2, B_2), as follows

$$A_1 + B_2 \rightleftharpoons B_1 + A_2. \tag{10.70}$$

An example of this is

$$CH_3COOH + NH_3 \rightleftharpoons CH_3COO^- + NH_4^+. \tag{10.71}$$

If K_1 and K_2 are equilibrium constants for the two schematic equilibria of type 10.69, then the equilibrium constant for 10.70 is

$$K = K_1/K_2. \tag{10.72}$$

Relative scales of acid and base strength can be established for each solvent (these scales will depend slightly on temperature) and it is customary and convenient to use the solvent itself as the standard. For example, in water, acid strength is measured relative to the strength of H_3O^+ by examining the equilibrium

$$A + H_2O \rightleftharpoons B + H_3O^+. \tag{10.73}$$

In dilute solutions the activity of water can be taken as constant, hence the equilibrium constant for 10.73 is given by

$$K_a = \frac{a_B a_{H_3O^+}}{a_A}, \tag{10.74}$$

and this is called the acid dissociation constant of A. The stronger the acid A the more it will protonate the water molecule and the greater will be K_a.

A standard of base strength can be established relative to the deprotonated solvent as standard. Thus in water solutions we examine the equilibrium

$$B + H_2O \rightleftharpoons A + OH^-, \tag{10.75}$$

and define base strength by the value of

$$K_b = \frac{a_A a_{OH^-}}{a_B}. \tag{10.76}$$

By taking the product of 10.74 and 10.76 we see that acid and base strengths are related:

$$K_a K_b = a_{H_3O^+} a_{OH^-} = K_s, \tag{10.77}$$

where K_s is the equilibrium constant for autoionization of the solvent, in this case water. K_w has the value 1.00×10^{-14} at 298 K.

As equilibrium constants can take values covering many powers of ten it is traditional to use a logarithmic scale to measure acid and base strengths

$$pK = -\log_{10} K. \tag{10.78}$$

This is called the pK scale. Table 10.3 lists some values for acids and bases in

Table 10.3 Dissociation constants for some common acids and bases in water at 298 K. For carbonic and phosphoric acids dissociation constants are given for successive ionization of the protons

Acid	pK_a	Base	pK_b
Phenol	9.89	Aniline	9.37
Acetic acid	4.75	Pyridine	8.75
Benzoic acid	4.19	Methylamine	3.34
Formic acid	3.75	Trimethylamine	4.19
Trichloracetic acid	0.70	Ammonium hydroxide	4.75
Hypochlorous acid	7.53	Hydroxylamine	7.97
Hydrofluoric acid	3.45		
Carbonic acid (1)	6.37		
(2)	10.25		
Phosphoric acid (1)	2.12		
(2)	7.21		
(3)	12.67		

Data from CRC *Handbook of Chemistry and Physics*, 59th edn, 1978–79.

water at 298 K. Strong acids have $pK_a < -1$ and are more than 90% ionized: nitric acid, for example, has a pK_a of approximately -1.4. The other common strong acids, hydrochloric, sulphuric and perchloric are effectively 100% ionized in water and cannot be differentiated in acid strength. However, we shall see later that they can be differentiated in solvents which are less good proton acceptors than water.

pH measurement

It is important to distinguish between the strength of an acid as measured by the degree to which it protonates the solvent (i.e. pK_a) and the acidity, which is the concentration of hydrogen ions (protonated solvent molecules) in the solution. In 1909 Sörensen proposed that the logarithm of the hydrogen ion concentration be taken as a measure of acidity and he introduced the term pH defined by

$$pH = - \log[H^+]. \qquad (10.79)$$

There are two ways in which this simple definition can be extended. First, we can recognize that protons are attached to solvent molecules and, in the case of water, write

$$pH = - \log[H_3O^+]. \qquad (10.80)$$

However, aqueous solutions are not ideal and any thermodynamic measurement will give in the first place activities of the ionic species. The most widely accepted definition of pH today is

$$pH = - \log a_{H_3O^+} \qquad (10.81)$$

but this encounters the problem that the activities of individual ions are not absolutely determined. It should be recalled that thermodynamic measurements on ionic solutions give the mean activity coefficients of the positive and negative ions (9.43).

The procedure recommended by the National Bureau of Standards for accurately determining pH according to the recipe 10.81 is to measure the e.m.f. of the cell

$$\text{Pt, } H_2(1 \text{ atm}) \,|\, \text{buffer with } Cl^- \,|\, AgCl(s), \text{ Ag} \qquad (10.82)$$

as a function of Cl^-. One can then use certain well established formulae for the activity of Cl^- and determine a_{H^+} from 10.49.

This procedure is rather tedious and the hydrogen electrode is not a very easy standard to use because the catalytic activity of the platinum is subject to poisoning. The most common way to measure pH is with a glass electrode which consists of a $Ag\,|\,AgCl$ electrode contained within a thin glass bulb with an HCl solution of known pH. This electrode is immersed in the solution whose pH is required and its e.m.f. measured against some other standard electrode. The glass wall behaves as a membrane which is transparent to hydrogen ions and it has been found that the glass electrode potential is linearly proportional to the pH of the solution being examined. The glass electrode has also been found useful for measuring the pH in water–organic solvent mixtures providing that they contain more than 10% by weight of water.

For strong acids in aqueous solutions at concentrations appreciably greater than $10^{-7} \, m$ the concentration of H_3O^+ is approximately equal to the concentration of acid. Thus $10^{-3} \, m$ HCl has pH ≈ 3. At concentrations less than $10^{-6} \, m$ the amount of H_3O^+ produced by the autodissociation of the water must be allowed for. The pH of a very dilute acid can never be greater than 7 nor the pH of a base be less than 7.

Buffer solutions

When studying a chemical reaction which consumes or produces hydrogen ions it is often useful to create conditions under which the pH is nearly constant over the course of the reaction. This can be achieved by the use of a buffer solution which contains a weak acid and its conjugate base. If hydrogen ions are produced in the reaction they react with the base to increase the amount of weak acid. If hydrogen ions are consumed then the weak acid dissociates to give more hydrogen ions. The overall effect is to resist any change in pH. Solutions containing a weak base and its conjugate acid have the same effect.

As an illustration of the buffer effect we will consider a reaction that produces $10^{-3} \, m$ HCl. Adding HCl to neutral water to produce this concentration would change the pH from 7 to 3, that is by 4 units. We will now see what happens if $10^{-3} \, m$ HCl is produced in a buffer solution containing $10^{-2} \, m$ acetic acid and $10^{-2} \, m$ sodium acetate.

The acid dissociation constant of acetic acid is 1.75×10^{-5}. If we approximate activities by concentrations then the concentration of ions is determined by the two equations

$$m_{H_3O^+} \cdot m_{Ac^-} = 1.75 \times 10^{-5} m_{HAc}, \tag{10.83}$$

$$m_{H_3O^+} \cdot m_{OH^-} = 1.00 \times 10^{-14}. \tag{10.84}$$

Before the HCl is produced we have the condition of charge balance

$$m_{H_3O^+} + m_{Na^+} = m_{OH^-} + m_{Ac^-}, \tag{10.85}$$

and the mass balances

$$m_{Na^+} = 0.01; \, m_{HAc} + m_{Ac^-} = 0.02. \tag{10.86}$$

Equations 10.83–10.86 can be solved assuming that $m_{H_3O^+}$ and m_{OH^-} are negligible in 10.85 (K_a is small for acetic acid and there is no other source of acid). This assumption leads to

$$m_{Ac^-} = m_{HAc} = 0.01, m_{H_3O^+} = 1.75 \times 10^{-5}, \text{pH} = 4.76. \tag{10.87}$$

After $10^{-3} m$ HCl the charge balance 10.85 is replaced by

$$m_{H_3O^+} + m_{Na^+} = m_{OH^-} + m_{Ac^-} + m_{Cl^-}, \tag{10.88}$$

and we have the additional mass balance

$$m_{Cl^-} = 0.001. \tag{10.89}$$

These equations can again be solved by neglecting $m_{H_3O^+}$ and m_{OH^-} in 10.88 (for $m_{H_3O^+}$ this may not be obvious as HCl has been added but it can be confirmed by the self-consistency of the resulting solution). We arrive at the following result

$$m_{Ac^-} = 0.009, m_{HAc} = 0.011, m_{H_3O^+} = 2.14 \times 10^{-5}, \text{pH} = 4.67 \tag{10.90}$$

In summary, adding $0.001 m$ HCl to the buffer solution has moved the HAc/Ac$^-$ equilibrium by 10% and changed the pH by only 0.09 units.

For an effective buffer, that is, one capable of absorbing a reasonably large change in acid concentration, the concentrations of neither component must be too small. The range of buffer activity is therefore limited to about 1 pH unit on either side of the pH for a 50:50 mixture. Acetic acid–acetate buffers can be prepared covering the pH range of about 3.5–5.5 and outside this other acid–base pairs must be used.

If a weak acid is titrated with a strong base, or a weak base with a strong acid then before neutrality is reached there will be a range over which the pH varies slowly because the mixture is behaving as a buffer. When the end point is reached there will be a sharp change in pH with further addition of the titrant. Figure 10.4 shows a typical titration curve for this situation. The ideal indicator in this case will be one that shows a colour change at approximately pH = 8.

Figure 10.4   Titration curve for $0.10\,m$ acetic
acid with NaOH

Hammett acidity function

Concentrated solutions of acids generally show large deviations from ideality. This is particularly true for strong acids, which, when concentrated, often have a much greater ability to protonate weak bases than would be expected from an extrapolation of the properties of their dilute solutions. The activity coefficient $\gamma_\pm$ for an acid like HCl has a concentration dependence similar to that for a simple salt like LiCl; it decreases up to a concentration of approximately $0.5\,m$ and then increases to values much greater than one at high concentrations.

The most widely used measure of acidity in concentrated strong acid solutions is that introduced by Hammett and Deyrup and called the Hammett acidity function. If we take the logarithm of 10.74 and use 10.81 as the definition of pH, we have

$$pH = pK_a + \log\left(\frac{a_B}{a_A}\right). \tag{10.91}$$

This is an identity in so far as both pH and pK_a are defined in terms of activities. However, it must be remembered that pK_a is a constant only for dilute solutions because 10.74 is the equilibrium constant for 10.73 only on the assumption that the activity of the water (more generally the solvent) is unity. If K'_a is the exact equilibrium constant for 10.73, allowing for water activity,

230

then the expression analogous to 10.91 is

$$pH = pK'_a + \log\left(\frac{a_B}{a_A a_{H_2O}}\right) \qquad (10.92)$$

The Hammett scale of acidity is based upon an experiment in which a small amount of a weak neutral base B is added to the acid solution and the ratio of the concentrations of B and its conjugate acid BH^+ determined by colorimetric methods. The system B/BH^+ is usually an indicator. From this ratio a quantity H_0 called the acidity function is calculated from the equation

$$H_0 = pK_{BH^+} + \log\left(\frac{m_B}{m_{BH^+}}\right) \qquad (10.93)$$

the suffix zero indicates that the function applies only to neutral bases; similar functions for charged bases have been investigated.

By comparing 10.93 with 10.91 we see that H_0 is identical with pH for dilute solutions but in concentrated solutions the two functions differ appreciably. The ratio of activities a_B/a_{BH^+} is very different from the ratio of molalities because the charged species BH^+ deviates much more from ideality than does neutral B. It has, however, been found that the ratio γ_B/γ_{BH^+} is roughly constant for a wide range of organic indicators at a given acid concen-

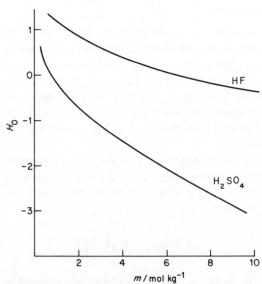

Figure 10.5 The Hammett acidity function for aqueous solutions of H_2SO_4 and HF. (Data from M. A. Paul and F. A. Lang, *Chem. Rev.*, **57**, 1 (1957) and R. P. Bell and K. N. Bascombe, *Disc. Faraday Soc.*, **24**, 162 (1957))

tration so that H_0 determined from 10.93 is roughly independent of the nature of B.

Figure 10.5 shows the acidity function that has been deduced for sulphuric acid as a function of molality. Very similar graphs are obtained for other very strong acids such as HBr, HCl and $HClO_4$ but weaker acids such as HF and H_3PO_4 give quite different H_0 curves as is shown in Figure 10.5.

It appears to have been well established that the main determining factor for the behaviour of concentrated strong acid solutions is the decrease in water activity. If one assumes that the dominant hydrated proton species in water is $H_9O_4^+$ (described in Chapter 8) then the dependence of H_0 on molality for very strong acids can be satisfactorily explained up to concentrations $m \approx 8$ mol kg^{-1}.† However, a cautionary note should be sounded. Although the Hammett acidity function has been shown to be valuable for correlating thermodynamic and kinetic data for organic indicators in concentrated strong acid solutions there is probably little justification for using it to describe the protonation of other types of weak base.

10.5 Equilibria in non-aqueous polar solvents

We have already noted that in water the strong acids such as hydrochloric and perchloric cannot be differentiated in their acid strengths. The reason for this is that water is a relatively good proton acceptor and all of these acids donate, effectively completely, their protons to water molecules. In the Brönsted–Lowry definition of an acid the strongest acid that is stable in water is H_3O^+; anything stronger would protonate water according to the equation

$$BH + H_2O \rightleftharpoons B^- + H_3O^+, \tag{10.94}$$

with the equilibrium being established far to the right.

Stronger acids than H_3O^+ are only stable in solvents which are less good proton acceptors than water. For example, in 100% sulphuric acid even perchloric acid has a low dissociation constant, $K_a \approx 10^{-4}$. Very few acids indeed are strong in sulphuric as a solvent: $H_2S_3O_{10}$ and $B(HSO_4)_3$ are two with moderately high dissociation constants.

To parallel the above points we note that OH^- is the strongest base that can exist in water; anything stronger would be protonated by water according to the equation

$$B + H_2O \rightleftharpoons BH^+ + OH^-. \tag{10.95}$$

Ammonia, however, liberates protons much less readily than water and hence liquid ammonia can tolerate a much stronger base. Thus if one needs a very strong base to carry out a chemical reaction it is likely to be better to use $NaNH_2/NH_3(l)$ rather than $NaOH/H_2O(l)$.

†K. N. Bascombe and R. P. Bell, *Disc. Faraday Soc.*, **24**, 158 (1957).

Figure 10.6 Range of existence of acids and bases in different solvents. (From R. P. Bell, *The Proton in Chemistry*,
Methuen, London (1959))

Figure 10.6 shows the ranges over which different solvents can discriminate acid strengths. To take an extreme example, hexane cannot be detectably protonated or deprotonated hence no acid or base would be dissociated in this solvent and the complete range of acid strengths is, in principle, available (but restricted of course by problems of solubility). Sulphuric acid can discriminate amongst the strong acids but the overall range of discrimination is small because most compounds are protonated in sulphuric acid, that is, most compounds behave as strong bases.

The discrimination width is related to the autoionization constant of the solvent. For water we have seen (10.77) that $pK_w = 14.0$. For liquid ammonia autoionization is much less

$$2NH_3 \rightleftharpoons NH_4^+ + NH_2^-, \quad -\log K = 29.8 \tag{10.96}$$

and for sulphuric acid it is much greater

$$2H_2SO_4 \rightleftharpoons H_3SO_4^+ + HSO_4^-, \quad -\log K = 3.6 \tag{10.97}$$

Solvents also limit the range of redox strengths that are attainable in solution. However, an important difference from the acid–base situation is that redox reactions are often slow so that an oxidizing or reducing agent that is thermodynamically unstable may nevertheless be kinetically stable.

The strongest oxidizing agent that is thermodynamically stable in water is O_2; anything stronger will liberate O_2 from water. The strongest reducing agent that is stable is, similarly, H_2. Redox strengths are measured by standard electrode potentials. In water under acid conditions we have

$$H^+ + e \rightleftharpoons \tfrac{1}{2}H_2, \qquad \mathscr{E}^\ominus = 0 \text{ (definition)},$$
$$\tfrac{1}{4}O_2 + H^+ + e \rightleftharpoons \tfrac{1}{2}H_2O, \qquad \mathscr{E}^\ominus = 1.229 \text{ V.} \tag{10.98}$$

Thus reducing agents with negative $\mathscr{E}^\ominus$ values (see Table 10.1) are unstable in water and oxidizing agents with $\mathscr{E}^\ominus > 1.229$ V are unstable (for example Ce^{4+}).

In liquid ammonia, N_2 is the strongest thermodynamically stable oxidizing agent and H_2 the strongest reducing agent. The relative standard electrode potential is

$$\tfrac{1}{6}N_2 + H^+ + e \rightleftharpoons \tfrac{1}{3}NH_3, \qquad \mathscr{E}^\ominus = 0.04 \text{ V,} \tag{10.99}$$

the reference again being zero for the H^+/H_2 couple. A much smaller range of oxidizing agents is thermodynamically stable in liquid ammonia than in water but as the equilibrium 10.99 is established very slowly this is not a severe limitation. Solutions of alkali metals in liquid ammonia are powerful reducing solutions although the $\mathscr{E}^\ominus$ value for say Li^+/Li is negative.

Chapter 11

Solutions of polymers

11.1 Introduction

Solution properties form the basis of many techniques for the quantitative characterization of polymer molecules, e.g., molecular weight determination. In addition, solutions of synthetic polymers find widespread technological applications, e.g., as paints, varnishes and adhesives. Polymer fabrication techniques, such as the spinning of fibres, involve polymer melts (not mentioned further) or solutions. Biological systems, however difficult they may be to unravel, consist in the main of macromolecular structures in solution or dispersed, or forming membranes in contact with liquids. This chapter deals with some of the basic aspects of polymer solutions;[†] the next two chapters contain references to polymer molecules adsorbed at interfaces and forming colloidal systems. It will become clear that in many respects polymer molecules in solution do not behave like small molecules. Also, because of the nature of polymer solutions, the emphasis is often on techniques and properties not given much prominence in earlier chapters.

11.2 Polymer molecules

Table 11.1 shows the chemical formulae of the repeating unit in several common polymers. The vinyl polymers $+CH_2CHX)_n$ form a particularly important class, including poly(vinly chloride), $X = -Cl$, polyacrylonitrile, $X = -CN$, polystyrene, $X = -C_6H_5$, and the water-soluble species poly(vinyl alcohol), $X = -OH$. The biological macromolecules are represented by the general polypeptide or linear protein repeat unit, and by an example of a polysaccharide, cellulose which is a major constituent of plant cell walls. In addition, there exist more complex chemical structures, e.g., the nucleic acids.

[†]P. J. Flory, *Principles of Polymer Chemistry*, Cornell, New York (1953); C. Tanford, *Physical Chemistry of Macromolecules*, Wiley, London and New York (1961); H.-G. Elias, *Macromolecules*, Vol. 1, Plenum, London and New York (1977); H. Morawetz, *Macromolecules in Solution*, 2nd edn, Wiley, Chichester (1975).

Table 11.1   Representative formulae of simple polymers

Name	Repeating unit	Comment
Vinyl polymers	$-CH_2CH-$ $\quad\quad\mid$ $\quad\quad X$	X = OH, Cl, CN, etc.
Polyethylene	$-CH_2CH_2-$	
Polyamide, nylon-6,6	$-NH(CH_2)_6NHCO(CH_2)_4CO-$	One of a family: the numbers denote no. of C in sequences
Polypeptides, proteins	$\quad\quad R$ $\quad\quad\mid$ $-NHCHCO-$	Large natural family
Poly(methyl methacrylate)	$-CH_2C(CH_3)COOCH_3-$	
Natural rubber cis-polyisoprene	$-CH_2\quad\quad CH_2-$ $\quad\quad\searrow C=C \nearrow$ $CH_3 \quad\quad H$	
Polyacrylamide	$-CH_2CHCONH_2-$	Water-soluble: so is the parent acid
Poly(ethylene oxide)	$-CH_2CH_2O-$	Water-soluble
Cellulose		Many cellulose derivatives are used for processes in solution

It will be seen from the table that nylons, or polyamides, prepared by condensing $\alpha\omega$-diamines and $\alpha\omega$-dicarboxylic acids are similar in some respects to polypeptides which can be synthesized by condensing N-carboxy anhydrides. A standard textbook on polymer science should be consulted for a wider appreciation of polymeric species.† Solutions of polymer molecules in a suitable solvent will consist of anything from tens to thousands of repeating units per molecule in a solvent whose molecules are comparable in size to one repeat unit. The polymer molecules may be polar or non-polar and in the case of many biological macromolecules and the synthetic polyelectrolytes they will carry charges which dramatically affect some solution properties compared to those of uncharged polymers.

The variety of physical entities possible in solution is considerable: polymer molecules can be linear, branched or cross-linked (forming gels at a critical

†E.g. M. P. Stevens, *Polymer Chemistry: an Introduction*, Addison-Wesley, New York (1975).

(a)   (b)   (c)

Figure 11.1   Schematic representation of: (a) linear, (b) branched and (c) cross-linked polymer molecules

cross-linking concentration), as indicated in Figure 11.1. Copolymers, which are common, consist of at least two different repeating units denoted A and B (with composition ranging from pure A to pure B) in Figure 11.2; and the polymer molecules can range in degree of structuring from flexible random coils to rigid solids having a fairly definite shape, when they are best regarded as colloidal particles dispersed in a liquid medium. The important polymer entity the random coil is described in more detail below. Figure 11.3 shows atactic, syndiotactic and isotactic microstructure types of a general vinyl polymer. The tacticity or stereochemical structure of a polymer sample will depend on the species and on the polymerization conditions. The configurations of a polymer molecule in space, and the strength of intermolecular attraction depend on tacticity.

11.3   Properties of polymer solutions

Table 11.2 summarizes some of the more straightforward techniques which are used to study the properties of polymer solutions, and the kinds of information which can be obtained, ranging from viscosity measurements to give molecular weights and molecular dimensions to separatory techniques using

Figure 11.2   Schematic representation of copolymers with repeat units A and B: (a) random, (b) alternating, (c) block and (d) graft

Figure 11.3 Representation of the stereochemical configurations or tacticity of vinyl polymers

electrophoresis (movement in an applied electric field) of charged species. Discussion of some of these reveals the distinct nature of polymer solutions. A polymer sample generally consists of molecules covering a wide size distribution, and average properties are of interest.

A slight digression is needed to explain polymer molecular weights, which are important quantities in polymer characterization. Due to the nature of the chemical reactions involved in forming a polymer from monomer molecules, a sample of the product will consist of polymer molecules having a wide range of numbers of repeat units. The distribution of molecular size depends on the polymerization mechanism, and the manner in which it is described depends

Table 11.2 Techniques for polymer solution properties

Technique	Properties
Osmotic pressure	Number-average m.w., theta conditions, virial coefficients
Light scattering	Weight-average m.w., diffusion
Viscosity	Viscosity-average m.w., particle shape factors, configurational information including random-coil dimensions
Ultracentrifugation	Molecular weight (e.g., of proteins).
Solvent vapour pressure measurement	Thermodynamic activity and χ-parameters
Electrophoresis	Surface charge (zeta potential): also used for separation —see Chapter 13

on the nature of the solution property to which it relates.† Colligative properties such as the osmotic pressure of a polymer solution depend on the number of solute molecules in the solution rather than the kind of solute molecules, and are therefore related to the number-average degree of polymerization or the number-average molecular weight. For simplicity all units of a polymer will be treated as equivalent, i.e., the particular nature of end groups will be ignored. A sample containing N_i molecules each having i repeating units of molecular weight M_0, has a number-average molecular weight

$$\bar{M}_n = M_0 \sum_i i N_i / \sum_i N_i. \tag{11.1}$$

However, properties which are sensitive to the size of the solute molecules, e.g., light scattering, can be used as explained below to give the weight-average degree of polymerization. In this average quantity the moderate number of molecules of a moderate weight (strictly mass) outweigh large numbers of small molecules and small numbers of large molecules:

$$\bar{M}_w = M_0 \sum_i i^2 N_i / \sum_i i N_i. \tag{11.2}$$

A convenient measure of the spread of molecular size in a sample is $\bar{M}_w / \bar{M}_n \geq 1$, which is unity for a hypothetical uniform sample.

Osmotic pressure

The most important colligative property as far as polymer solutions are concerned is the osmotic pressure. Its use as a primary method of molecular weight determination has declined in recent years, but the concept and its relation to solution models and biological phenomena remains valuable. In a system where a semipermeable membrane separates pure solvent from polymer solution, Figure 11.4, the condition for physicochemical equilibrium is that at temperature T, the chemical potential of the pure solvent equals that of the solvent species in the solution. A general form of the dependence of the osmotic or applied hydrostatic pressure π, needed to establish equilibrium for solute concentration c_2, is the virial expansion‡

$$\pi/c_2 = RT(A + Bc_2 + Cc_2^2 + \dots). \tag{11.3}$$

Figure 11.4 shows schematically how π/c_2 varies with c_2. The upper curve is used to illustrate how the $c_2 = 0$ intercept, the limiting slope and the curvature can be used to obtain the virial coefficients A, B and C. The first virial coefficient gives the number-average molar mass, $\bar{M}_n$, defined by equation 11.1,§

$$\bar{M}_n = 1/A. \tag{11.4}$$

†P. J. Flory *loc. cit.*
‡Analogous to the virial expansion for real gases, section 3.6.
§The ideal solution behavior conforms to the more general van't Hoff law $\pi/c_2 = RT/M$ with $M = \bar{M}_n$.

Figure 11.4   (a) Representation of osmotic pressure apparatus. (b) Dependence of π/c_2 on c_2 for polymer in a theta solvent and in a good solvent

The second and third virial coefficients give, respectively, a measure of the interaction of a pair of polymer molecules and of three contacting molecules. B is proportional to the excluded volume u,

$$B = \mathcal{N}u/2\bar{M}_n^2, \tag{11.5}$$

where $\mathcal{N}$ is Avogadro's number. C can be related to B,

$$C = gB^2/\bar{M}_n, \tag{11.6}$$

by means of the constant g, which is $\frac{1}{2}$ for the interaction of random coils in what is known as a good solvent. A good solvent is one with solvent–polymer segment interaction favouring an open polymer configuration (below). The upper curve in Figure 11.4 represents a good solvent with $B > 0, C > 0$. The horizontal line identifies a system with $B = 0$ and $C = 0$ at finite concentrations. For a particular solvent and a particular polymer species there may be a temperature, Θ, at which the solution behaves ideally and in this case the solvent is called a theta solvent. The solvent in these circumstances will be a poor one for the polymer, e.g., cyclohexane at $T = 308$ K is a theta solvent for polystyrene, whereas benzene and toluene are good solvents for polystyrene and show non-ideal behaviour.

Light scattering

When light of intensity I_0 falls on a substance, some of it is in general transmitted, some is absorbed and some is scattered at the same frequency.

240

Figure 11.5 Schematic representation of apparatus for measuring light scattering as a function of angle θ

Rayleigh laid the theoretical foundations by considering scattering from small particles. The subject has developed into one of considerable complexity, which is capable in the case of polymers and colloids of giving information on size, shape and dynamics.

Rayleigh scattering of unpolarized light (using apparatus depicted in Figure 11.5) from particles of size less than about $\lambda/20$ shows that at a distance r from the specimen, and at an angle θ to the axis of the transmitted beam, the intensity of scattering I_θ is proportional to λ^{-4} and to α^2, where α is the polarizability of the particle substance:[†]

$$I_\theta r^2 / I_0 = 8\pi^4 \alpha^2 (1 + \cos^2\theta)/\lambda^4. \tag{11.7}$$

It is possible to eliminate α from equation 11.7 by relating it to the relative permittivity, which in turn is related to the refractive index, n, and depends on particle concentration.

Treatments based on fluctuation theory by Einstein and Debye led to equations applicable to the scattering of monochromatic radiation (e.g., $\lambda = 435.8$ or 546.1 nm) by polymers in real solutions. The Rayleigh ratio,

$$R_\theta = I_\theta r^2 (N/V)/I_0, \tag{11.8}$$

where there are N molecules in volume V, is measured and used to obtain the molecular weight average in the limit as $c \to 0$,

$$\frac{\mathcal{K}c}{R_\theta} = \frac{1}{\bar{M}_w} + 2Bc + 3Cc^2 + \ldots, \tag{11.9}$$

where $\mathcal{K}$ the optical constant (with solvent refractive index n_0) is

$$\mathcal{K} = 2\pi^2 n_0^2 (dn/dc)^2 / \mathcal{N}\lambda^4. \tag{11.10}$$

The specific refractive index increment dn/dc is determined independently in a differential refractometer. The weight-average molecular weight given by this technique has been defined by equation 11.2.

A more complete theory involves the particle scattering factor $P(\theta)$. When

[†]The intensity I_θ is measured relative to I_0 for scattering at distance r from unit volume of sample at angle θ, defined in Figure 11.5.

the virial coefficient C is neglected the relevant expression is

$$\frac{\mathscr{K}c}{R_\theta} = \frac{1}{\bar{M}_w P(\theta)} + 2Bc. \tag{11.11}$$

With large particles, typically for $\bar{M}_w$ of several hundred thousand, there will be intraparticle effects, due to differences in phase and in path length for scattering from a particle, and the intensity I_θ will be reduced by $P(\theta)$. The value of $P(\theta)$ depends on the size and shape of the particle and on θ. One method of dealing with the problem of interference is to make light scattering measurements over a range of c and θ and extrapolate to the limits $c \to 0$, $\theta \to 0$ using what are known as the Zimm plots, Figure 11.6, of $\mathscr{K}c/R_\theta$ against $\sin^2\theta/2 + kc$, where k is an arbitrarily chosen constant.

Recent advances in the use of light scattering include the use of photon correlation spectroscopy to study particle size, translational diffusion and intermolecular or interparticle interactions of polymer molecules and colloidal particles.

Solution viscosity

The presence of polymer molecules in solution raises the viscosity relative to that of pure solvent. In practice flow times t at a series of concentrations, and t_0 for pure solvent are determined using an Ostwald or an Ubbelohde dilution viscometer, Figure 11.7. After the elimination of polymer–polymer molecule interactions by extrapolation to infinite dilution, the effect of polymer molecules is given by the following relationships:

$$\eta_r = \frac{\eta}{\eta_0} = \frac{t}{t_0} \quad \text{viscosity ratio} \tag{11.12}$$

Figure 11.6 Representation of a Zimm plot according to equation 11.11

Figure 11.7   Ubbelohde suspended level dilution viscometer

$$\eta_{red} = (\eta - \eta_0)/\eta_0 c \quad \text{viscosity number} \tag{11.13}$$

$$[\eta] = \lim_{c \to 0} \eta_{red} \quad \text{limiting viscosity number} \tag{11.14}$$

The limiting viscosity number $[\eta]$ is related to the viscosity-average molar mass $\bar{M}_v$ by the empirical expression,

$$[\eta] = K\bar{M}_v^a, \tag{11.15}$$

where K and a are constants (from independent calibration) for the solvent + polymer pair at a specified temperature. Table 11.3 gives three values. The three averages have values in the order

$$\bar{M}_n < \bar{M}_v < \bar{M}_w.$$

There are two extreme models which can be invoked: the free draining model in which the polymer consists of connected beads enabling solvent to pass through the random coil, and the rigid-particle model. The draining model gives $a \simeq 1.0$–1.2, whereas a is found to be usually in the range 0.5–0.8 with $a = \frac{1}{2}$ for theta conditions. If the polymer molecule moves as a random coil taking the solvent with it, a hard particle model might be more appropriate: certainly this applies to ordered proteins and viruses. Einstein, and later Simha, considered the problem and arrived at the relationship

$$\eta = \eta_0(1 + kv_2), \tag{11.16}$$

where v_2 is the polymer volume fraction. For rigid spheres, $k = 2.5$; it exceeds

Table 11.3   Values of constants K and a†

Polymer	Solvent	Temp./K	$10^2 K/\text{cm}^3\,\text{g}^{-1}$	a
Polystyrene	Cyclohexane	298	1.63	0.68
Polystyrene	Cyclohexane	308Θ	8.6	0.5
Polystyrene	Benzene	298	1.0	0.74

†See *Polymer Handbook*, 2nd end, J. Brandrup and E. H. Immergut eds., Wiley, Chichester (1975), section IV for additional values: they vary with the m.w. range, and in many cases the correct values to use have not been decided.

this value for oblate and prolate ellipsoidal particles. Values of k are also affected by particle solvolysis (hydration) and by asymmetry of the particles. The size of flexible polymer molecules, given as the root-mean-square end-to-end distance $\langle r^2 \rangle^{\frac{1}{2}}$, can also be obtained from $[\eta]$. The limiting viscosity number is proportional to the hydrodynamic volume of the polymer molecules, leading to

$$[\eta] = \Phi \langle r^2 \rangle^{3/2} / \bar{M}_n. \tag{11.17}$$

Values of the constant Φ in the range $2.0-2.5 \times 10^{21}$ have been found by comparing theory with experiment; a value of 2.5×10^{21} is often used. Measurements of $[\eta]$ and $\bar{M}_n$ yield $\langle r^2 \rangle^{3/2}$. If measurements are also carried out on a system satisfying theta conditions, the expansion of a polymer molecule relative to its size under theta conditions is given by

$$\alpha = ([\eta]/[\eta]_\Theta)^{1/3} \tag{11.18}$$

In a theta solvent the polymer is said to have unperturbed dimensions, e.g. the root-mean-square end-to-end distance denoted $\langle r^2 \rangle_0^{1/2}$: see account below of polymer configurations.

11.4 Phase behaviour

Under certain circumstances a polymer and a solvent at temperatures T may be miscible in all proportions. However, it is generally true in principle that if the temperature is raised or lowered from a completely miscible state instability will occur, signified by clouding of the solution. The temperature at

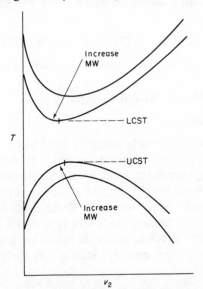

Figure 11.8 Phase diagram for a polymer solution showing the LCST and UCST for the higher MW sample: the system is completely miscible only between these temperatures

the onset of which clouding occurs depends on the species and the polymer volume fraction. Figure 11.8 indicates this phenomenon and identifies the upper and lower critical solution temperatures (UCST and LCST). In practice the entire phase diagram may not be attainable, e.g. because the solvent freezes, but sealed tubes under pressure can be used for the upper curve (below solvent critical conditions). In the partially miscible region the system separates into two solutions: dilute and concentrated with respect to polymer. The position and shape of the curves depend on the polymer molecular weight, and in the limit, that for polymer of infinite molecular weight would intersect the ordinate $v_2 = 0$ at $T = \Theta$. Also $\chi = \frac{1}{2}$ (see section 11.5).

Polymer recovery from solution (e.g., after polymerization) and polymer fractionation into samples of more uniform molecular weight can be brought about using non-solvent. A liquid in which the polymer is not soluble but which is miscible with the solvent is added in successive aliquots to the polymer solution. Higher molecular weight fractions precipitate first.

The solubility of certain polymers in water is often very sensitive to the addition of inorganic salts. Synthetic and non-ionic water-soluble polymers include poly(vinyl alcohol), poly(ethylene oxide), poly(acrylic acid) and poly-acrylamide. The addition of salt to aqueous solutions affects polymer–polymer and polymer–solvent interactions, and also affects water structure (hydrogen bonding): Chapter 8. It is usually found, e.g. for poly(ethylene oxide), that the ability to cause salting-out increases with anion valence. The order of decreasing ability, at a given molar concentration of salt, to bring about clouding, or 'salting out', usually referred to as the Hofmeister series, is approximately,

$$PO_4^{3-} > SO_4^{2-} \approx CO_3^{2-} > S_2O_3^{2-} > F^- > CH_3COO^- > Cl^- > NO_3^-$$

when compared on a molar concentration basis with a common cation.

11.5 Statistical and thermodynamic models

Models of polymer solutions

To attempt to explain the wide range of phenomena found for polymer solutions (related to practical aspects of polymer recovery, purification, fractionation and use), theoretical models have been developed. In over forty years various models have been produced to account for various aspects, but the all-embracing model—if one were ever thought possible—is elusive. The configurational nature of random coils will first of all be examined in the absence of solvent. The account below is based on analytical expressions. Polymer configurations can also be studied theoretically by numerical computation.

Configurations

Those polymer molecules which are linear, rather than branched, and flexible are expected to exist as random coils in solution, and in the amorphous solid state. For entropic reasons the molecules will not exist as extended chains, but even if these were likely, the steric hindrance and interaction between atoms or groups attached to the backbone, would, except in the case of polyethylene, ensure some distortion away from a planar zig-zag configuration. More specific interactions can also occur, e.g., hydrogen bonding.

The simplest hypothetical molecule for configurational analysis consists of n bonds of length l freely jointed at their ends, without restriction on orientation or rotation. Bond angles, restricted rotation about single bonds and the notion of an excluded volume are, for the time being, completely ignored. Statistically the molecule behaves like a gas of point atoms having a fixed mean free path. For a large number of bonds, $\mathcal{O}(10^3)$ or more, the molecule is expected to lie within a roughly spherical envelope. The root-mean-square end-to-end distance is

$$\langle r^2 \rangle^{1/2} = ln^{1/2} \tag{11.19}$$

The next level of refinement is to specify a bond angle θ, which leads to

$$\langle r^2 \rangle_{\text{of}}^{1/2} = ln^{1/2} \left(\frac{1 - \cos\theta}{1 + \cos\theta} \right)^{1/2} \tag{11.20}$$

where the additional factor is $2^{1/2}$ for $\theta = 109°28'$.

When restriction is placed on rotation in the form of limited movement about an average angle ϕ of rotation, shown in Figure 11.9, specified by $\overline{\cos\phi}$, the size becomes

$$\langle r^2 \rangle_0^{1/2} = \sigma \langle r^2 \rangle_{\text{of}}^{1/2}; \quad \sigma = \left(\frac{1 + \overline{\cos\phi}}{1 - \overline{\cos\phi}} \right)^{1/2} \tag{11.21}$$

The steric factor σ usually lies between 1.5 and 3.0. By specifying the bond angle and by taking account of localized restrictions, short-range interactions can be expressed as the characteristic ratio $C_n = \langle r^2 \rangle_0 / l^2 n$, making use of the unperturbed dimension already referred to for a molecule in a theta solvent.

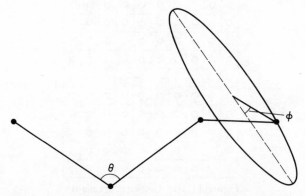

Figure 11.9 Spoke model used to describe the configuration of the backbone of a polymer molecule

246

For polyethylene $C_n = 6.7$. The additional expansion α given by equation 11.18 in a good solvent thus takes account of long-range interactions, i.e., it is a measure of the excluded volume effect since two polymer segments cannot occupy the same space. Solution viscosity, section 11.3, can be used to measure C_n and α.

Lattice models

The ability to measure quantities pertaining to polymer molecules and to calculate chain properties does not alone account for polymer solution behaviour. Polymer solutions show large negative deviations from Raoult's law at finite concentrations, in addition to which, solution theories should be able to explain phase separation. The forty-year old Flory–Huggins model and its modifications provide a basis for discussion.

A square lattice as depicted in Figure 11.10 with coordination number z is chosen, and the number of configurations of a mixture of n_1 solvent and n_2 polymer molecules was estimated. Starting with an initially empty lattice, it is then supposed that $\zeta - 1$ chains have already been added. Attention centres on the number of ways of adding the ζth polymer molecule. It is supposed that a solvent molecule occupies the space of a single polymer segment, and that a polymer molecule occupies r segments. The total number of lattice sites is then $n_0 = n_1 + rn_2$ where r is approximately the ratio of the molar volumes of the two components. When adding the ζth molecule it is assumed that $(\zeta - 1)r$ sites are already occupied randomly and that r contiguous sites must be found. The number of possible configurations Ω of the n_2 chains obtained in this manner gives the configurational entropy in terms of volume fractions (k is Boltzmann's constant),

$$S_{\text{config}} = kn_2\{(r - 1)\ln[(z - 1)/e] + \ln r\} - k(n_1 \ln v_1 + n_2 \ln v_2)$$

$$(11.22)$$

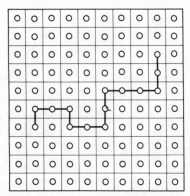

Figure 11.10 Lattice representation of a polymer molecule surrounded by solvent

The first term represents the entropy of disorientation of pure liquid polymer, and the second term is the entropy change of diluting the polymer with solvent, i.e., including the minus sign it is the combinatorial entropy—a quantity independent of z. The combinational entropy of mixing arises from the greater volume over which the molecules of both components are distributed compared to the volumes of the pure components, with $n_1 \ln v_1$ dominating at intermediate compositions.

The interior of the polymer molecules is accessible to the solvent molecules. On the other hand, a globular polymer represented by hard spheres will have centres inaccessible to other molecules, and the entropy of mixing will be reduced. The activity a_1 of the solvent will tend to unity as these spheres increase in size, whereas, as the open chains increase in molecular weight a limit $a_1 < 1$ is reached for intermediate compositions since $n_1 \ln v_1$ will not change, but $n_2 \ln v_2$ tends to zero.

The enthalpy of mixing is formally expressed in the original Flory–Huggins model as an interchange energy Δw in the manner of van Laar relationships,

$$\Delta H = n_1 v_2 \chi k T; \qquad \chi = z \Delta w / k T \tag{11.23}$$

which defines the dimensionless interaction parameter χ per solvent molecule. The Gibbs free energy of mixing is

$$\Delta G = kT(n_1 \ln v_1 + n_2 \ln v_2 + n_1 v_2 \chi) \tag{11.24}$$

and the partial molar Gibbs free energy gives the chemical potential of solvent component 1,

$$(\mu_1 - \mu_1^*)/RT = \ln(1 - v_2) + (1 - 1/r)v_2 + \chi v_2^2 \tag{11.25}$$

where μ_1^* is the chemical potential of pure solvent. The left-hand side of equation 11.25 defines $\ln a_1$, and with $1/r \ll 1$, simplification gives

$$a_1 \approx v_1 \exp[v_2(1 + \chi v_2)] \tag{11.26}$$

Experimental methods giving the chemical potential of the solvent, e.g., determinations of osmotic pressures and of vapour pressures, lead to values of χ. According to the above conventional theory, at moderate compositions where $v_2 \approx 1$, equation 11.26 shows that χ should be independent of v_2; it rarely is in practice (see below).

The main success of the theory is in its qualitative or semiquantitative ability to account for solution behaviour, and the basis which it provides for modified treatments. It can account for the occurrence of phase separation in polymer solutions.

The critical temperature for phase separation (UCST) encountered as a solution is cooled satisfies the condition that both $(\partial \mu_1 / \partial v_2)_{T,P}$ and $(\partial^2 \mu_1 / \partial v_2^2)_{T,P}$ are zero. From equation 11.25, critical phenomena (subscript c) occur when

$$1/(1 - v_{2,c}) - (1 - 1/r) - 2v_{2,c}\chi_c = 0 \tag{11.27}$$

$$1/(1 - v_{2,c}) - 2\chi_c = 0 \tag{11.28}$$

Table 11.4 Values of χ, χ_H and χ_S[†]

Polymer solvent	χ	χ_H	χ_S
Natural rubber + benzene	0.42	0.1	0.3
Polystyrene + ethylbenzene	0.40	−0.02	0.42
Poly(methyl methacrylate) + chloroform	0.38	−0.1	0.48

[†]From the compilation by Flory, *Disc. Faraday Soc.*, No. 49, 1970.

The critical volume fraction at which phase separation can first be detected on cooling is

$$v_{2,c} = 1/(1 + r^{1/2}) \approx r^{-1/2} \qquad (11.29)$$

where

$$\chi_c = \tfrac{1}{2} + r^{-1/2} + (2r)^{-1} \qquad (11.30)$$

For a sample of infinite molecular weight, $\chi_c \to \tfrac{1}{2}$, corresponding to theta conditions.

Values of χ can be obtained from the determination of colligative properties and from light-scattering measurements. The interaction parameter can, for instance, be related to the second virial coefficient for polymer–polymer interaction:

$$B = \bar{v}_2^2(\tfrac{1}{2} - \chi)/NV_1 \qquad (11.31)$$

where $\bar{v}_2$ is the specific volume of the polymer, and V_1 is the molecular volume of the solvent. Table 11.4 gives a few representative values. It is usually found that χ values are close to $\tfrac{1}{2}$ in poor solvents, and are otherwise usually less than $\tfrac{1}{2}$ but rarely negative. The dissolution of a polymer in a solvent is therefore generally an endothermic process. There should be no dependence of χ on v_2 according to the simple theory, but it is often found experimentally that χ increases with polymer concentration.

It is now usual to replace the rigid interchange energy definition of χ by a pragmatic empirical interpretation. It is also divided into enthalpy and entropy contributions, $\chi = \chi_H + \chi_S$,

$$\chi_H = -T(\partial\chi/\partial T); \qquad \chi_S = \partial(\chi T)/\partial T \qquad (11.32)$$

which can be obtained from the temperature dependence of χ or from calorimetric enthalpy of mixing data. Generally χ_S dominates χ_H as a contribution to χ: Table 11.4.

Theoretical developments since the original lattice model include the Flory–Krigbaum theory to take account of the non-uniform distribution of polymer molecules in dilute solutions, and, more recently, equation-of-state theories following from corresponding-states theories of Prigogine and co-workers.[†]

[†]*Disc. Faraday Soc.*, No. 49, 1970.

Chapter 12

Liquid interfaces and adsorption phenomena

12.1 Introduction

A liquid can form three types of interface: (1) with its vapour or a mixture of vapour and gas; (2) with another liquid with which it is immiscible or only partially miscible; and (3) with a solid. There are two other types of interface, solid–gas and solid–solid. The science of interfaces is concerned with the nature of the boundary region between phases and the consequences of its existence. The word surface as applied to solids and liquids is generalized to interface. Systems involving interfaces are broadly classified into those with phases of relatively large extent, and into a separate class when at least one of the dimensions of a phase is in the submicrometer region—called colloids— and usually implying the presence of a dispersed phase (Chapter 13). Confining the discussion here to interfaces with at least one liquid, it will be appreciated that there are many facets to the subject because the liquids can, for instance, be solutions of electrolytes or non-electrolytes and can include synthetic and biological macromolecules.

Interfacial and colloidal phenomena play important roles in animate and inanimate natural systems and in man-made systems: the behaviour of natural water surfaces (e.g., lakes and water in soils); the structure and physical and chemical function of biological systems; a variety of analytical techniques such as liquid–solid and gas–liquid chromatography; numerous industrial processes and products; and many household and pharmaceutical commodities rely strongly on them.

When the surface of a liquid is extended reversibly by area $d\mathscr{A}$ at constant temperature, volume and chemical composition, the change in the Helmholtz free energy of the system is

$$dA = \left(\frac{\partial A}{\partial \mathscr{A}}\right)_{T,V,n_i} d\mathscr{A} . \tag{12.1}$$

The partial differential coefficient is one definition of the surface tension of the liquid:

$$\gamma = (\partial A / \partial \mathscr{A})_{T,V,n_i} . \tag{12.2}$$

249

Table 12.1 Surface and interfacial tensions

	$\gamma/\text{mN m}^{-1}$		$\gamma/\text{mN m}^{-1}$
Water	72.8	Acetone	23.7
Ethanol	22.3	Propylene carbonate	41
Benzene[†]	28.9	Liquid argon (at 90 K)	12
Carbon tetrachloride	26.8	Mercury	485

	$\gamma/\text{mN m}^{-1}$		$\gamma/\text{mN m}^{-1}$
Water/carbon tetrachloride	45	Water/hexane	51
Water/mercury	375		

[†]See also Table 12.3.

The surface tension is the force per unit length acting in the liquid surface. (The hitherto common unit dyn cm^{-1} for surface tension has been replaced by the SI unit mN m^{-1}, its numerical equivalent.)[†] Table 12.1 gives a few representative values of surface and liquid–liquid interfacial tensions. The value of the surface tension of water is greater than for other simple liquids, values for which fall in the range 20–40 mN m^{-1}. Methods of measuring γ can be classified as static, involving the relation of interface shape to the shape for a dimensionless model system, e.g., the pendent-drop method, or as dynamic such as the determination of the volume of the detaching portion of a pendent drop (drop-volume method). The underlying principles are embraced in a branch of interfacial science known as capillarity (below). The reader is referred to standard textbooks for methods of interfacial tension determination.[‡] When one phase is a solid it is difficult to determine the analogous solid–solid interfacial tensions and indirect methods are used.

The concept of surface tension can also be introduced from microscopic or statistical mechanical theory, since it originates from intermolecular attraction.[†] One advantage of the microscopic approach is that it enables computer modelling to be carried out of some interfacial properties which it would be difficult to measure experimentally.[‖] Elegant treatments exist to account for the existance of surface energy, but it is instructive to use a simple approach. A typical molecule embedded in the bulk liquid requires its share of the molar enthalpy (and free energy) of vaporization to lose its neighbouring 'liquid' contacts and escape to the vapour. To create new liquid surface requires the loss by each new surface molecule of about one-quarter of the

[†]The symbols and nomenclature in this chapter closely follow IUPAC recommendations (*Pure Appl. Chem.*, **31**, 579 (1972)). It is appropriate in this section to use the Helmholtz free energy $A = U - TS$ rather than the Gibbs function. Phases are denoted by superscripts.
[‡]e.g. Adamson, *Physical Chemistry of Surfaces*, 3rd edn, Interscience, Chichester (1977).
[§]G. Navescues, *Report. Progr. Phys.*, **72**, 1131, 1979.
[‖]J. S. Rowlinson, *Chem. Soc. Rev.* 1978.

Figure 12.1 Representation of the surface region where bulk phase concentrations exist up to AB and CD: the Gibbs surface is SS

neighbouring contacts (say, 3 out of 12) it had in the bulk liquid. On this basis the surface energy is about a quarter of the energy of vaporization.

12.2 Adsorption at interfaces

When at least one of the phases forming an interface is a solution, the composition of the system in the vicinity of the interface is expected to differ from that of the bulk phases. One component, at least, will usually have an enhanced concentration and be said to be adsorbed. The interfacial region whose thickness is at most a few molecular diameters might intuitively be regarded as being physically a heterogeneous layer sandwiched between the bulk phases: between AB and CD in Figure 12.1. To quantify the amount adsorbed, reference is made to a hypothetical system of the same volume as the real system. The surface excess amount or the Gibbs absorption, denoted n_i^σ, of component i is defined as the excess amount of this component actually present over that present in the reference system in which the bulk concentrations of the two phases remain uniform up to what is called the Gibbs dividing surface. Accordingly,

$$n_i^\sigma = n_i - V^\alpha c_i^\alpha - V^\beta c_i^\beta, \tag{12.3}$$

where n_i is the total amount of component i in the system, c_i^α and c_i^β are the concentrations in the two bulk phases α and β, and V^α and V^β are the volumes of the phases defined by the Gibbs surface. There is no volume specially assigned to an adsorbed substance in this description.

Figure 12.2 shows how the concentration c_i in an actual system might vary in the z-direction of Figure 12.1, and it also shows the Gibbs dividing surface positioned between the surfaces which are in the bulk phases. In the vicinity of the Gibbs surface, c_i^α and c_i^β do not exist as bulk values, but there is a variable concentration c_i depending on the position in the z direction of the volume element dV:

$$n_i^\sigma = \int_\alpha (c_i - c_i^\alpha)\, dV + \int_\beta (c_i - c_i^\beta)\, dV. \tag{12.4}$$

252

Figure 12.2   Concentration changes within the surface region

If the surface area $\mathscr{A}$ is known, the Gibbs surface concentration or the surface excess concentration Γ_i^σ is given by

$$\Gamma_i^\sigma = n_i^\sigma / \mathscr{A}. \tag{12.5}$$

Corresponding definitions can be given in terms of numbers of molecules or of mass.

In general the choice of position of a Gibbs surface is arbitrary: the amounts of the components in a reference system do, however, depend on its position. Quantities can be obtained which do not depend on its precise location, and their specification forms the basis for experimental measurements which cannot take the arbitrary nature of the Gibbs surface into account. For a multicomponent system the surface excess concentrations of components 1 and i, Γ_1 and Γ_i, respectively, for an arbitrarily chosen Gibbs surface lead to the relative adsorption $\Gamma_i^{(1)}$ of component i with respect to component 1,

$$\Gamma_i^{(1)} = \Gamma_i^\sigma - \Gamma_1^\sigma \left(\frac{c_i^\alpha - c_i^\beta}{c_1^\alpha - c_1^\beta} \right), \tag{12.6}$$

which corresponds to choosing the Gibbs surface so that $\Gamma_1^\sigma = 0$ and $\Gamma_1^{(1)} = 0$ in the reference system.

For liquid–vapour interfaces when the vapour pressure is low a useful approximation is

$$\Gamma_i^{(1)} = (n_i - n_1 x_i^l / x_1^l) / \mathscr{A}, \tag{12.7}$$

where x_1^l and x_i^l are the mole fractions of components 1 and i in the liquid phase.

The above description of an interface can be extended to give a system of surface thermodynamics which takes surface areas, interfacial tensions and adsorption phenomena into account. Important relationships are to be obtained by this method. An energy U^σ and an entropy S^σ are assigned to the surface to make the model system equivalent in these respects to the real system,

$$U = U^\sigma + U^\alpha + U^\beta; \quad S = S^\sigma + S^\alpha + S^\beta. \tag{12.8}$$

The Helmholtz free energy of the system is

$$A = A^\sigma + A^\alpha + A^\beta; \quad A^\sigma = U^\sigma - TS^\sigma. \tag{12.9}$$

Quantities can be referred to unit surface area, e.g., the surface free energy per unit area is

$$a^\sigma = A^\sigma/\mathscr{A}. \tag{12.10}$$

The total differential of the system is

$$dA = -S\,dT - P^\alpha\,dV^\alpha - P^\beta\,dV^\beta + \gamma\,d\mathscr{A}$$
$$+ \sum_i \bar{\mu}_i^\alpha\,dn_i^\alpha + \sum_i \bar{\mu}_i^\beta\,dn_i^\beta + \sum_i \mu_i^\sigma\,dn_i^\sigma, \tag{12.11}$$

involving obvious bulk terms, but the chemical potentials $\bar{\mu}_i^\alpha$, $\bar{\mu}_i^\beta$ and μ_i^σ must be defined. Partial differentiation of equation 12.9, subject to the usual constraints, gives

$$\bar{\mu}_i^\alpha = \mu_i^\alpha + (\partial A^\sigma/\partial n_i^\alpha)_{n_j^\alpha, n_i^\beta, n_i^\sigma}, \tag{12.12}$$

with an analogous equation for $\bar{\mu}_i^\beta$, where μ_i^α is the usual bulk chemical potential defined in terms of the Helmholtz as opposed to the Gibbs free energy,[†] and, at constant surface area,

$$\mu_i^\sigma = \partial A^\sigma/\partial n_i^\sigma. \tag{12.13}$$

The second term on the right-hand side of equation 12.12 arises because the surface is not strictly autonomous; its properties depend on variables pertaining to phases α and β. In equilibrium studies this second term can be neglected and autonomy assumed, but the power of surface thermodynamics to apply to certain non-equilibrium situations has been indicated.

Using standard thermodynamic formulae it can be shown that

$$dA^\sigma = -S^\sigma\,dT + \gamma\,d\mathscr{A} + \sum_i \mu_i^\sigma\,dn_i^\sigma. \tag{12.14}$$

Appropriate integration gives

$$A^\sigma = \gamma\mathscr{A} + \sum_i \mu_i^\sigma n_i^\sigma, \tag{12.15}$$

[†]Chemical potentials of form $\partial A/\partial n_i = \mu_i$ can be defined involving the Helmholtz function; in the context of interfaces the set of chemical potentials is slightly more complicated than for bulk phases alone.

which, recalling that $\Gamma_i^\sigma = n_i^\sigma / \mathscr{A}$, yields

$$\gamma = a^\sigma - \sum_i \Gamma_i^\sigma \mu_i^\sigma. \tag{12.16}$$

Clearly the interfacial tension γ and the surface free energy per unit area are not identical quantities. Indeed, γ is experimentally measurable, independently of any choice of Gibbs surface, whereas the value of a^σ depends on the position of the dividing surface.

When equation 12.15 is differentiated and compared with equation 12.14 under conditions of constant temperature,

$$\mathrm{d}\gamma = -\sum \Gamma_i \, \mathrm{d}\mu_i, \tag{12.17}$$

is the adsorption isotherm often referred to as the Gibbs equation. It is the fundamental equation for relating the interfacial tension to the amount adsorbed when $\mathrm{d}\mu_i$ is suitably expressed in experimentally measurable terms. The use of the Gibbs adsorption equation will now be illustrated.

Adsorption at liquid–vapour and liquid–liquid interfaces

In many cases the adsorption of one component of a solution at a liquid–vapour or at a liquid–liquid interface, although the latter type is much less studied, gives a layer one molecule thick, called a soluble monolayer. Certain insoluble substances can be made to spread at a liquid surface (usually aqueous) giving insoluble monolayers which are discussed later (section 12.3). Appropriate forms of the Gibbs adsorption equation can be used to obtain the amount of a soluble substance adsorbed.

For solute component 2 in solvent 1, the chemical potential of 2 can be written as a function of its activity,

$$\mu_2^l = \mu_2^{\ominus,l} + RT \ln a_2^l. \tag{12.18}$$

The relative adsorption, equation 12.6, of component 2 with respect to 1, $\Gamma_2^{(1)}$, corresponds to putting $\Gamma_1 = 0$ in equation 12.17 which becomes

$$\mathrm{d}\gamma = -\Gamma_2^{(1)} RT \ln a_2^l. \tag{12.19}$$

Equation 12.19 is applicable to a component which does not dissociate in solution, e.g., a simple alcohol in water. The adsorption at a liquid–liquid interface can similarly be obtained. For an ideal or sufficiently dilute solution the concentration c_2 can replace a_2^l, and the slope of experimentally determined γ against c_2 plots gives $\Gamma_2^{(1)}$.

There is considerable interest in amphipathic molecules having a hydrocarbon and a polar hydrophilic portion, which are known as surfactants (including soaps and detergents). They may be anionic, cationic or non-ionic, and will be discussed in more detail in Chapter 13. The anionic surfactant sodium n-dodecylsulphate, $C_{12}H_{25}SO_4Na$, is a convenient example. The appropriate form of the Gibbs equation for this molecule in water is

$$\mathrm{d}\gamma = -2RT\Gamma_2^{(1)} \ln a_\pm, \tag{12.20}$$

where $a_{\pm}$ is the mean ion activity of the surfactant. Values of $\Gamma_2^{(1)}$ obtained in this way give the area $\sigma = 1/\Gamma_2^{(1)}$ occupied by a surfactant molecule at, say, the surface of water, or at the surface of an aqueous solution containing an inorganic salt (the factor 2 in equation 12.20 is eliminated in these circumstances). Values of σ obtained in this manner, compatible with surfactant anions close-packed perpendicular to the aqueous surface are 53 Å^2 for $C_{12}H_{25}SO_4Na$ and 59 Å^2 for $C_7H_{15}CH(SO_3Na)COOC_6H_{13}$ in 0.01 M sodium chloride.

Adsorption at liquid–solid interfaces

Apart from the division of solutions into electrolytes and non-electrolytes, it will be recognized that binary mixtures with miscibility in all proportions have a symmetry not present when one component is a solute of limited solubility. Polymer adsorption from solution must take account of solvent qualities, e.g., good or theta, as already discussed (Chapter 11); further discussion is deferred to Chapter 13. The amount of a component adsorbed from solution onto a solid can be obtained by measuring the change in solution composition following immersion of the solid (often powdered) into the liquid. Solids are first of all cleaned by removal of adsorbed species by heating them under vacuum, they are then sealed in a container (ampoule) which is broken under the liquid surface. Adsorption processes are accompanied by enthalpy changes, in this case called the enthalpy of immersion of the solid, which can be interpreted in terms of liquid–solid interactions.

For a binary mixture of molecules 1 and 2 present in total amount n, equilibrated with mass m of solid adsorbent, the specific surface excess amount, $n(x_2^0 - x_2)/m$, where x_2^0 and x_2 are, respectively, the initial and final mole fractions of component 2 in the bulk mixture, can be measured. Figure 12.3 shows two typical forms of the corresponding surface excess isotherm. In this manner of representing adsorption, there is no adsorption of component 2 when $x_2 = 0$ and when $x_2 = 1$. In Figure 12.3(b) there is also a surface azeotrope signified by the zero adsorption at intermediate x_2. A monomolecular model of competitive adsorption on the solid surface can explain many systems, especially when the molecules occupy similar areas when adsorbed, e.g. benzene + cyclohexane. Unlike the case of adsorption of a single component gas or vapour onto a solid, there is now a balance between the state when a molecule is attracted to the surface and surrounded on the other sides by molecules of kind 1 and 2, and the state where a particular molecule is surrounded by 1 and 2 in the bulk.[†] Many attempts have been made to deduce individual (component) isotherms from composite or excess ones using extra-thermodynamic assumptions and vapour adsorption isotherms: they are outside the scope of this chapter. Many adsorption-from-solution isotherms, e.g. of amino acids in water, only cover a portion of the composition range before reaching solute saturation.

[†]D. H. Everett, Spec. Period. Report, Chem. Soc., *Colloid Science*, 1, 49 (1973).

256

Figure 12.3 Two common types of composite isotherm for adsorption from solution on a solid. Type (a) is, for example, shown by benzene (1) + methyl acetate (2) on boehmite (alumina); and type (b) is shown by ethanol (1) + benzene (2) on carbon, with the surface azeotrope of bulk composition at x_2 ca. 0.8

12.3 Capillarity

There are many surface phenomena which do not depend on adsorption, but which are associated with the properties of fluid–fluid interfaces. They are related to the laws of capillarity.

When an interface between phases i and j is increased in area by $d\mathscr{A}^{ij}$ the work done on the system is

$$dW = \gamma^{ij} d\mathscr{A}^{ij} + \mathscr{A}^{ij} d\gamma^{ij}. \tag{12.21}$$

It will subsequently be assumed that γ^{ij} is constant. For finite reversible changes to a system involving liquid–solid, liquid–vapour and solid–vapour interfaces,

$$\Delta W = \gamma^{ls}\Delta\mathscr{A}^{ls} + \gamma^{lv}\Delta\mathscr{A}^{lv} + \gamma^{sv}\Delta\mathscr{A}^{sv}. \tag{12.22}$$

Figure 12.4   Sessile drop of liquid showing definition of contact angle θ. Contact-angle hysteresis can lead to two limiting values θ_a and θ_r. When the three-phase confluence is at a solid edge, 'hinging' is possible between limits where θ (assumed single value) is shown applying to the two solid surfaces meeting at the edge

When no other changes are significant, e.g., no chemical reaction and neglecting gravitational effects, the Helmholtz free energy change for a finite reversible change to a closed system is $\Delta F = \Delta W$.

Figure 12.4 shows a sessile drop of liquid on a solid surface. The contact angle θ is defined as the angle between the liquid–vapour interface and the solid, and is always taken, by convention, through the denser phase. Contact angles generally pertain to the chemical composition of the three phases involved (one solid and two fluids), but the contact angle is often found to vary over a range of values, giving rise to contact-angle hysteresis. The limits of the range, $\theta_a > \theta > \theta_r$, as Figure 12.4 depicts, are the advancing angle θ_a and the receding angle θ_r depending, respectively, on whether the static configuration has arisen from forward or backward movement of the denser fluid phase over the surface. Possible causes of contact-angle hysteresis are chemical heterogeneity of the solid surface, surface roughness and the presence of impurities. To simplify the following discussion a unique contact angle θ will be assumed. The limiting case is $\theta = 0°$ when the liquid spreads over the solid surface. The cases of $\theta > 0°$ are divided, by convention, into wetting and non-wetting conditions:

$$0° < \theta < 90° \qquad 90° < \theta < 180°$$
$$\text{wetting} \qquad\qquad \text{non-wetting}$$

By an analysis involving the free energy change of the system, when the three-phase confluence is displaced with concomitant area changes, one of the general conditions for equilibrium when θ is not zero is obtained,

$$\gamma^{sv} = \gamma^{sl} + \gamma^{lv} \cos \theta, \qquad (12.23)$$

which is known as Young's equation. A fluid–fluid interface may meet a solid surface at an edge which allows the interface some amount of 'hinging', without forming the contact angle θ, and equation 12.23 is not applicable. The range of movement of the interface at a fixed edge will, however, be governed by θ with respect to the solid surfaces meeting at the edge as Figure 12.4 also indicates.

Water, for example, gives a contact angle of about 112° on solid paraffin and polyethylene surfaces, and would be said to be non-wetting; such surfaces are termed low energy. On many clean inorganic solids, minerals and oxides and metals, known as high energy surfaces, water spreads ($\theta = 0°$). A useful empirical concept, the critical surface tension of a solid surface, γ_c, has been found to be capable of separating solids on which a liquid will spread from those on which a finite contact angle is formed. The quantity γ_c for a solid can be obtained by extrapolating plots of $\cos \theta$ against γ^{lv} for a series of liquids, e.g., alkanes, to $\cos \theta = 1$, or $\theta = 0°$. Other liquids with $\gamma^{lv} < \gamma_c$ will spread over the solid. Table 12.2 gives a few values of γ_c. Values of γ_c for a solid can be increased to give better wetting by chemical modification, e.g. using electrical discharge (plasma) or by flaming. These are important considerations in achieving good adhesive joints; generally good wetting favours good adhesion. The semiqualitative classification into low and high energy surfaces arises because spreading will only be spontaneous when there is a free energy decrease, which means the free energy associated with the creation of liquid–solid and liquid–vapour interfacial areas must be more than compensated for by the decrease in solid–vapour interfacial free energy: equations 12.22 and 12.23.

The interfacial tension between two fluid phases, whereby the interface behaves like a membrane in tension, has important consequences when the interface is curved. The mean surface curvature, which can vary over the interface, is

$$J = \frac{1}{r_1} + \frac{1}{r_2}, \qquad (12.24)$$

where r_1 and r_2 are the the principal radii of curvature. Figure 12.5 shows

Table 12.2   Critical surface tensions

Solid surface material	γ_c/mN m^{-1}
Polyethylene	31
Poly(vinyl chloride)	39
Polytetrafluoroethylene	18
Perfluorolauric acid monolayer on solid ($-CF_3$ exposed)	6

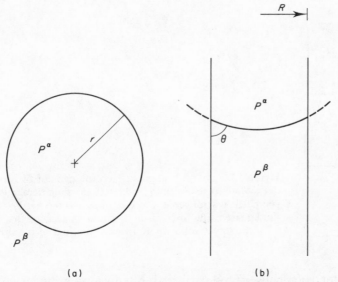

Figure 12.5   For the spherical drop of liquid (a) the mean surface curvature is $J = 2/r$ and $P^\alpha > P^\beta$. For liquid (b) in a solid
cylinder (e.g., a pore) where the contact angle is θ, the mean
surface curvature is $J = -(2/R)\cos\theta$ and $P^\alpha > P^\beta$. The vapour
pressure, equation 12.28, when one phase is a vapour or a mixture of vapour and gas may need to be distinguished from these
hydrostatic pressures

values of J for two simple interface shapes, but for complicated interfacial
configurations the evaluation of J is often difficult. At any position on a
curved interface there is a component of γ acting inwards giving rise to a
pressure difference across the interface called the capillary pressure,

$$\Delta P = P^\alpha - P^\beta = \gamma J. \qquad (12.25)$$

Equation 12.25 is usually referred to as Laplace's equation, although the
underlying principle is attributable to both Young and Laplace. The greater
pressure is always on what can loosely be called the concave of the interface.

For a small spherical drop of liquid of radius r (see Figure 12.5) surrounded
by air the capillary pressure, given by equation 12.25, is $2\gamma/r$. For a spherical
soap bubble of radius r, to a good approximation $J = 2\gamma/r$, also, but 2γ represents the inner and outer surfaces of the soap film and replaces γ in 12.25.
The force exerted on two solid particles separated by a fluid bridge, shown for
two cylindrical solids in Figure 12.6, provides a more subtle problem, even
neglecting gravity. The component of the fluid–fluid interfacial tension
resolved axially, and acting around the edge of the solids, combined with the
capillary pressure acting across the end faces of the solids, gives

$$f = 2\pi r\gamma \cos \phi - \pi r^2 \gamma J. \qquad (12.26)$$

Figure 12.6 Fluid bridge between the ends of two solid cylinders. Many types of fluid bridge are possible depending on the geometrical arrangement of the solids and the nature of the two fluid phases. The force given by equation 12.26 is that acting on the upper solid where it joins the fluid of the bridge

The interaction between soil particles is often via water bridges which can draw the particles together or hold them apart depending on the volume and geometrical shape of the bridge. In a gravitational field the hydrostatic pressure in a fluid phase α decreases in the upward vertical direction z by $\rho^\alpha g z$ (Pascal's laws), and so the capillary pressure, or J at constant γ according to equation 12.25, must also vary. The most straightforward cases to deal with are those having an axis of rotation aligned in the vertical direction.[†] Figure 12.7 shows the meridian curves of some of the more common examples. In dealing with such static systems the quantities determining interface shape and stability are γ and the density difference $\Delta\rho$ between the fluid phases, which can be combined to define the capillary constant

$$a = (2\gamma/\Delta\rho g)^{1/2}. \tag{12.27}$$

An alternative definition omits the factor 2. What this effectively means is that a distance z in an actual system can be scaled by a to give a reduced or dimensionless quantity $Z = z/a$, regardless of the chemical composition. Furthermore, conditions of zero gravity, $g = 0$, can also be met by choosing two fluids of the same density, $\Delta\rho = 0$: the above dimensionless form is then not appropriate.

Hydrostatic pressures P^α and P^β must be distinguished from the vapour pressure p when one phase is a vapour in a gas. A plane liquid surface at temperature T will have above it a vapour pressure p° when the hydrostatic pressure in the liquid phase is one atmosphere. For a liquid component 1 separated from the vapour phase by a curved interface the hydrostatic pressure in the liquid will change, and so will its chemical potential μ^1_1. The change in chemical potential of the vapour phase component 1 compensating

[†]E. A. Boucher, *Reports Progr. Phys.*, **43**, 497 (1980).

Figure 12.7 Eight types of meridian curve which on rotation about the vertical axis give the following axisymmetric fluid bodies in a gravitational field: (a) pendent drop, (b) emergent bubble, (c) sessile drop, (d) captive bubble, (e) raised holm, (f) submerged holm, (g) light bridge, and (h) heavy bridge

for this will be due to a change in fugacity, or, assuming ideal vapour, to a change from p° to p given at equilibrium by

$$RT \ln p/p^\circ = 2\gamma V_m^l J, \qquad (12.28)$$

where V_m^l is the molar volume of the liquid. Equation 12.28 is known as Kelvin's equation. For a spherical liquid droplet of radius r surrounded by its vapour, $J > 0$ and $p > p^\circ$: the increase in vapour pressure for water at room temperature is $p/p^\circ \approx 1.1$ for $r = 10$ nm.

A droplet of liquid will be unstable with respect to a plane liquid surface at the same temperature. It would evaporate, transferring by vapour diffusion to the plane surface. The sign of J in equation 12.28 determines whether $p > p^\circ$ or $p < p^\circ$. Examples of $p < p^\circ$ are given by water in a glass capillary tube and water adsorbed (capillary condensation) by many porous solids, since the water–vapour interface is concave on the vapour side ($\theta < 90^\circ$). On a plane solid surface in contact with water vapour there would be adsorbate increasing in thickness to give a layer a few molecules thick with increase in p, and eventually becoming thicker so that at saturation bulk condensation occurs ($\theta = 0^\circ$ for simplicity).

Liquid lenses and spreading phenomena

When a drop of liquid is placed on a second with which it is not miscible, three basic phenomena represented schematically in Figure 12.8 can occur: (a) the drop can form a lens; (b) the drop can spread to give a duplex film whose thickness depends on the area available for spreading; and (c) some of the drop can spread to form a monolayer on top of the liquid. A spreading liquid solvent can be used to facilitate the spreading of an insoluble substance yielding an insoluble monolayer when the solvent evaporates.

Figure 12.8 Representation of lens formation and spreading phenomena: (a) simple lens of one liquid on another; (b) spread film of liquid; (c) lens and spread monolayer; and (d) specification of a lens leading to equation 12.29

The condition for mechanical equilibrium of the stable drop (Figure 12.8) is usually expressed as Neumann's triangle of forces,

$$\gamma^{wa} \cos \phi_1 = \gamma^{oa} \cos \phi_2 + \gamma^{ow} \cos \phi_3. \qquad (12.29)$$

The shape and position of the lens will depend on the densities of the three fluid phases, and on the three interfacial tensions.

Spreading can be dealt with by introducing the spreading coefficient or tension S,

$$S = \gamma^{wa} - \gamma^{oa} - \gamma^{ow}. \qquad (12.30)$$

If the full horizontal force γ^{wa} exceeds the sum of the other two, then spreading will occur:

$$S > 0 \text{ spreading;} \qquad S < 0 \text{ lens formation.} \qquad (12.31)$$

It is more satisfactory to consider the possibility of spreading in terms of the free energy change arising from area changes according to equation 12.22, but the conclusions will be the same for spreading conditions. Table 12.3

Table 12.3 Behaviour of oily liquids on water[†]

Liquid	γ^{oa}/mN m^{-1}	γ^{ow}/mN m^{-1}	S/mN m^{-1}	Comment
n-Octane	21.8	50.8	+0.2	Can just spread
n-Octanol	27.5	8.5	+36.8	Spreads
n-Hexadecane	30.0	52.1	−9.3	Lens, no spreading
Benzene	28.9	35.0	+8.9 to −1.4	Initially spreads, then gives lens with surrounding monolayer

[†]Using γ^{wa}/mN m^{-1} = 72.8 at 293 K.

illustrates the use of S, and it shows how the situation can be altered when interfacial tensions change, as in the case of benzene due to mutual saturation being achieved starting from pure benzene and pure water. Benzene after initially spreading retracts to a lens, but with a monolayer of benzene on the remaining surface. A lower value of γ^{wa} due to an impure water surface would, other things being equal, reduce the chances of spreading occurring.

Spread monolayers of molecules such as hexadecanol can reduce the rate of evaporation from lakes. Artificially spread monolayers (apart from the role of natural ones) may sufficiently affect lake surfaces to alter the ecology, e.g. by preventing mosquito larvae from maintaining a location for breathing.

Insoluble monolayers

The aspect of insoluble monolayers to which this account is limited concerns the manner in which the two-dimensional pressure exerted by the monolayer depends on the surface area occupied by a known amount of substance. The use of a Langmuir–Adam trough for this purpose has a considerable history. It is still used for understanding intermolecular interactions, particularly (these days) those of biologically significant species. Figure 12.9 shows a highly schematic representation of the principle of operation.

The insoluble monolayer is to be contained between the movable barrier and the float attached to the torsion balance. The substance to be spread is dissolved in e.g., petroleum ether, and placed in small quantities at various locations on the clean water surface. A uniform layer of adsorbate should be obtained when the solvent has evaporated. The presence of the adsorbed layer reduces the surface tension relative to that, γ_0, of the still clean water on the other side of the float, giving a spreading pressure π,

$$\pi = \gamma_0 - \gamma. \tag{12.32}$$

The force needed (measured with the torsion mechanism) to maintain the float in position as the movable barrier is used to compress the adsorbed layer is (per unit length of float) a direct measure of π. The area available to the amount of spread substance is given from the geometrical area of the enclosed surface. Plots of π against the area per molecule can be constructed, as shown schematically for stearic acid and myristic acid (octa- and tetradecanoic) in

Figure 12.9 Schematic representation of the principle of operation of the Langmuir–Adam trough

264

Figure 12.10 Dependence of surface pressure, π, on the area available per molecule of spread substance, shown schematically for (a) stearic acid on water (—) and dilute HCl (– –) at 293 K, and (b) myristic acid on 0.1 mol dm^{-3} hydrochloric acid at 288 K. The area scale in (b) is distorted to show the main features—see text

Figure 12.10. Plots are usually interpreted in terms of an analogy to a hypothetical two-dimensional gas which on compression changes 'state'. Straight chain fatty acids, e.g. stearic, at room temperature give very low pressures when there is a large area available per molecule: the oriented molecules form two-dimensional clumps or islands due to hydrocarbon chain interactions. On compression they pack tightly and the surface pressure rises steeply. Myristic acid molecules, by comparison, separate at large available areas and behave like a two-dimensional gas. This can be compressed to give a so-called liquid-expanded region, and eventually compression gives a condensed state: the film cannot withstand further compression and would buckle. The phospholipid molecules discussed in Chapter 13 have been studied using the Langmuir–Adam trough.†

†M. N. Jones, *Biological Interfaces*, Elsevier, London and Amsterdam (1975).

12.4 Nucleation phenomena

Nucleation concerns the onset of a phase change, e.g. vapour → liquid or liquid → solid; the discussion of the phase diagrams in Chapters 1, 4 and 7 assumed that there are no impediments to the changes. In practice, different phase changes can cover a wide range of time scales due to energy barriers, and the time scale of a particular change can be varied by altering the height of the energy barrier. While microscopic treatments of nucleation are available† it is instructive to deal here with macroscopic quantities.

A common illustrative experiment involves observing the crystal growth from the melt of sodium thiosulphate, which once started occurs rapidly from a few locations. These locations are the positions of nuclei which, as will be seen, depend on the cleanliness of the system; crystal growth would be greatly helped by providing a few crystals to the supercooled melt. The slow crystallization of clear honey represents a situation where nucleation is not readily achieved. Many natural phenomena, e.g. cloud (liquid droplet) formation and ice (snow or hail) formation, involve nucleation phenomena. The production of a new phase such as a liquid from vapour, or solid from liquid, even though thermodynamically favourable in terms of the chemical potentials of the bulk phases, requires a mechanism often entailing an embryo or nucleus of the new phase. When only a single component or a phase of uniform composition is involved the process is termed homogeneous nucleation. When the embryo of the new phase forms on a different (inert) solid surface the process is termed heterogeneous nucleation.

Figure 12.11 Schematic representation of (a) homogeneous nucleation, and (b) heterogeneous nucleation on a solid substrate

†A. C. Zettlemoyer (ed.), *Nucleation*, Dekker, New York (1969).

Figure 12.12 Dependence of ΔG for liquid water droplet formation on droplet size for various saturation ratios S

Figure 12.11 depicts both kinds of process. Clearly all the molecules of a liquid cannot suddenly adopt positions required for the solid. By forming tiny clusters an interface is produced between solid and liquid with an increase in free energy. For liquid droplet formation from a vapour, for instance,

$$\Delta G = \Delta G_{\text{bulk}} + 4\pi r^2 \gamma^{\text{lv}}. \tag{12.33}$$

Figure 12.12 shows how ΔG depends on the radius r of the cluster for several values of the supersaturation ratio S of the vapour. There is a critical nucleus size r^* corresponding to the maximum ΔG^* in the free energy change. Only if a cluster of atoms or molecules can grow and slightly exceed this critical size will the subsequent spontaneous growth of the new phase be possible. The rate j of nucleation depends strongly on ΔG^*,

$$j \sim \exp(-\Delta G^*/RT), \tag{12.34}$$

and any way of reducing ΔG^* will increase the rate of growth to a size $r > r^*$. In heterogeneous nucleation the corresponding energy barrier is lowered by energetically favourable cluster formation on the solid surface. The dependence on the exponent in equation 12.34 is often so sharp that a small temperature change can result in very rapid nucleation and growth when effectively the rate was nil before. Solid atmospheric particles (for example) nucleate ice from supercooled water vapour in the presence of liquid droplets at a characteristic threshold temperature: for the artificial cloud-seeding agent silver iodide the threshold temperature is 267 K.

Chapter 13

Colloidal systems

13.1 Introduction

Colloidal systems consist of two or more phases and have a large interfacial area to volume ratio. Systems can acquire properties not displayed by simple true solutions or by bulk matter when at least one dimension of a phase is in the submicron region. Many systems of natural occurrence, animate and inanimate, of technological or domestic importance and of fundamental novelty fall within the scope of colloid science.

Table 13.1 gives the technical names of the colloid types of dispersed system where one phase is a liquid; other types are included for comparison. The table only includes cases which are straightforward to classify, since colloids are often complex. There are also numerous examples which cannot be described as consisting of a dispersed phase in a continuous medium, including membranes where only one dimension is small. There are two other important classes not included in the table: association colloids consisting of aggregates of surfactant molecules, and macromolecules (polymers) in solution, in dispersion or existing as gels. True solutions of polymers are sometimes referred to as lyophilic (liquid-liking) colloids, and dispersions of, say, silver iodide in water are referred to as being lyophobic. It will not be possible to deal here with other than the physical nature of colloids,† in spite of the significance to biology.‡ The physical structures of biological systems, e.g., membranes, bones, and fluids are colloidal and, therefore, colloid science is important to an understanding of them in the absence of chemical reactions. Biochemical processes of a colloidal nature occur which can be classed as physical (e.g., the micellization of fatty substances by bile) or chemical; reactions are greatly influenced in kind and in their kinetic rate by the colloidal framework in which they occur.

Soils provide many examples of the importance of colloid and interfacial

†D. J. Shaw, *Introduction to Colloid and Surface Chemistry*, 3rd edn, Butterworths, London (1981).
‡M. N. Jones, *Biological Interfaces*, Elsevier, London and Amsterdam (1975).

Table 13.1   Some colloid types

Phases			
dispersed	continuous	Name	Example
Liquid	Gas	Liquid aerosol	Fog, spray
Gas	Liquid	Foam	Froth
Liquid	Liquid	Emulsion	Milk, pharmaceutical bases
Solid	Liquid	Sol or colloidal suspension: paste at high solid content	Silver iodide sol: toothpaste
Liquid	Solid	Solid emulsion	
Solid	Gas	Solid aerosol	Dust
Gas	Solid	Solid foam	Expanded polystyrene
Solid	Solid	Solid suspension	TiO_2 in plastics

phenomena. Clay minerals fall into colloidal dimensions and are greatly affected by adsorption from solution, and by the dependence of particle–particle interactions on the nature of the continuous medium. The stability of clays, affecting agriculture and civil engineering, is a colloidal phenomenon. Bricks and other building materials, e.g., cement, are also colloidal, and phenomena such as rising damp and frost damage represent aspects of the science of porous solids. Atmospheric particles, e.g., clay minerals, volcanic dust and soluble salts from the sea and from industrial processes, are colloidal, as are smokes. The chemical industry generally relies on many colloidal systems, e.g. finely divided solid catalysts, but it is perhaps with household chemicals such as cosmetics, toothpaste, pharmaceutical creams and greases, foodstuffs e.g. flour and bread represent different colloid types (and the art of cooking), inks and paints that one has most contact with colloidal systems.

13.2   Formation of dispersions

In many cases the source of the colloidal type under consideration will be obvious, but a brief outline of methods of dispersion preparation is needed. The bases of most methods of forming dispersions are either the aggregation of smaller species or the breaking-down (milling and grinding) of bulk material. Grinding usually gives particle sizes at the upper end of the range and a wide size distribution. Certain chemical reactions can be carefully controlled to prevent the formation of bulk precipitate, e.g. $AgNO_3(aq)$ + KI(aq) can be used to give a AgI sol which is stable when the concentration of one of the reactants is in excess. Also, $HAuCl_4(aq)$ can be reduced, e.g. with HCHO, to give gold sols. Sulphur sols can be prepared by grinding bulk solid, by adding a dilute solution in alcohol to hot water or by the reduction of $Na_2S_2O_3$. It will be clear from the final section of Chapter 12 that nucleation can lead, if controlled, to colloid formation. If nucleation can be made to occur over a relatively short period of time, subsequent growth will sometimes give monodisperse systems (narrow size range). Nuclei for gold sol formation can be prepared by reducing $HAuCl_4$ (neutralized with K_2CO_3) with white phosphorus. Model colloids of monodisperse polystyrene latex particles can be prepared by carefully initiated emulsion polymerization.

13.3 Colloid stability

General considerations

Colloids consisting of solutions of macromolecules or aggregates of surfactant molecules may be thermodynamically stable. Many colloidal dispersions are not thermodynamically stable, but are able to remain in an essentially unchanged state for long periods of time (years). Particles in a fluid dispersion medium will experience Brownian motion, analogous to the translational motion of the molecules of the medium, but collision between colloid particles need not lead to coalescence or aggregation. The particles will be attracted to one another by van der Waals forces (Chapter 2), the magnitude of the attraction depending on the species, but a dominating repulsive component may also be present, preventing coagulation. Two basic mechanisms conferring stability arise from the existence of an electric double layer at the particle surface, or from the presence of neutral molecules, e.g. of polymer, adsorbed from solution at the particle surface.

Electric double layers

Proteins, e.g., bovine serum albumin, and similar molecules dispersed in water can acquire charge, dependent on the pH of the dispersion medium, by ionization to give either $-NH_3^+$ or $-COO^-$ groups. Due to the strong electrostatic interaction between ions, whichever ionic group is present will have around it counterions of opposite charge giving an electric double layer. Inorganic particles in water can acquire charge by adsorbing ions from solution, or by one ion species of an ionic solid preferentially dissolving leaving a charged surface; an electric double layer will exist in both cases. The establishment of a double layer close to the surface causes a redistribution of ions around it, compared to the bulk liquid. This outer region is subjected to thermal agitation and is called the diffuse double layer. It is analogous to the ionic atmosphere around the central ion in the Debye–Hückel model (Chapter 9). The ionic species at the particle surface is called the potential-determing ion: the variation of electrical potential ψ with distance from the surface where it is ψ_0, is a major feature of charged colloids. Naturally occurring aqueous colloidal dispersions are often, but not inevitably, negatively charged, probably because large polarizable anions can adsorb strongly whereas the cations are more readily hydrated.

270

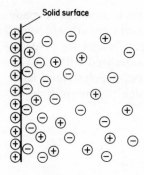

Figure 13.1   Schematic representation of the ionic distribution adjacent to a positively charged surface in the Gouy–Chapman model

In dealing with models for electric double layers it is necessary to examine separately the diffuse layer and the inner or Stern layer. Simple treatments assume point charges in a Boltzmann distribution and a plane surface, thus Figure 13.1 is a highly schematic representation. In the diffuse region the net density of charge is related to ψ by Poisson's equation giving, with the approximation $Ze\psi_0/2kT \ll 1$, the dependence of ψ on distance x as

$$\psi = \psi_0 \exp(-\kappa x) \tag{13.1}$$

where $1/\kappa$ is the thickness of the diffuse double layer:

$$\kappa = \left(\frac{2e^2 n_0 Z^2}{\varepsilon_0 K_r kT}\right)^{1/2} \tag{13.2}$$

The permittivity of the medium is K_r, the number density of ions is n_0 (the product of the electrolyte concentration and Avogadro's number), e is unit charge and Z is the number of charges on an ion. Figure 13.2(a) depicts the electrical potential variation implied by this model.

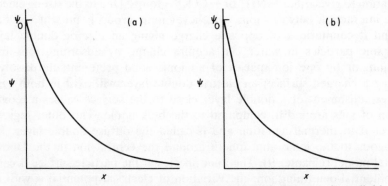

Figure 13.2   Dependence of the electrical potential ψ near the colloid particle on distance x: (a) for the diffuse region, and (b) for the Stern model of Figure 13.3 with the diffuse model applying except very close to the surface (the precise dependence of ψ on x near the surface depends on the system, but that shown is thought to be the usual behaviour)

Figure 13.3 Schematic representation of the region very close to the solid, showing the Stern plane where the potential is ψ_δ and the shear plane where it is ζ

Close to the solid surface the finite size of the ions and their hydration become more important. The centres of hydrated ions in the vicinity of the charged surface are not able to approach closer than a hydrated-ion radius, defining the Stern plane shown in Figure 13.3: these ions become specifically but not permanently adsorbed. They modify the dependence of ψ on x as is shown in Figure 13.2(b), whereas further away from the surface the exponential decay of ψ from $\psi = \psi_\delta$ instead of $\psi = \psi_0$ is adequate. Specific adsorption of ions can lead to more complicated properties including the reversal of sign of the charge (i.e., giving negative ψ_δ). Apart from their effect on $\psi(x)$, the specific adsorption of (hydrated) ions affects the mobility of the surface relative to the liquid, since movement is expected to occur at the shear plane where the potential is ζ. The zeta potential is the most important single characteristic and measurable quantity pertaining to charged surfaces.

The electric double layer stabilizes colloids against coagulation (flocculation) by the potential energy barrier arising from the overlap of regions of ψ (depending on x) as is shown schematically in Figure 13.4. It is thought that there can exist under some circumstances a shallow secondary minimum further out than the maximum in Figure 13.4 which can give rise to loose and readily reversible flocculation. The amount of protection afforded by the maximum in the energy is strongly dependent on its height. Addition of so-called indifferent electrolyte to the aqueous phase increases the concentration of ions in the vicinity of the charged surface with the result that ψ decays more rapidly. Increase in ionic charge has the same effect, namely that the double layer is compressed. The height of the energy barrier (Figure 13.4) is accordingly reduced, possibly to a value where coagulation occurs. The dependence of colloid stability on ion charge (usually called the Schulze–Hardy rule) is very strong. For the coagulation of a negatively charged silver

Figure 13.4   Potential energy barrier for two stabilized colloid particles. The primary minimum and
'hard-sphere' repulsion curve are omitted

iodide sol the critical concentrations for coagulation are approximately 140, 2.5 and 7×10^{-2} mmol dm^{-3} for 1:1, 2:1 and 3:1 electrolytes, i.e., lanthanum nitrate is of the order of 10^3 more effective than potassium nitrate.

Electrokinetic phenomena

The four basic types of electrokinetic phenomena are associated with:

(1) the electrophoretic mobility of a charged particle in an electric field;

(2) the electro-osmotic pressure (or liquid flow) developed when an electrical potential difference is applied across liquid within a fixed solid porous plug or compact of solid particles having a charged surface;

(3) the streaming potential developed across a similar porous bed when the liquid is forced through it;

(4) the sedimentation potential developed between the top and bottom of a liquid in which charged particles are settling.

Particle electrophoresis, a powerful technique for the separation of charged species and for characterizing their surface (ζ-potential) serves to illustrate these phenomena. Paper electrophoresis and gel electrophoresis, used extensively for biochemical separations, are more complicated methods with similar principles. Figure 13.5 shows the basic electrophoresis cell and the method of observing particle movement. Because the inner surface of the

Figure 13.5 Schematic arrangement for particle electrophoresis. The central portion of the capillary joining the
electrode compartments is shown in enlarged section. Scattered light from the particles is viewed at right angles to the
incident beam through a microscope

glass cell in contact with water will be charged, there will be electro-osmotic
flow near the walls and return flow in the centre of the bore. True electrophoretic mobility must be measured where these flows cancel out, which is at
0.146 of the bore diameter from the inner cell wall. An individual particle is
picked out by the light it scatters (Tyndall effect; the particles are usually too
small for direct observation with visible light), and timed over a fixed distance,
e.g. 0.1 nm, with a suitable voltage drop. In addition to enabling the zeta
potential to be measured, the determination of electrophoretic mobility can
be used to assess the effect of particle surface modification, including the
influence of adsorbed species such as surfactants or the change in pH. A
significant feature of electrically charged colloids is the point of zero charge,
i.e. when conditions are such that ζ becomes zero.

Steric stabilization

The adsorption of non-charged molecules from solution, e.g. poly(ethylene
oxide) or non-ionic surfactants, can also protect colloids against coagulation
by what is known as steric stabilization. A most effective procedure to attain
this kind of stability is to use block copolymers, one portion of which is
readily adsorbed onto the colloidal particles, the other portion of which
prefers solvent contact and the freedom to adopt configurations. The fundamental basis for steric stabilization is to imagine the adsorption of polymer
molecules which will involve surface contact at intervals as shown schematically in Figure 13.6. It was explained in Chapter 11 that random coil
configurations of polymer molecules in solution tend to exist in isolation, i.e.,
without interpenetration on collision except under theta conditions (see also the

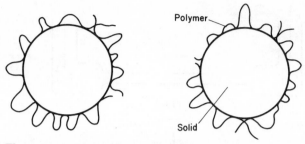

Figure 13.6 Schematic representation of polymer adsorption on solid particles. Some segments of each polymer molecule adsorb but others are surrounded by solvent

following section). A colloidal particle with adsorbed polymer encountering a similarly clad particle will be of an approximately similar thermodynamic nature, the barrier to polymer penetration providing a barrier to coagulation of the particles. Under these circumstances there is reasonable agreement between conditions for coagulation and theta conditions for the polymer + solvent combination in the absence of the colloid. Poly(ethylene oxide) in water shows phase separation (Chapter 11) on heating (LCST with $\Theta \simeq 369$ K), the temperature of separation being lowered in the presence of inorganic salts. A colloidal particle stabilized with poly(ethylene oxide) in the presence of salts becomes unstable on heating to near the theta temperature. With smaller adsorbed species containing $-CH_2CH_2O-$ units other factors are also involved. The term steric implies an entropic effect, but it is the free energy which is important and the enthalpic contribution may dominate in some cases.

Polymers can also bring about colloid instability by the mechanism known as bridging flocculation. If in dilute solution a polymer molecule, e.g., poly-acrylamide in water, adsorbs to two particles simultaneously, they will be unstable and further aggregation will ensue.

13.4 Association colloids and macromolecules

Some types of molecule when placed in water will under certain circumstances form discrete aggregates. Molecules prone to aggregation are those described in Chapter 12 as being strongly adsorbed at interfaces—the surfactants which were broadly classified as being either water soluble or insoluble. The aggregates formed from water-soluble surfactants, e.g. sodium dodecyl sulphate (SDS), are called micelles (Figure 13.7): these only exist above a certain surfactant concentration called the critical micelle concentration, e.g. the c.m.c. for SDS is about 0.08 mol dm^{-3}.

It was explained in Chapter 12 that changes of surface tension with concentration can be used with the Gibbs adsorption equation to measure the amount of surfactant adsorbed at the liquid–vapour interface. When the c.m.c. is reached there is no further decrease in γ with increase in bulk surfactant concentration. Also the variation of other properties with surfactant concentration, e.g. electrical conductivity and osmotic pressure, show a change of slope denoting the c.m.c.

The interiors of micelles are able to solubilize oily substances, or to envelop solid particles with oily surfaces or surfaces on which the hydrocarbon chains can adsorb. The use of soap and detergent solutions for washing depends in part on the solubilization of dirt once it has been removed from a surface. Solubilization of reactive organic molecules can greatly increase reaction rates due to the increase in local concentration. In the human body bile acids (and salts) solubilize fatty substances by micelle formation. In some cases of so-called emulsion polymerization, e.g. of styrene, the polymerization occurs within what are initially micelles (e.g. of sodium dodecyl sulphate in water containing solubilized monomer). These micelles subsequently become polymer particles stabilized against aggregation by adsorbed surfactant molecules.

It is thought that micelles of simple surfactants are basically spherical in shape at concentrations just above the c.m.c. For straight chain surfactants with 12–14 carbon atoms, micelle size ranges from about 30 to 50 molecules, being about 5 nm in diameter. The formation of a micelle can in simple terms be envisaged as involving two processes:

(1) the collection together of hydrocarbon tails, which, although energetically favourable is not appreciably more so than the water–hydrocarbon interaction of isolated surfactant molecules;
(2) the liberation of water molecules from around surfactant resulting in

Polar   Hydrocarbon

Figure 13.7 Representation of a spherical micelle. The outer surface may consist of an electrical double layer or may be non-charged, depending on the surfactant species

Figure 13.8 Bilayer structures as (a) cylindrical aggregates, (b) spherical concentric layers and (c) liposomes. The schematic bilayer arrangement shows the phospholipid molecules, e.g., phosphatidylcholine (lecithin)

'water structure' in the form of the relatively strong, but transient, hydrogen-bonded network existing in pure water.

The net result can be attributed to the hydrophobic effect† which manifests itself to a greater or lesser extent in all water–hydrocarbon systems.

Many surface active molecules, e.g., those giving insoluble monolayers (Chapter 12), are not soluble in water. However, by strong mechanical agitation or the use of ultrasonics they can be dispersed into aggregates in water, called liposomes (biologically similar entities are called vesicles). Figure 13.8 depicts the basic enclosed bilayer structure of liposomes, and shows that they may be of variable shape and that concentric structures are also possible. Rather than being the simple amphipathic model surfactant with a single hydrocarbon chain and a hydrophilic group at one end, the insoluble species have a more complex structure often with at least two distinct hydrocarbon portions. When a naturally occurring phospholipid is dispersed in water with the water content in excess of about 50%, aggregates are obtained of cylindrical bilayers concentrically arranged and separated by water. Spherical structures of bilayers can be obtained from these by gentle shaking. These in turn can give roughly spherical liposomes when subjected to sonication. Liposomes will only form at temperatures below what is known as the chain-melting temperature of the phospholipid. In the solid state a particular phospholipid will exhibit polymorphism (several crystalline forms) which on heating show thermotropic mesomorphism (Chapter 5). The critical temperature for the change from crystalline to liquid–crystalline states is the chain-melting temperature. Incidentally, lyotropic mesophases occur when the phospholipid is heated in the presence of water: analogous transitions occur in spread monolayers.

†C. Tanford, *The Hydrophobic Effect*, 2nd edn, J. Wiley Chichester (1980).

The current view, simply presented, is that biological membranes consist of lipoprotein bilayers within which are protein molecules, with other protein molecules coating the inner and outer surfaces. Liposomes go some way to being model membrane entities, and have been used to study transport properties, e.g. diffusion coefficients for ions passing from the interior through to the bulk aqueous phase. Liposomes are also of considerable interest as carriers of drugs in the pharmacological field. Because of their essentially liquid crystal nature they can be made of molecules such that the particular liposomes are very sensitive to changes in body temperature in the region of infection within the blood stream. They breakdown sufficiently at the site to release the drug.

Macromolecules in solution have largely been dealt with in Chapter 11. Random coil configurations of flexible polymers in solution scatter light, behaving as particles, and can as such be regarded as colloidal. Their role in conferring stability when adsorbed on particle surfaces, and their ability to cause bridging flocculation have already been discussed. Biological macromolecules by their chemical and physical variety extend the range of properties of particles, often being insoluble and therefore dispersed rather than dissolved in an aqueous phase. Gel systems are of many kinds, but the prevalent attribute is of a system of cross-linked (reversibly or irreversibly) polymeric species.

13.5 Aerosols, foams and emulsions

Parts of the above account of interfaces and colloids apply directly to liquid-in-gas, gas-in-liquid and liquid-in-liquid colloidal systems known, respectively, as liquid aerosols, foams and emulsions. In addition they have distinctive features and properties.

Aerosols can be formed by vapour condensation or by dispersing liquid in a gas, as from an 'aerosol can', by forcing it through a nozzle. Aerosol formation by condensation involves either homogeneous or heterogeneous nucleation (Chapter 12), e.g. clouds readily form as water droplets in air because at a water vapour pressure very close to saturation (dew point) there are plenty of atmospheric particles to act as nuclei for the vapour $\rightarrow$ liquid phase change. Liquid droplets have an equilibrium vapour pressure $p > p^\circ$, given by equation 12.28, especially when their radius is less than about 1 μm. The relative stability of aerosols depends on how effective collisions are in bringing about coalescence, and on the ease with which evaporation or further condensation can occur, keeping in mind that transport is often by diffusion. Again using atmospheric droplets as examples, smog particles acquire some stability against evaporation by having a surface film of oily substance. Cloud droplets may contain dissolved salts which partially offset the elevation of vapour pressure according to Kelvin's equation. They are often able to withstand supercooling to well below 273 K without ice formation.

Foams are broadly of two types: with a large gas-to-liquid ratio, as in a froth of polyhedral gas cells, but including soap bubbles; dilute-in-gas variety where the bubbles in a liquid remain essentially separate and approximately spherical, as in carbonated water, but usually the liquid phase is highly viscous. The essentials of concentrated foam stability can be dealt with by examining a single soap film drawn from bulk liquid. Initially drainage and thinning occurs under gravity (like water down a window pane), but then liquid is squeezed out in all directions due to capillary pressure differences, equation 12.25, giving further thinning. The presence of surfactant molecules increases the liquid viscosity, but more importantly the stability of the film is greatly influenced by their presence. Electric double layers at opposite sides have a large effect, and with very thin films, e.g. black soap films of *ca*. 5 nm thickness, surfactant hydrocarbon moieties are essentially end-to-end in a bilayer. When viewed with reflected white light, coloured interference fringing indicates film thinning until constructive interference occurs at all visible frequencies.

The adsorption of surfactant molecules, e.g. proteins by foams, helps to stabilize the head on beer, and provides a means of purification by foam fractionation of surfactant solutions. Impurities adsorb with some of the surfactant at the liquid–vapour interface, then on continued foaming by bubbling gas through the bulk solution the foam rises away from the surface where it can be skimmed off.

The production of gas bubbles in liquid, while not strictly a foam because the system is neither static nor stable, provides the basis for mineral flotation. Some solid particles attach to the liquid–vapour bubble interface and are carried away to the surface.

Emulsions, consisting of droplets of one liquid dispersed in another are of two main types called oil-in-water, o/w, and water-in-oil, w/o. The term oil is used in its widest sense. Simple organic hydrocarbons when shaken with water do not form a proper emulsion because the components readily separate. Usually a surface active component is required, e.g. a little soap will allow benzene and water to be emulsified and then to remain fairly stable. The two types of emulsion differ in properties, e.g. o/w emulsions are better conductors of electricity than the w/o variety, and the former may be creamy and the latter greasy: as used as bases for pharmaceutical preparations. Ice creams, salad dressings and margarines also represent some of the commercial emulsions. Often the particles in emulsions exceed the nominal 1 μm diameter colloid size upper limit. On account of light scattering normal emulsions are rarely transparent, but an exception is a kind called microemulsions.

Adsorption at the oil–water interface is important to emulsion stability. The adsorbed material may be able to operate by electrical and/or steric mechanisms, but the precise details of any particular example are usually complex. Emulsions can be stabilized by proteins, glucosides, lipids, including gelatine, pectin and albumin. Emulsions can also be stabilized by the capillary attraction of small solid particles to the oil–water interface, which will be their favoured position with contact angles greater than 0°. The solid particles may themselves also acquire electric double layers adding to their ability to keep the droplets apart and reduce the possibility of coalescence. Emulsions are a good subject with which to end because they represent systems of considerable scientific and practical interest: the art of emulsions goes along with the science of emulsions in the attainment of satisfactory formulations.

Bibliography

This bibliography contains most textbooks on liquids and solutions and a selection of textbooks on some of the subjects that we have dealt with such as liquid crystals and colloids. Most of these books are more suitable for postgraduate than for undergraduate reading—even some with titles beginning 'Introduction to . . .'. They will, however, be useful for students who wish to look at certain topics in more detail than we have provided.

Adamson, A. W., *Physical Chemistry of Surfaces*, 3rd edn, Interscience, Chichester (1977)

Albert, A., and Serjeant, E. P., *The Determination of Ionization Constants: a Laboratory Manual*, Chapman and Hall, New York (1971)

Amis, E. S., and Hinton, J. F., *Solvent Effects on Chemical Phenomena*, Vols. 1 and 2, Academic Press, London and New York (1973)

Aveyard, R. and Haydon, D. A., *An Introduction to the Principles of Surface Chemistry*, C.U.P., Cambridge (1973)

Barker, J. A., *Lattice Theories of the Liquid State*, Pergamon Press, Oxford (1963)

Barton, A. F. M., *The Dynamic Liquid State*, Longman, London (1974)

Bell, R. P., *Acids and Bases: their Quantitative Behaviour*, 2nd edn, Methuen, London (1969)

Blackburn, T. R., *Equilibrium: a Chemistry of Solutions*, Holt, Rinehart and Winston, New York (1969)

Blander, M. (Ed.), *Molten Salt Chemistry*, J. Wiley, London and New York (1964)

Boublik, T., Nezbeda, I. and Hlavaty, K., *Statistical Thermodynamics of Simple Liquids and their Mixtures*, Elsevier, London and Amsterdam (1980)

Brown, G. H. (Ed.) *Liquid Crystals* (conference report), Kent State Univ., Ohio (1968)

Buckingham, A. D., Lippert, E., and Bratos, S., *Organic Liquids*, J. Wiley, Chichester (1978)

Burgess, J., *Metal Ions in Solution*, Ellis Horwood, Chichester (1978)

Butler, J. N., *Solubility and pH Calculations: the Mathematics of the Simplest Ionic Equilibria*, Addison-Wesley, New York (1964)

Butler, J. N., *Ionic Equilibrium, a Mathematical Approach*, Addison-Wesley, New York (1964)

Charlot, G., Collumeau, A., and Marchon, M. J. C., *Selected Constants: Oxidation–Reduction Potentials of Inorganic Substances in Aqueous Solution* (IUPAC) Butterworths, London (1971)

Coetzee, J. F., and Ritchie, C. D., *Solute–Solvent Interactions*, Marcel Dekker, New York (1969)

Cole, G. H. A., *An Introduction to the Statistical Theory of Classical Simple Dense Fluids*, Pergamon Press, Oxford (1967)

Conway, B. E., *Electrochemical Data*, Elsevier, London and Amsterdam (1952)

Conway, B. E., and Barradas, R. G., *Chemical Physics of Ionic Solutions* (symposium), J. Wiley, London and New York (1966)

Covington, A. K. and Jones, P., *Hydrogen Bonded Solvent Systems* (symposium), Taylor and Francis (1968)

Croxton, C. A., *Liquid State Physics—a Statistical Mechanical Introduction*, C.U.P., Cambridge (1974)

Croxton, C. A., *Introduction to Liquid State Physics*, J. Wiley, Chichester (1975)

Croxton, C. A., *Statistical Mechanics of the Liquid Surface*, J. Wiley, Chichester (1980)

Dack, M. R. J. (Ed.), *Solutions and Solubilities*, Parts I and II, J. Wiley, Chichester (1976)

Durrans, T. H., *Solvents*, 8th edn, Chapman and Hall, New York and London (1971)

Egelstaff, P. A., *An Introduction to the Liquid State*, Academic Press, New York and London (1967)

Eisenberg, D., and Kauzmann, W., *The Structure and Properties of Water*, Clarendon Press, Oxford (1969)

Eyring, H., and Jhon, M. S., *Significant Liquid Structures*, J. Wiley, London and New York (1969)

Faber, T. E., *Introduction to the Theory of Liquid Metals*, Cambridge University Press, Cambridge (1972)

Falkenhagen, H., *Electrolytes*, Clarendon Press, Oxford (1934)

Faraday Society Discussion, **43**, Structure and properties of liquids (1967)

Faraday Discussions of the Chemical Society, **66**, Structure and motion in molecular liquids (1978)

Fisher, I. Z., *Statistical Theory of Liquids*, Univ. of Chicago Press, Chicago (1964)

Flory, P. J., *Principles of Polymer Chemistry*, Cornell, New York (1953)

Franks, F. (Ed.), *Physico-chemical Processes in Mixed Aqueous Solvents*, Heinemann, London (1967)

Franks, F. (Ed.), *Water: a Comprehensive Treatise*, vols. 1–7, Plenum Press, London and New York (1972)

Gennes, P. G. de, *The Physics of Liquid Crystals*, Clarendon Press, Oxford (1974)

Gerrard, W., *Solubilities of Gases and Liquids, a Graphic Approach*, Plenum Press, London and New York (1976)

Gerrard, W., *Gas Solubilities*, Pergamon Press, Oxford (1980)

Gold, V., *pH Measurements: their Theory and Practice*, Methuen, London (1956)

Gray, G. W., *Molecular Structure and the Properties of Liquid Crystals*, Academic Press, New York and London (1962)

Guggenheim, E. A., Mixtures, the theory of the equilibrium properties of some simple classes of mixtures, solutions and alloys, Clarendon Press, Oxford (1952)

Guggenheim, E. A., and Stokes, R. H., *Equilibrium Properties of Aqueous Solutions of Single Strong Electrolytes*, Pergamon Press, Oxford (1969)

Hamer, W. J. (Ed.), *The Structure of Electrolytic Solutions* (symposium), J. Wiley, London and New York (1959)

Hansen, J. P., and McDonald, I. R., *Theory of Simple Liquids*, Academic Press, London (1976)

Harned, H. S., and Owen, B. B., *The Physical Chemistry of Electrolytic Solutions*, Reinhold, New York (1943 and 1958)

Hildebrand, J. H., Prausnitz, J. M. and Scott, R. L., *Regular and Related Solutions*, Van Nostrand-Reinhold, New York (1970)

Hildebrand, J. H., and Scott, R. L., *The Solubility of Non-electrolytes*, Dover, London (1964)

282

Hildebrand, J. H., and Scott, R. L., *Regular Solutions*, Prentice-Hall, Englewood Cliff, New Jersey (1962)

Hirschfelder, J. O., Curtis, C. F., and Bird, R. B., *Molecular Theory of Gases and Liquids*, J. Wiley, London and New York (1964)

Hughel, T. J., *Liquids: Structure, Properties, Solid Interactions* (symposium), Elsevier, London and Amsterdam (1965)

Inman, D., and Lovering, D. G., *Ionic Liquids*, Plenum Press, London and New York (1981)

Jander, G., Spandau, H., and Addison, C. C., (Eds.), *Chemistry in Non-aqueous Ionizing Solvents*, Vols. 1–4, J. Wiley, London and New York (1963)

Janz, G. J. and Tomkins, R. P. T., *Non-aqueous Electrolytes Handbook*, Vols 1, 2, Academic Press, New York and London (1972)

Jones, M. N., *Biological Interfaces*, Elsevier, London and Amsterdam (1975)

Kavanau, J. L., *Water and Solute–Water Interactions*, Holden-Day, San Francisco (1964)

King, E. J., *Acid–Base Equilibria*, Pergamon Press, Oxford (1965)

Kohler, F., Findenegg, G. H., Fischer, J., Posch, H., and Weissenbock, F., *The Liquid State*, Verlag Chemie, Berlin (1972)

Kratochvil, B., Gutman, V., and Smith, S. L., *Non Aqueous Chemistry* (*Topics in Current Chemistry*, Vol. 79), Springer, Berlin and New York (1972)

Kruus, P., *Liquids and Solutions*, Marcel Dekker, New York (1977)

Lagowski, J. J. (Ed.), *The Chemistry of Non Aqueous Solvents*, Vols. 1–5, Academic Press, London and New York (1966)

Latimer, W. M., *Oxidation potentials*, 2nd edn, Prentice-Hall, Englewood Cliff, New Jersey (1958)

Linke, W. F., *Solubilities of Inorganic and Metal Organic Compounds* (data), Vols. 1 and 2, Van Nostrand, New York (1958)

Malesinski, W., *Azeotropy and Other Theoretical Problems of Vapour–Liquid Equilibrium*, Interscience, London and New York (1965)

Mamankov, G. (Ed.), *Molten Salts, Characterization and Analysis*, Marcel Dekker, New York (1969)

Marcus, Y., *Introduction to Liquid State Chemistry*, J. Wiley, Chichester (1977)

McBain, M. E. L. and Hutchinson, E., *Solubilization and Related Phenomena*, Academic Press, New York and London (1955)

Morawetz, H., *High Polymers*, Vol. 21, *Macromolecules in Solution*, 2nd edn, Wiley–Interscience, Chichester (1975)

Munster, A., *Theory of the Liquid State*, North-Holland, Amsterdam (1965)

Nancollas, G. H., *Interactions in Electrolyte Solutions*, Elsevier, London and Amsterdam (1966)

Nyvlt, J., *Solid–Liquid Phase Equilibria*, Elsevier, London and Amsterdam (1977)

Parsons, R., *Handbook of Electrochemical Constants*, Butterworths, London (1959)

Pings, C. J., *Physics of Simple Liquids*, North-Holland, Amsterdam (1968)

Popvych, O., and Tomkins, R. P. T., *Nonaqueous Solution Chemistry*, J. Wiley, Chichester (1981)

Prigogine, I. (with Bellemans, A., and Mathot, V.), *The Molecular Theory of Solutions*, North-Holland, Amsterdam (1957)

Prigogine, I., and Rice, S. A. (Eds.), *Non Simple Liquids, Adv. Chem. Phys.*, **31**, J. Wiley, Chichester (1975)

Pryde, J. A., *The Liquid State*, Hutchinson, London (1966)

Reid, R. C., Prausnitz, J. M. and Sherwood, T. K., *The Properties of Liquids and Gases*, 3rd edn, McGraw-Hill, Maidenhead (1981)

Reisman, A., *Phase Equilibria*, Academic Press, London and New York (1970)

Rice, S. A., and Gray, P., *The Statistical Mechanics of Simple Liquids*, Interscience, London and New York (1965)

Rice, S. A. and Nagasawa, M., *Polyelectrolyte Solutions*, Academic Press, New York and London (1961)

Robbins, J., *Ions in Solution, an Introduction to Electrochemistry*, Clarendon Press, Oxford (1972)

Robinson, R. A., and Stokes, R. H., *Electrolyte Solutions*, Butterworths, London (1959)

Rochester, C. H., *Acidity Functions*, Academic Press, London and New York (1970)

Rowlinson, J. S., *Liquids and Liquid Mixtures*, 2nd edn, Butterworths, London (1969)

Scatchard, G., *Equilibrium in Solutions and Surface and Colloid Chemistry*, Harvard University Press (1976)

Seidell, A., *Solubilities of Organic Compounds* (data), Vols. 1 and 2, Van Nostrand, New York (1941)

Shaw, D. J., *Introduction to Colloid and Surface Chemistry*, 3rd edn, Butterworths, London (1981)

Shinoda, K., *Principles of Solution and Solubility*, Marcel Dekker, New York (1978)

Sisler, H. H., *Chemistry in Non Aqueous Solvents*, Chapman and Hall, New York and London (1962)

Stokes, R. H. and Mills, R., *Viscosity of Electrolytes and Related Properties*, Pergamon Press, Oxford (1965)

Sundheim, B. R. (Ed.), *Fused Salts*, McGraw-Hill, Maidenhead (1964)

Tanford, C., *Physical Chemistry of Macromolecules*, J. Wiley, London and New York (1961)

Tanford, C., *The Hydrophobic Effect*, 2nd edn, J. Wiley, Chichester (1980)

Temperley, H. N. V., Rowlinson, J. S., and Rushbrooke, G. S., *Physics of Simple Liquids*, North-Holland, Amsterdam (1968)

Temperley, H. N. V., and Trevena, D. H., *Liquids and their Properties*, Ellis Horwood, Chichester (1978)

Timmermans, J., *The Physico-chemical Constants of Binary Systems in Concentrated Solutions*, Vols. 1–4, Interscience, London and New York (1959)

Ubbelohde, A. R., *The Molten State of Matter*, J. Wiley, Chichester (1978)

Waddington, T. C., *Non-aqueous Solvents*, Nelson, Walton-on-Thames (1969)

Waddington, T. C. (Ed.), *Non-aqueous Solvent Systems*, Academic Press, London and New York (1965)

Williamson, A. G., *An Introduction to Non-electrolyte Solutions*, Oliver and Boyd, Edinburgh (1967)

Zingaro, R. A., *Non-aqueous Solvents*, Heath, Lexington (1968)

Zundel, G., *Hydration and Intermolecular Interactions*, Academic Press, New York and London (1969)

Index